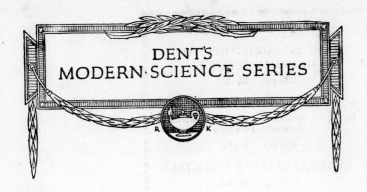

DENT'S MODERN SCIENCE SERIES

GENERAL SCIENCE PHYSICS

GENERAL SCIENCE
PHYSICS

BY

A. SPENCER WHITE
B.Sc., L.C.P.

ILLUSTRATED WITH
310 DIAGRAMS

J. M. DENT AND SONS LTD.
BEDFORD ST. LONDON W.C.2

by
J. M. DENT & SONS LTD
Aldine House · Bedford Street · London
Made in Great Britain
at
The Temple Press · Letchworth · Herts
First published 1936
Last reprinted 1952

Z 312/16 m

PREFACE

THE aim of this book is to cover the Physics papers set by the various examining bodies for candidates taking General Science at Ordinary Level.

Throughout the book the apparatus described is quite simple ; every school will certainly possess most of the appliances mentioned. If the laboratory has more elaborate equipment, this is an added joy to teacher and taught. It is certainly very disappointing to be in the opposite situation. Many of the experiments can be repeated at home by the keen pupil.

It seems hardly necessary to mention that contact with daily life has been maintained, for at this stage Physics hardly ever gets away from daily life.

It is claimed that the pupil who works through the book will have a useful knowledge of the subject if he goes no further, and a sound foundation if he is able to proceed to " higher " things. Where lack of space has forbidden the exhaustive treatment of some particularly attractive part of the subject as in " Colour " and " Alternating Current," references are made to recent articles in the *School Science Review*.

Numerous calculations have been included and great stress has been laid on graphical methods. In the section on Light all the lens and mirror problems can be worked in this way. Although lens and mirror formulæ are not essential for the Physics of a General Science Course, these have been included because many pupils like to be able to check their graphical work. In this connection the Cartesian method recommended by the Physical Society's Committee (1934) has been adopted. To fit in with this scheme the early lens and mirror diagrams have been drawn with a " left to right " progression of the light. If the teacher prefers the alternative recommendation of that Committee, it should be an easy matter for the pupils themselves to make the few necessary alterations in the text on pages 191, 222 and 226.

The section on Electricity has been written in such a way that Electrostatics can be read before or after Current Electricity.

The General Editor of this series, Dr. E. J. Holmyard, has made many valuable improvements in the text for which I am very grateful. The writer of a school textbook is always indebted to his colleagues on account of the many ideas put forward on those numerous occasions when they foregather to talk "shop," and here I must thank my colleagues, Mr. T. Templeton Smith and Mr. A. Williamson. The Publishers for their friendly spirit and infinite patience are also deserving of my best thanks.

Many questions have been taken from back papers of the eight examining boards, and these sources are indicated. Where "part question" appears, this means that the remainder of the question was not appropriate to that particular chapter. My thanks for permission to use such questions are due to the following: The University of Bristol; the University of Cambridge Local Examinations Syndicate; the University of Durham; the Joint Matriculation Board of the Universities of Manchester, Liverpool, Leeds, Sheffield, and Birmingham; the University of London; the Delegates of the University of Oxford Local Examinations; the Oxford and Cambridge Schools Examination Board; and the Central Welsh Board.

A. SPENCER WHITE.

CONTENTS

MECHANICS

CHAPTER I

LENGTHS, AREAS, AND VOLUMES

In ordinary life we measure lengths with ruler, tape or surveyor's chain, but in science we frequently need to measure a length with great accuracy or to measure a thickness too small for these everyday methods. For these purposes we have two instruments called the **vernier** and the **micrometer screw gauge.**

The Vernier. Draw a narrow rectangle and mark off the length in centimetres (fig. 1). This may be called the *main*

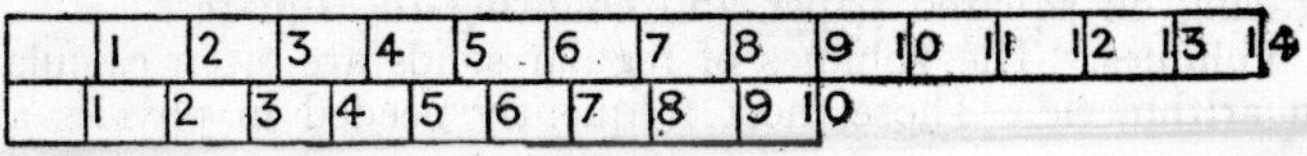

Fig. 1.

scale. Mark off a second narrow rectangle with divisions arrived at by taking 9 of the main divisions and dividing into 10 equal parts, in other words, make these divisions 9 mm. long. This will be the *vernier scale.* By causing the vernier scale to slide along the main scale various readings, *e.g.* 3·4 cm., 5·2 cm., etc., may be illustrated. With a vernier we are thus able to read to a millimetre while still using divisions very easy to see.

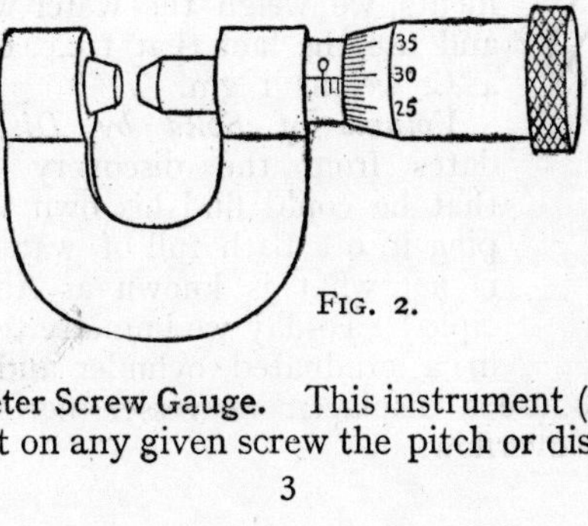

Fig. 2.

The Micrometer Screw Gauge. This instrument (fig. 2) depends on the fact that on any given screw the pitch or distance between successive turns of the thread is constant. When the screw is given a complete turn, the screw point moves one pitch. If the pitch is $\frac{1}{2}$ mm. and the screw is twisted $\frac{1}{50}$ of a complete turn, the screw point moves $\frac{1}{100}$ mm. The screw and "collar" form one piece. Complete turns are recorded on the frame while fractions of a turn are registered on the collar. With such an instrument the thickness of a hair is easily determined.

Areas. The areas met with in physics are those which are ordinarily treated in arithmetic. The following may be noted:

Area of circle $= \pi \times (\text{radius})^2$ or πr^2
Area of ellipse $= \pi \times$ semi major axis $\times$ semi minor axis
Curved surface of cylinder $= 2\pi \times (\text{radius}) \times (\text{length}) = 2\pi rl$
Surface of a sphere $= 4\pi r^2$

The area of an irregular plane surface may be found by tracing on squared paper and counting the squares.

Volumes. The volumes of regular solids are often calculated in arithmetic. Those most frequently needed in physics are:

Volume of sphere $= \frac{4}{3}\pi \times (\text{radius})^3 = \frac{4}{3}\pi r^3$
Volume of cylinder $= \pi \times (\text{radius})^2 \times \text{height} = \pi r^2 h$.

Volume of Liquid is measured by pipette, burette, graduated cylinder or graduated flask. In all cases the instrument is so made that the bottom of the meniscus must be read. The eye should always be on a level with the meniscus. To check the accuracy of one of these instruments, we weigh the water which it delivers and use the fact that 1 c.c. of pure water at 4° C. weighs 1 gm.

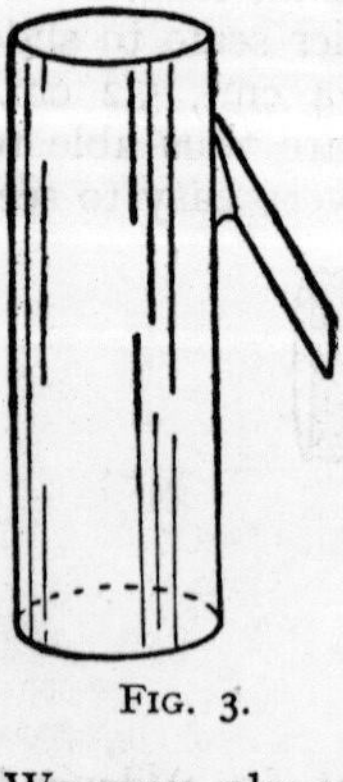

FIG. 3.

Volume of Solid by Displacement. This dates from the discovery by Archimedes that he could find his own volume by stepping into a bath full of water. (*N.B.*—This is *not* what is known as Archimedes' Principle.) To-day we immerse the solid in water in a graduated cylinder and note the rise. We may also use a displacement vessel (fig. 3) measuring or weighing the overflow.

Useful Numerical Data.

1 litre	= 1 cubic decimetre = 1000 c.c.		
1 kilogram	= Mass of 1000 c.c. of pure water at 4° C.		
1 metre	= 39·37 in.	1 foot	= 30·5 cm.
1 litre	= 1·76 pints	1 inch	= 2·54 cm.
1 kilogram	= 2·2 lb.	1 lb.	= 454 gm.

QUESTIONS AND EXERCISES

1. Draw a main scale and vernier scale, and set to show a reading of 1·8 cm. Repeat for 2·3 cm., 3·6 cm.

2. A main scale is marked off in inches and quarters. A vernier scale is made by taking 7 quarters and dividing into 8 equal parts. To what degree of accuracy will the vernier read? Draw the arrangement.

3. Describe and explain an instrument for measuring the diameter of a half-penny to one-hundredth of an inch. (C. part question.)

4. Measure the thickness of an exercise book with a ruler. Count the pages and calculate the thickness of one page. Check with screw gauge.

5. Coil a length of thin copper wire tightly round a pencil. Measure the length occupied by 20 or 30 turns and thus determine the diameter of the wire. Check with screw gauge.

6. How could you arrange three rectangular blocks of wood to measure the diameter of a cylinder or sphere?

7. Make a perspective drawing of a cubic decimetre (a litre). Mark off the base into cubic centimetres alternately plain and shaded.

8. Draw the best instrument you know for measuring (*a*) 21·6 c.c. of water, (*b*) 180 c.c., (*c*) 25 c.c. Give reasons for your choice of instrument.

9. How would you find the volume of an irregular solid lighter than water?

10. A rectangular tank is 1½ metres long, 50 cm. wide and 550 mm. deep. Find its volume in litres.

11. You are provided with a foot rule graduated in tenths of an inch. How would you construct a vernier so that you could measure in fiftieths of an inch? Show in a diagram the position of the vernier on the scale if the reading is 7·64 in. (D.)

CHAPTER II

FORCE, MASS, WEIGHT, AND DENSITY

Force.

Sir Isaac Newton, who has been described as the greatest philosopher of all time, stated three *Laws of Motion.* At present we are only concerned with the **First Law : Every body continues in its state of rest or of uniform motion in a straight line unless it is acted upon by a force.**

The first part of the law is readily understood and a little thought will provide many illustrations of the second. We do not see bodies moving on indefinitely because there is always a force, generally friction, stopping them. If you are standing in a moving train when the brakes are put on, you fall forward because the brakes stopped your feet, but the upper part goes on in a straight line. Stepping off a moving vehicle gives another illustration.

The law really provides us with a good definition of *force* and we may say : **Force is that which changes or tends to change a body's state of rest or of uniform motion in a straight line.**

The best-known force is undoubtedly the force of gravity, and concerning this also Newton made a very important discovery. It was realized before his time that the falling of unsupported bodies was due to the earth's attraction on them. Newton wondered why the moon should go round the earth instead of keeping on in a straight line to disappear ultimately in space. He came to the conclusion that here again it was a case of attraction. The motion of the earth and other planets round the sun could be similarly explained. He accordingly stated his Law of Gravitation : **Every body attracts every other body with a force proportional to the product of their masses and inversely proportional to the square of the distance between the bodies.**

Apart from their agreement with everyday experience, Newton's Laws have enabled astronomers to calculate the times of eclipses, the paths of comets and led to the discovery of new planets. Such a successful prediction of new facts is, of course, the very best support any theory can have.

Mass and Weight. We are now in a position to understand the meaning of the terms "mass" and "weight" and the difference between them. The mass of a body is the amount of matter in it, while weight is the earth's attraction on the body. Mass is a fundamental property of a body, while its weight is more or less an accident depending on its position in the universe. If we could make a journey to the moon, our provisions for the journey would have the same mass all the way, but at some point in between, the earth's attraction would be just cancelled by that of the moon. On the moon itself the weight would be about one-sixth of the terrestrial weight. But we need not wait for a journey to the moon; a body taken from the equator to the poles will increase in weight because it will be nearer to the centre of the earth. Such variations in weight could, of course, be observed only by using a spring balance.

Now, although mass is constant and weight varies, we find it very convenient to measure and compare masses by means of their weights; for at the same place equal masses have the same weight and the greater the mass the greater the weight. There is in London a certain lump of platinum called a **mass of 1 lb.** Elsewhere there are copies of this in brass and iron. If we want to buy sugar having a mass of 1 lb., one of these lumps of metal is put on one scale-pan and the sugar on the other. The amount of sugar is adjusted until the earth pulls equally on both. We then say that since the weights are the same, the masses must be the same.

Besides providing us with a unit of mass, the same lump of platinum affords a convenient unit of **force.** Thus the practical unit of force is the pull exerted by the earth on that mass of 1 lb. We should always refer to a *mass of 1 lb.* and a *force of 1 lb.-wt.*

Just as in London there is a lump of platinum called a mass of 1 lb., so in Paris there is a lump of platinum called a *mass of 1 kilogram.* In science the common balance is always accompanied by a box of masses (generally called "weights") based on this kilogram.

The chief difference between the shop balance and the science balance is that the latter is more sensitive, *i.e.* a very small difference in load causes the beam to turn. Correspondingly the instrument requires more careful treatment. In particular the moving parts should not be touched while the beam is raised. Apart from careless misuse the most frequent mistakes are (*a*) not using the weights in the strict order of the box, (*b*) miscounting the weights. *N.B.*—The 50 and 500 mgm. weights when reversed look very much like 20 and 200 and vice versa.

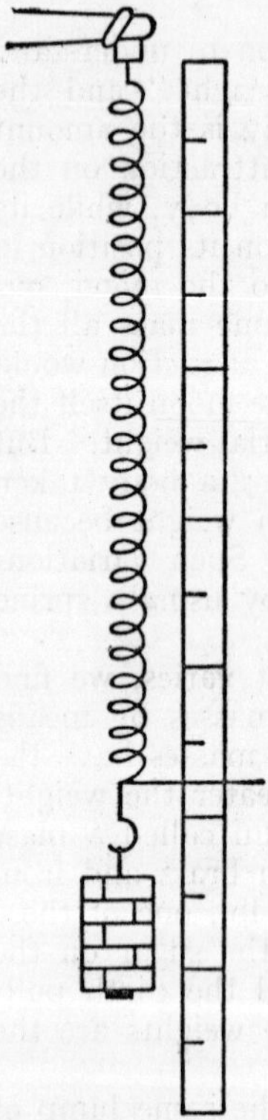

FIG. 4.

Extension of a Spiral Spring. Fix up a spiral spring carrying a pointer against a scale as shown in fig. 4. Take a number of readings of load, scale reading, and extension during increase and decrease of load. Draw a graph showing load on the X axis and extension on the Y axis. Unless we have exceeded the elastic limit of the spring, we shall find that the graph is a straight line going through the origin. We conclude that the extension is directly proportional to the load (Hooke's Law). This is the principle of the spring balance, a convenient instrument not only for the measurement of mass but also for the measurement of force.

Density. The non-scientific man would say that lead is "heavier" than aluminium. He quite understands, and would explain if asked, that equal volumes must be taken for the comparison. In science we say lead is *denser* than aluminium. **Density is defined as the mass of unit volume.** To find the density of a body we only need to know its mass and its volume. It is obvious that

$$\text{Density} = \frac{\text{Mass}}{\text{Volume}}, \text{ and Mass} = \text{Volume} \times \text{Density}.$$

The densities of water, aluminium, and lead may be stated thus:

Water.	*Aluminium.*	*Lead.*
1 gm. per c.c.	2·7 gm. per c.c.	11·3 gm. per c.c.
62·5 lb. per cu. ft.	168·75 lb. per cu. ft.	706·25 lb. per cu. ft.
10 lb. per gallon.		

We notice that aluminium is 2·7 times denser than water and this is true no matter what units are used. In industrial physics we more frequently say the *relative density* or *specific gravity* (S.G.) of aluminium is 2·7.

Relative Density or Specific Gravity may be defined:

$$\text{S.G. of a body} = \frac{\text{Wt. of body}}{\text{Wt. of an equal vol. of water}} \text{ or } \frac{\text{Density of the body}}{\text{Density of water}}.$$

Therefore Density of a body = Density of Water × Rel. Density.

If metric units are used, the number expressing density and specific gravity will be the same, but when speaking of density the units of mass and volume must be stated; specific gravity is a number and will be the same in any country. Again, the density of lead is 706·25 lb. per cubic foot or 11·3 gm. per c.c. or S.G. = 11·3.

To find the density of any Regular Solid. The density of a brick, a metal or wooden cylinder, or a piece of wire can be found by *calculating* the volume and determining the weight on the balance most suitable for the particular solid.

To find the density of a Small Irregular Solid. Here the volume is determined with a burette, graduated cylinder or beaker according to the size of the solid. The method of using the beaker for a large solid is as follows: Place the solid in the beaker and fill to a mark with water from a graduated cylinder. Note volume of water required. Remove the solid and again fill to the mark. Note volume of water required. The difference between the volumes required will be the volume of the solid.

To find the density of a Liquid. Mark the neck of a small flask. Weigh empty, then full of water, then full of the liquid.

Wt. of flask $= a$ gm.
Wt. of flask + water $= b$ gm.
Wt. of flask + liquid $= c$ gm.
∴ Wt. of liquid $= (c - a)$ gm.
∴ Wt. of water $= (b - a)$ gm.
∴ Vol. of water, flask or liquid $= (b - a)$ c.c.

Density of liquid $= \dfrac{c - a}{b - a}$ gm. per c.c.

Repeat the experiment with a specific gravity bottle (fig. 5) and explain the advantage of it.

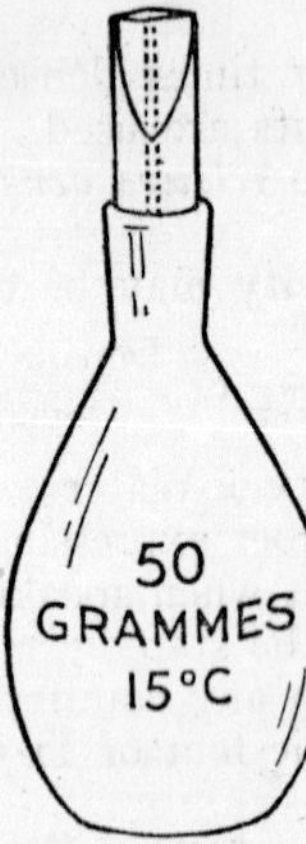

FIG. 5.

FIG. 6.

To find the density of Air. Into a round-bottomed flask of about 250 c.c. capacity pour about 50 c.c. of water. Fit the flask with a rubber stopper, glass tube, rubber tube and clip (fig. 6). Boil the water for a few minutes so as to drive out the air. Remove burner and close clip simultaneously. Cool, dry and weigh the apparatus. Open the clip and weigh again. This gives the weight of the air. Fill flask from a graduated cylinder noting volume required. Calculate the mass per litre.

QUESTIONS AND EXERCISES

1. Explain the difference between—

(*a*) A law of nature and a law of a country.

(*b*) Mass and weight.

(*c*) Density and Specific Gravity.

2. A 10-c.c. graduated cylinder weighs 19·43 gm. empty and 155·89 gm. when full of mercury. What is the density of mercury ?

3. A rectangular block of wood measures 150 cm. × 40 cm. × 14 cm. If it weighs 67·2 kilograms, what is its density ?

4. Find the weight of a column of mercury of height 30 in. and cross-section 1 sq. in. [S.G. of mercury = 13·6.]

5. A bottle weighs x gm. Full of water it weighs y gm., full of milk z gm. What is the density of milk?

6. A flask partly filled with water is boiled, then corked, cooled and weighed. It is now opened and reweighed. The two weighings are 70·56 and 70·71 gm. respectively. To fill the bottle completely requires another 120 c.c. Calculate the density of air.

7. A piece of steel wire of length 20 in. and cross-section 0·2 sq. in. weighs 1·12 lb. What is its specific gravity?

8. Find the relative density of a salt solution from the following data: Wt. of bottle = 20·12 gm. Bottle + water, 70·22 gm. Bottle + solution, 71·72 gm.

9. A thread of mercury 20 cm. long is blown out of a capillary tube and found to weigh 0·623 gm. Find the average diameter of the tube. [S.G. of mercury = 13·6.]

10. Make an equation connecting V, s, M, and d where V is the volume of a body, s its specific gravity, M its mass and d is the density of water.

Calculate the mass of 4 cu. ft. of lead, aluminium, mercury.

11. Newton's First Law is sometimes stated as a property of matter called "Inertia" thus:

Inertia is that property by reason of which every body continues in its state of rest. . . .

Complete the statement. How does the inertia of your body make itself evident when you are travelling by train or bus?

12. The flywheel of an engine is said to have *inertia*. What does this mean? When is this inertia an advantage?

13. The comedian on the stage suddenly whisks off the table-cloth, but, behold, the tea things remain undisturbed! Why?

14. From the following readings plot *loads* on the Y axis and *extensions of spring* on the X axis:

Load	100 gm.	120 gm.	140 gm.	160 gm.	180 gm.	200 gm.
Length	7·5 cm.	10·2 cm.	12·9 cm.	15·6 cm.	18·2 cm.	20·9 cm.
Load	110 gm.	130 gm.	150 gm.	170 gm.	190 gm.	
Length	9·0 cm.	11·6 cm.	14·2 cm.	16·9 cm.	19·6 cm.	

Does your graph agree with Hooke's Law?

CHAPTER III

FLUID PRESSURE

In physics we define matter as anything which occupies space, and we classify it into *solids, liquids, and gases.* We sometimes put the last two together and have two classes—*solids and fluids.*

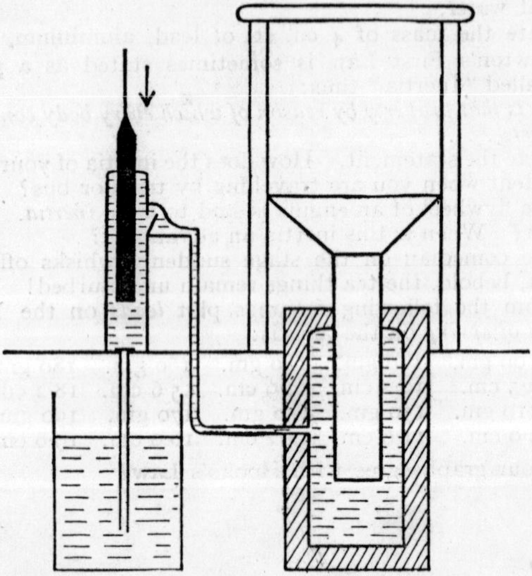

Fig. 7.

The most striking difference between solids, liquids, and gases is that solids have definite size and definite shape, liquids definite size and indefinite shape, while gases have indefinite size and shape.

Another important difference between solids and fluids is the way in which they pass on or *transmit* a force applied to them. If you sit on a cycle saddle, the tyres bulge out at the sides. If you lean on a crutch or a walking-stick, the force is transmitted in a straight line; there is no bulging out at the sides. Again, if a hole were drilled anywhere in a water pipe, the water would always spirt out at right angles to the pipe. Our experience with fluids is summed up by a natural law called Pascal's Law: **Fluids transmit pressure equally in all directions.**

There is no doubt that a fluid like water presses downwards and sideways. In a swimming bath we get ample proof that water also exerts an upward pressure. The fact that water finds its own level depends on this upward pressure; the fountain in the public gardens is a good illustration of this.

Bramah Press. The working of this machine (fig. 7) is an excellent application of the fact that liquids transmit pressure equally in all directions. A force pump drives water from a well or tank into a cylinder fitted with a large plunger.

Suppose that the sectional area of the small plunger is 1 sq. in. and that of the large plunger 100 sq. in. If a force of 10 lb. is applied to the small plunger, a pressure of 10 lb. per square inch is transmitted through the water to every square inch of the large plunger. We thus have an upward force of 1000 lb.-wt.

$$\frac{\text{Area of small plunger}}{\text{Area of large plunger}} = \frac{\text{Force on small plunger}}{\text{Force on large plunger}}.$$

Atmospheric Pressure.

An Italian physicist, Torricelli, in 1643 carried out an experiment which laid the foundations of our knowledge of atmospheric pressure. He took a glass tube 36 in. long and closed at one end. This was filled with mercury, closed with the thumb and inverted in a bowl of mercury (fig. 8). The mercury dropped until its height above the mercury level in the bowl was round about 30 in.

Torricelli realized that this was an illustration of Pascal's discovery; air pressure was squeezing on the mercury in the bowl, and this pressure was *transmitted through the liquid* and up the tube.

The normal air pressure was just able to support 30 in. of mercury and above the mercury would be a vacuum. When the tube was sloped, the mercury ran to the top with a characteristic click, but all the time the air could support a *vertical* column of 30 in. of mercury.

When Pascal heard of this experiment he suggested to his brother-in-law Périer that a similar apparatus should be fitted up and carried to the top of a mountain. Périer did this and found, as Pascal had predicted, that the mercury column became shorter because of the diminished air pressure.

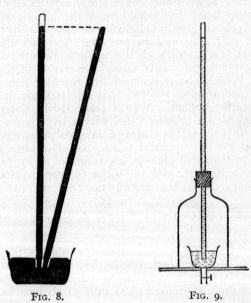

FIG. 8.

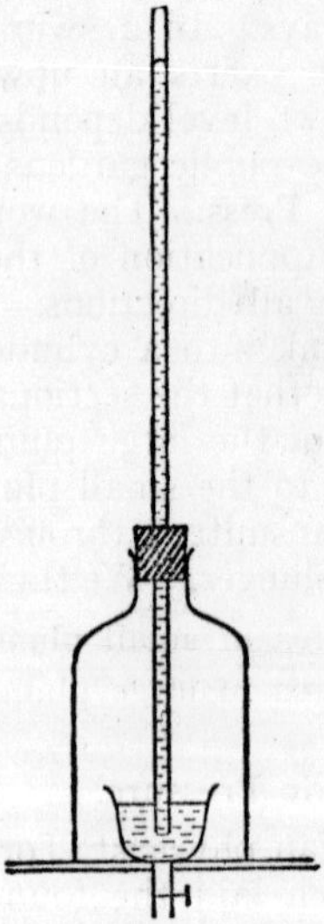

FIG. 9.

Torricelli's experiment taught the world that it was possible to produce a vacuum. Very soon Otto von Guericke in Germany and Boyle and Hooke in England produced the first air pumps.

Using any type of air pump it is possible to prove in a very striking way that the mercury in Torricelli's experiment is really kept up by air pressure. The apparatus (fig. 9) is set up on the air-pump plate. A bell-jar with a well-vaselined flange is then passed over the tube so as to rest on the plate. A rubber stopper with a little vaseline in the bore is then slipped down the tube into the neck of the bell-jar. On working the pump the mercury falls.

The Barometer. Boyle very soon found that Torricelli's apparatus gave some indication of weather changes. When the mercury rose it was generally a sign of fine weather and vice versa. This is because dry air exerts more pressure than air containing water vapour; water in the gaseous form is less dense than air.

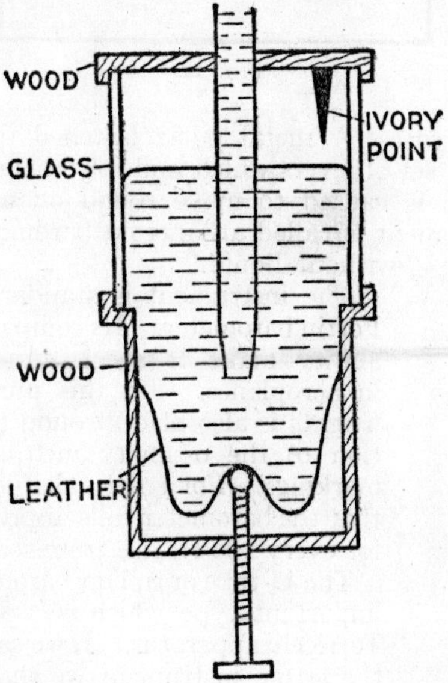

FIG. 10.

To use the Torricelli apparatus as a barometer, it is convenient to have a scale of inches or centimetres fixed to the tube. But immediately a difficulty arises; as the mercury rises or falls in the tube, the level in the bowl changes, in other words, there is a variable zero.

The difficulty is neatly overcome in the Fortin barometer (fig. 10). The mercury is contained in a leather bag which may be raised or lowered by an adjusting screw. Before taking a reading, the mercury is brought into contact with an ivory pin which is the zero of the scale.

The barometer common in houses has a flat case of thin corrugated metal (fig. 11) which has been made nearly vacuous. Variations in the atmospheric pressure cause in-and-out movements of the case.

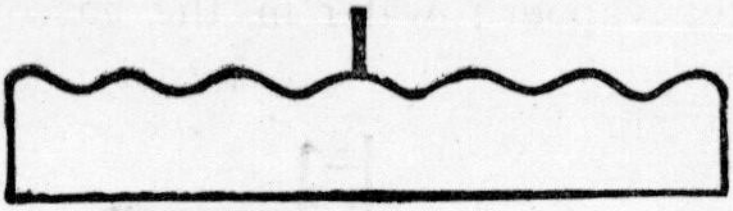

FIG. 11.

A metal pillar fastened to the centre is connected to a set of levers which multiply this movement until finally a hand is caused to move round on a circular scale. Such an instrument is called an aneroid barometer from Greek words meaning " without liquid."

The instrument is standardized against a Fortin barometer. Its compactness and portability make it specially suitable for use in aeroplanes. For this purpose a scale of heights is also placed round the dial in addition to the ordinary inch and centimetre markings. For small altitudes the rule is that the barometer falls approximately $\frac{1}{10}$ in. for every 100 ft. rise from sea-level.

FIGS. 12 and 13.

The U-tube or siphon barometer is another important type which is a variation of the Torricelli apparatus. If we carefully consider the latter instrument we shall see that the mercury in the bowl merely serves to transmit the air pressure to the mercury in the tube (fig. 12). This can be done equally well by a U-tube of mercury (fig. 13).

The U may be of glass or rubber. Glass is more convenient if the apparatus is to be permanently fixed on a board, while rubber is better for easy filling in a quick demonstration.

Problem. To express the atmospheric pressure in lb. per square inch. Consider a siphon barometer in which the tube has a cross-section of 1 sq. in. Then evidently the atmospheric pressure per square inch is equal to the weight of 30 cu. in. of mercury.

Now 1728 cu. in. of water weigh 62·5 lb.

$\therefore$ 30 cu. in. of mercury weigh $30\left(\frac{62\cdot5 \times 13\cdot6}{1728}\right)$ lb.

or 14·7 lb.

We may note that the pressure is given by the product of a length and a density. This is an illustration of the fact that **the pressure at a point in a fluid at rest is proportional to the depth and the density.** Thus

$$p \text{ lb. per sq. in.} = h \text{ in.} \times d \text{ lb. per cu. in.}$$

similarly

$$p \text{ lb. per sq. ft.} = h \text{ ft.} \times d \text{ lb. per cu. ft.}$$

or

$$p \text{ gm. per sq. cm.} = h \text{ cm.} \times d \text{ gm. per c.c.}$$

We must also remember that **the pressure at a given depth is the same in all directions.**

Problem. What is the water pressure on a diver working in 60 ft. of sea water? [S.G. of sea water = 1·028.]

$$p \text{ lb. per sq. in.} = h \text{ in.} \times d \text{ lb. per cu. in.}$$
$$= (60 \times 12) \times \frac{62\cdot5 \times 1\cdot028}{1728}$$
$$= 26\cdot7.$$

A fluid pressure is sometimes referred to as a "head of water" or a "head of mercury." Thus the ordinary atmospheric pressure can be expressed as a 34-ft. head of water or 30-in. head of mercury. Fluid pressures can therefore be stated in

1. Atmospheres.
2. lb. per sq. in., gm. per sq. cm., etc.
3. Head of water or mercury.

N.B.—**Thrust = Pressure × Area.**

Archimedes' Principle.

Problem. A rectangular block of metal (fig. 14) measuring 15 cm. × 6 cm. × 4 cm. is suspended vertically in water so that its top surface is 5 cm. below the water surface. Calculate the downthrust on the top, the upthrust on the base, and the weight of water displaced.

Upthrust on base = Pressure × Area
= h cm. × d gm. per c.c. × Area
= 20 × 1 × 24 = 480 gm.-wt.
Downthrust on top = 5 × 1 × 24 = 120 gm.-wt.

Net upthrust = 360 gm.-wt.

Wt. of water displaced = 15 × 6 × 4 × 1 = 360 gm.-wt.

Problem. The same block (fig. 15) is suspended in water so

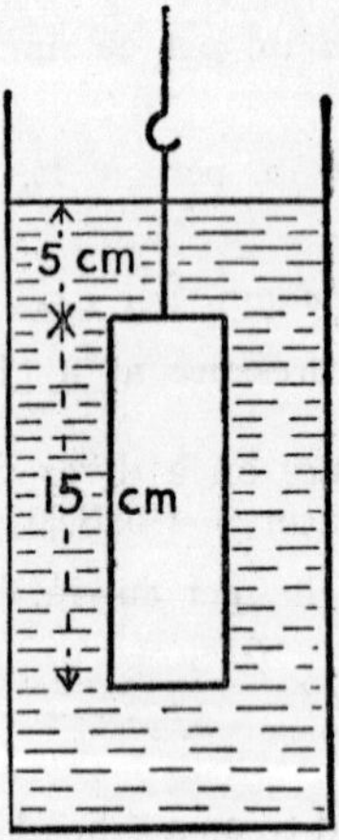

FIG. 14.

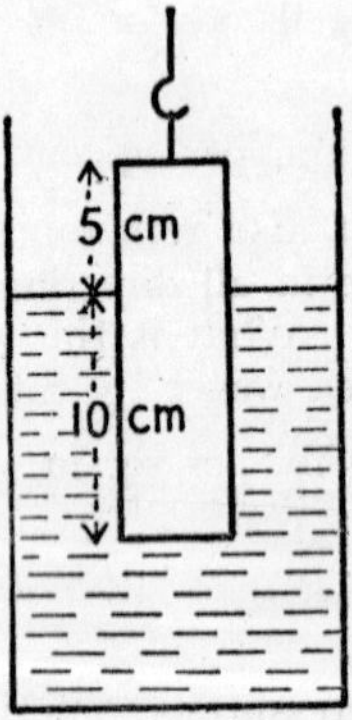

FIG. 15.

that a length of 10 cm. is immersed and 5 cm. exposed. Calculate upthrust on base and weight of water displaced.

Upthrust on base = Pressure × Area
= h cm. × d gm. per c.c. × Area
= 10 × 1 × 24
= 240 gm.-wt.
Wt. of water displaced = 10 × 6 × 4 × 1 = 240 gm.-wt.

In each of the above problems we notice that the upthrust = wt. of water displaced.

If the block is *weighed* in water the upthrust will be indicated by an apparent loss of weight on the balance. Again, if the block is of wood, it will float and apparently lose all its weight. So we have

Wt. of floating body = Upthrust = Wt. of water displaced.

The above facts are true not only for *regular* solids immersed in *water* but for all bodies immersed in any fluid. These facts are just particular cases of Archimedes' Principle, which states that **when a body is wholly or partly immersed in a fluid, it is acted upon by an upthrust. This upthrust or apparent loss of weight is equal to the weight of fluid displaced.**

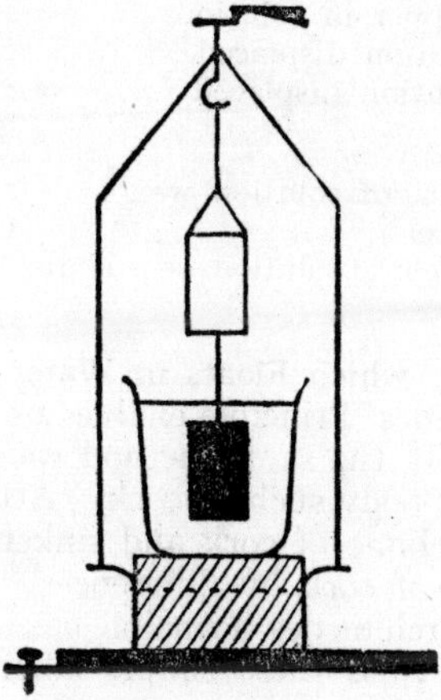

FIG. 16.

The principle can be illustrated experimentally by the well-known bucket and cylinder experiment (fig. 16). The volume of cylinder = internal volume of the bucket. The bucket and cylinder are first weighed in air, then bucket in air and cylinder in water. The loss of weight in the second case is just made up by filling the bucket with water.

We can use Archimedes' Principle to determine densities and specific gravities.

To find the density of Glass and of a Solution of Copper Sulphate. Tie a thread round a glass stopper and weigh it, first in air, then in water, then in the solution, using a "bridge" and beaker (fig. 16).

Wt. of stopper in air	= 35·54 gm.
Wt. of stopper in water	= 21·56 gm.
∴ Wt. of water displaced	= 13·98 gm.
∴ Vol. of water displaced	= 13·98 c.c.
∴ Vol. of stopper	= 13·98 c.c.
∴ 13·98 c.c. of stopper weigh	35·54 gm.
1 c.c. ,, ,, ,,	2·54 gm.

Density of stopper = 2·54 gm. per c.c. S.G. = 2·54

Again, Wt. of stopper in air	= 35·54 gm.
Wt. of stopper in solution	= 20·44 gm.
Wt. of solution displaced	= 15·10 gm.
Vol. of solution displaced	= 13·98 c.c. (same as stopper)
∴ 13·98 c.c. of solution weigh	15·10 gm.
1 c.c. ,, ,, ,,	1·08 gm.

Density of copper sulphate solution = 1·08 gm./c.c.

S.G. = 1·08.

Density of a Body which Floats in Water. From the above we see that Archimedes' Principle enables us to find the volume of a body in c.c. By the same method we can easily find the density of a floating body such as cork. Attach a piece of lead to sink it. Find volume of cork and sinker, volume of sinker alone, then volume of cork by difference.

Flotation. But Archimedes' Principle has a still wider application, ranging far beyond these simple laboratory experiments. Hydrometers for testing accumulator acid, lactometers for milk, rafts, ships, floating docks, balloons and airships all depend upon Archimedes' Principle. Most problems on floating bodies depend on the following fact—

Wt. of floating body = Upthrust or Wt. of liquid displaced.

Problem. A rectangular block of wood 6 ft × 2 ft. × 1 ft. is thrown into sea water having a density of 64 lb. per cubic foot. If the block weighs 600 lb., what additional weight will sink it?

$$600 \text{ lb.} + x \text{ lb.} = (6 \times 2 \times 1) \text{ cu. ft.} \times 64 \text{ lb.}$$
$$600 + x = 768 \text{ lb.}$$
$$x = 168 \text{ lb.}$$

Problem. A solid floats in glycerine (S.G. 1·25) with $\frac{3}{5}$ of its volume immersed. Find the specific gravity of the solid.

Let V = volume of the solid, s = its specific gravity, d = wt. of unit vol. of water, then

Wt. of floating body = wt. of glycerine displaced

But Wt. = Vol. × Spec. Grav. × Density of water

$$\therefore V \times s \times d = \frac{3}{5} V \times 1{\cdot}25 \times d$$

$$\therefore s = \frac{3}{5} \times 1{\cdot}25 \text{ or } 0{\cdot}75.$$

Problem. A cylinder of wood (fig. 17) floats in a liquid with 7 cm. of its length immersed and 3 cm. exposed. Compare the densities of the wood and the liquid.

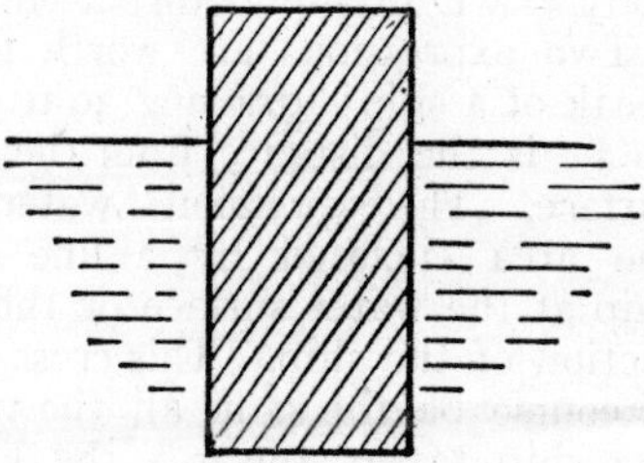

FIG. 17.

Let V c.c. = total volume

v c.c. = immersed volume

then Wt. of wood = $V \times d_W$

Wt. of liquid displaced = $v \times d_L$

but $Vd_W = vd_L$

$$\therefore \frac{d_W}{d_L} = \frac{v}{V} = \frac{7}{10}.$$

If the liquid is water, then d_L is 1 and $d_W = \frac{v}{V} = \frac{7}{10}$.

Problem. A block of wood of specific gravity 0·7 is placed in water, then in alcohol of specific gravity 0·8. What fraction of the volume will be immersed in each case?

(*a*) Wt. of block = Wt. of water displaced

$V \times 0{\cdot}7 \times d = v \times d$ where d = density of water

∴ Immersed volume v = 0·7 of total volume V.

(*b*) Wt. of block = Wt. of alcohol displaced

$V \times 0{\cdot}7 \times d = v \times 0{\cdot}8 \times d$

∴ Immersed volume = 0·7/0·8 of Total Volume

= 0·875 of Total Volume.

We notice that the block sinks farther in the light liquid. This is the principle of the hydrometer (fig. 18) so much used in daily life for determining the specific gravity of accumulator acid, milk, alcoholic mixtures. The acid from a charged accumulator gives a hydrometer reading of about 1220. This means that the specific gravity is 1·220. As the accumulator runs down, the specific gravity of the acid drops to, perhaps, 1160; this is a sign that recharging is necessary.

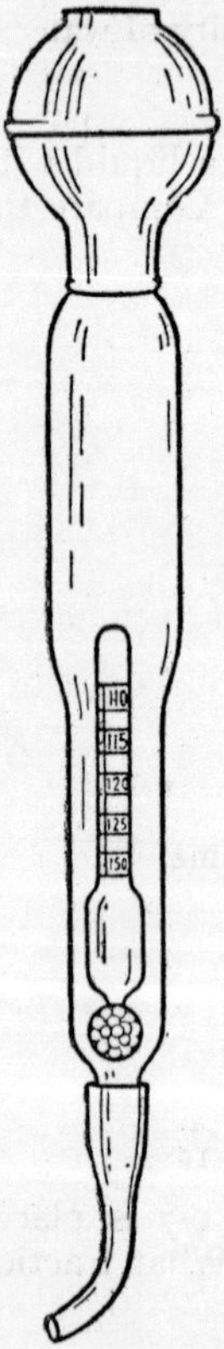

Fig. 18.

Ships and Floating Docks. Here again we have examples illustrating the fact that wt. of floating body = wt. of liquid displaced.

Two expressions are worth noting. We often speak of a ship "drawing 30 ft. of water." Here 30 ft. is the distance from the keel to the water surface. The expression "water line area" means the area enclosed by a line drawn round the ship at the water surface or the horizontal cross-section of the ship. This cross-section would not of course be the same all the way down because the ship tapers towards the keel, but it would not vary much for some distance above and below the "Plimsoll mark" (fig. 19). The letters L.R. signify that this safe loading line is considered reasonable for that particular ship by Lloyd's Insurance Company and that the fact is duly recorded in Lloyd's Register of Shipping. The mark is named after Samuel Plimsoll (1824–98), a Bristol M.P. who succeeded in getting a law passed to prevent the over-loading of ships. Before his time, unscrupulous owners sent to sea old heavily laden (and heavily insured) vessels and profited by the disasters so caused. Sailors often referred to these ships as "coffin ships."

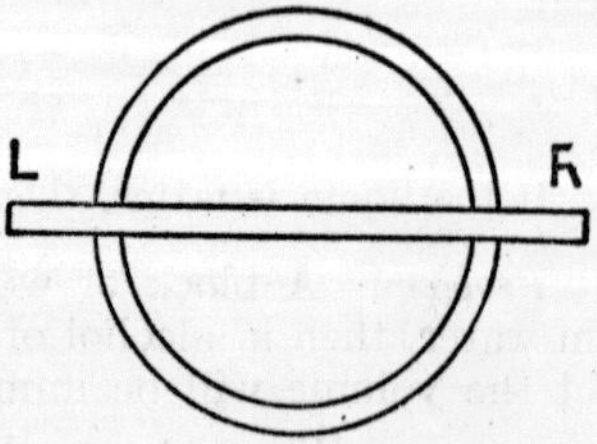

Fig. 19.

Problem. A sea-going ship without cargo draws 25 ft. of

water. If its water line area is 20,000 sq. ft., what load will make it draw 27 ft. of water?

$$\text{Extra vol. of water displaced} = 20{,}000 \times 2 \text{ cu. ft.}$$
$$\text{Wt. of water displaced} = 20{,}000 \times 2 \times 62{\cdot}5 \text{ lb.}$$
$$\text{Wt. of sea water displaced} = 20{,}000 \times 2 \times 62{\cdot}5 \times 1{\cdot}03 \text{ lb.}$$
$$\therefore \text{Load} = \frac{20{,}000 \times 2 \times 62{\cdot}5 \times 1{\cdot}25}{2240} \text{ tons.}$$

A floating dock has air chambers in its base. When these

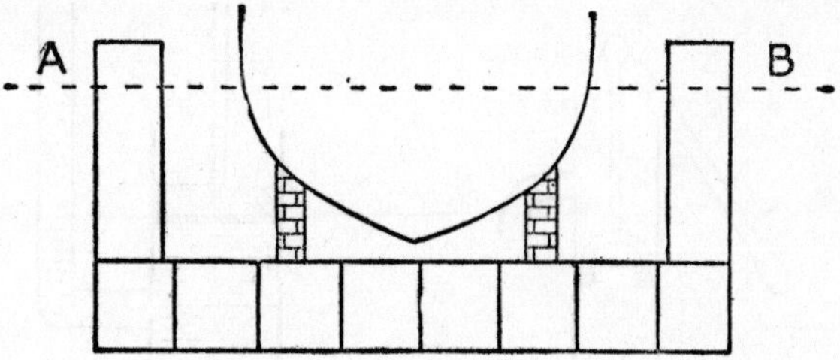

FIG. 20.

are full of water, the dock sinks to the line AB say (fig. 20), and the vessel floats in. The water is then pumped out of the chambers and the dock rises until the floor of the dock is clear of the water. Finally the upthrust due to water displaced is equal to the total weight of dock and ship.

The Siphon. A simple siphon is shown in fig. 21. To start the water running, suction is applied at C. Then the water will continue to run as long as C is lower than B.

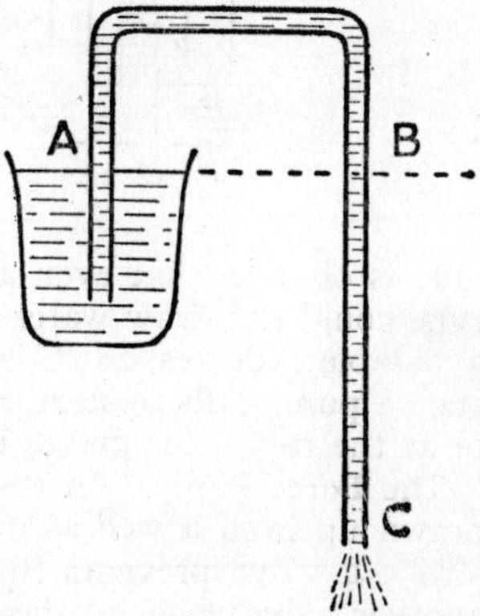

FIG. 2..

The action may be explained as follows. The external pressure at A and C is the same. The pressures inside the tube at A and B are also equal to this external pressure. But the pressure inside the tube at C is greater by the water column BC. It is therefore able to overcome the external pressure at C.

The Common or "Suction" Pump. The principle of the common water pump will be readily understood from fig. 22. As the piston rises, its valve closes and there is a tendency to form a vacuum in the cylinder. The atmospheric pressure acting on the water in the well forces water up through the lower valve to fill this partial vacuum. On the down stroke the bottom valve closes and the piston valve opens. On the next up stroke, water is driven out from the spout.

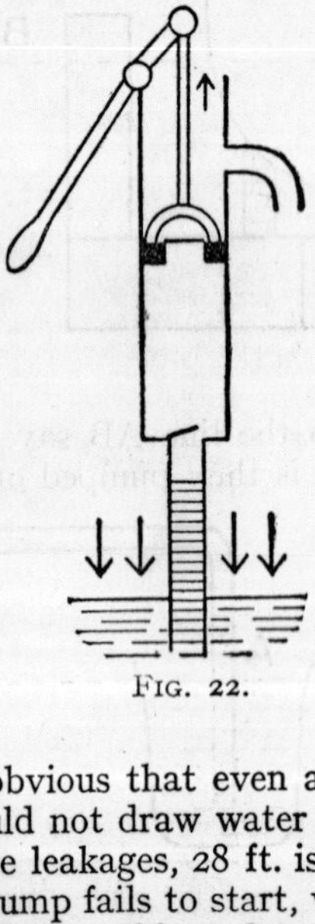

FIG. 22.

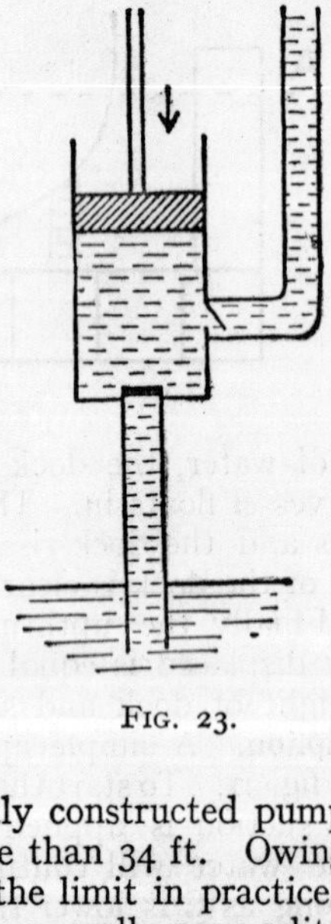

FIG. 23.

It is obvious that even a perfectly constructed pump of this type could not draw water up more than 34 ft. Owing to unavoidable leakages, 28 ft. is about the limit in practice. When such a pump fails to start, villagers generally pour a little water in at the top; this makes the piston and valve more air-tight.

The Force Pump. In the force pump (fig. 23) water may be drawn up from a well as in the common pump. On the down stroke a valve prevents the water returning to the well, while another valve opens to the delivery tube. The height to which water may be forced depends only on the power available for driving the piston.

Boyle's Law. When we refer to a litre of water or a cubic inch of iron, the idea is perfectly definite, but when a litre of air is mentioned the actual quantity of air is uncertain; the air may be hot or cold, rare or compressed. It is important to know exactly how pressure and temperature affect the volume of a gas. The effect of pressure was investigated by Robert Boyle in 1662. He found that when the pressure is doubled the volume is halved, if the pressure is trebled the volume diminishes to one-third and so on. Put in more general terms the result was this—**If the temperature is constant, the volume of a given mass of gas is inversely proportional to the pressure (Boyle's Law).**

This result may be verified for air by a modified form of Boyle's apparatus (fig. 24). Two glass tubes are connected by pressure tubing. One tube is closed at the top and contains the air enclosed by mercury. The other tube is open at the top. Provision is made for both tubes to slide up and down against a scale.

FIG. 24.

Since the cross-section of the tubes will not vary during the experiment, both pressure and volume can be measured in units of length. In the figure the volume of the air is AB, while the pressure is atmospheric + CD. The atmospheric pressure is first read on the barometer, then this is added to the various values of CD.

AB is placed as low as possible and the open tube raised step by step to the highest position. Then AB is placed as high as possible and the open tube moved step by step to the lowest position. In this way a considerable variation of pressure may be obtained. When necessary, mercury is added to the open tube. The results are drawn up as follows:

Atmospheric Pressure	*Mercury Pressure*	*Total Pressure P*	*Volume V*	*P × V*
cm.				
76·4 say	0	76·4	12·3	940
76·4	8·2	84·6	11·1	939
	and so on			

It should be found that PV is a constant within the limits of experimental error. If P is plotted against V on a graph a hyperbola is obtained. This is always an indication that one quantity is inversely proportional to the other.

Problem. A litre of hydrogen is collected when the atmospheric pressure is 740 mm. What will be the volume under a pressure of 760 mm.?

Vol. of air at 740 mm. pressure = 1000 c.c.
,, ,, ,, ,, 1 mm. ,, = 1000 × 740
,, ,, ,, ,, 760 mm. ,, = $1000 \times \frac{740}{760}$

$$\text{or } P_1V_1 = P_2V_2$$
$$740 \times 1000 = 760\ V_2$$
$$\therefore V_2 = 1000 \times \frac{740}{760}$$

QUESTIONS

1. Explain with the aid of a diagram the Principle of the Bramah Press. How could the same principle be used to work a lift?

2. The pistons in a Bramah Press have radii 2 in. and 25 in. If a weight of 30 lb. acts on the small one, what load will be supported by the other?

3. What would be the height of the liquid in a Torricellian barometer filled with (*a*) water, (*b*) glycerine? [S.G. of glycerine = 1·26.]

4. A man sitting on a football bladder can be gradually raised from the ground by pouring water into a long narrow tube which is attached to the bladder. Explain this. Describe briefly any one application of this principle. (J. M. B.)

5. A pipe "springs a leak" 24 ft. below the surface of the water in the supply cistern. Find the water pressure at the leak in lb. per square inch.

6. The pressure at a water tap is 150 lb. per square inch. How far is the tap below the reservoir?

7. The greatest recorded ocean depth is 32,000 ft. in the Pacific. Find the pressure in atmospheres and lb. per square inch. [S.G. of sea water 1·03.]

8. A brick measures $8\frac{1}{2}$ in. × 4 in. × $2\frac{1}{2}$ in. What will be the upthrust when it is suspended (*a*) in fresh water, (*b*) in sea water S.G. 1·03?

9. A solid cylinder 15 cm. long and 4 sq. cm. cross-section floats upright in water with 3 cm. of its length exposed. Calculate the weight of the cylinder and the density of the material.

10. A cube of metal with edge 2 cm. is suspended from a spring balance and immersed in water. The reading of the balance is 76 gm. What is the weight of the cube in air? What is the density of the metal?

11. A cylinder of oak 20 cm. long and 3 sq. cm. in cross-section floats in water with 18 cm. of its length immersed. Find (*a*) the weight of the cylinder, (*b*) the weight which must be put on the top to just sink it.

12. A solid weighs 126 gm. in air, 114 gm. in water and 112 gm. in a salt solution. Find the density of the solid and of the salt solution.

13. A piece of marble weighs 108 gm. in air, 68 gm. in water, and 76 gm. in alcohol. Find the specific gravity of the marble and of the alcohol.

14. A piece of cork weighs 2·5 gm. and a lump of lead 45·2 gm. When the cork and lead are tied together and weighed in water the result is 33·7 gm. The lead alone in water weighs 41·2 gm. Find the density of the cork.

15. A raft is made of logs of S.G. 0·7. If the raft has a volume of 100 cu. ft., what load will make it awash (*a*) in fresh water, (*b*) in sea water S.G. 1·03?

16. A log 12 ft. long, 2 ft. wide, and 10 in. thick, is floating horizontally in water so that 7 in. of its thickness is immersed. Find the weight of the log.

17. A beaker containing lead shot floats in water, with 8 cm. of its depth immersed. If the average radius of the beaker is $3\frac{1}{2}$ cm., find the weight of beaker and shot. What additional weight will sink the beaker another 2 cm.?

18. If ice and sea water have specific gravities 0·92 and 1·03 respectively, what fraction of the iceberg will be immersed?

19. A ship sinks $\frac{1}{2}$ in. when an elephant is taken aboard. If the water line area is 3456 sq. ft., find the weight of the elephant.

20. A cubical block of metal floats in mercury (S.G. 13·6). When a load of 170 gm. is placed on top it sinks $\frac{1}{2}$ cm. What is the length of one side of the cube?

21. If an airship has a capacity of one and a half million cubic feet, what weight will it lift when filled with (*a*) hydrogen, (*b*) helium? [Densities of air, helium and hydrogen are as 14·4, 2, 1; 1 cu. ft. of hydrogen weighs 0·0056 lb.]

22. Draw any hydrometer which you have seen. In which direction do the numbers increase? Why?

23. A floating dock is 324 ft. long, 105 ft. wide and the air chambers are 11 ft. 6 in. deep. Calculate the upthrust when the air chambers are just immersed.

24. The air in a certain room weighs 145 lb. when the barometer stands at 29 in. of mercury. Find the weight of the air in the same room, at the same temperature, when the barometer stands at 30·5. (O. part question.)

25. Half a litre of hydrogen is collected at a pressure of 754 mm.

What will be the volume at a pressure of 760 mm. if the temperature does not change?

26. What do you understand by the expression "the density of a solid"? A block of an insoluble substance, whose volume is 40 c.c., weighs 36 gm.; will this body float or sink in water? Give reasons for your answer, and state the principle involved. (L.)

27. A piece of glass weighs 24 gm. in air, and 16 gm. in water. A piece of wood weighs 60 gm. in air, and when fastened to the glass the two weigh 10 gm. in water. Find the specific gravity of the glass and of the wood. (L.)

28. Show that if one part by volume of liquid of specific gravity 1·84 is mixed with four parts of distilled water, the specific gravity of the resulting mixture is approximately 1·17. [Assume no change of volume in mixing.] (L.)

29. State the relation between the pressure and density of a gas at constant temperature.

A gas cylinder contains 40 litres of gas at 20 atmospheres pressure. Some of the gas is used and the pressure falls to 3 atmospheres. What volume of gas at atmospheric pressure has been used? (C.W.B.)

30. State Boyle's Law, and describe how it may be verified experimentally.

The mercury in a barometer tube stands at 75 cm., and the space above it is 5 cm. in length. 3 c.c. of air at atmospheric pressure are admitted to the tube, and the mercury falls 15 cm. Find the area of the cross-section of the tube. (B.)

31. Use the following data relating to men digging a trench; plot men on the *Y* axis and days on the *X* axis.

Men	1	2	3	6	8	12
Days	24	12	8	4	3	2

What kind of graph do you obtain? How are the two quantities related? How does the graph resemble a Boyle's Law graph?

CHAPTER IV

THE PARALLELOGRAM OF FORCES

IF two boys pull on a rope in the same direction with forces of 30 and 50 lb.-wt., the effect is the same as if a man pulled in the same direction with a force of 80 lb.-wt. We say the **resultant** of 30 and 50 lb.-wt. acting in the same direction is a force of 80 lb.-wt. acting in that direction. **The resultant of two or more forces is a single force which can replace the given forces.**

A force of 80 lb.-wt. acting in the opposite direction would produce a state of balance or equilibrium and is therefore called the **equilibrant.** *The equilibrant is a single force which can balance two or more forces.*

Suppose now that the two boys pull on the rope in opposite directions, say 30 lb.-wt. to the North and 50 lb.-wt. to the South. The resultant is now 20 lb.-wt. South and the equilibrant 20 lb.-wt. North. Note that the equilibrant is always equal and opposite to the resultant.

The problem is a little more complicated if we imagine the pulls exerted on two ropes inclined at an angle, say 60°. Fasten a large sheet of paper on a table and draw lines at an angle of 60°, making one 3 units long, the other 5 units long. Attach strings to three spring balances and join the free ends in one knot. Apply forces of 3 and 5 lb.-wt. along the two lines, holding the knot in a stationary position. Now pull the third balance, gradually varying the magnitude and direction until the equilibrant is obtained. Draw a line to represent its magnitude and direction. Complete the parallelogram and draw the diagonal which passes through the point of application. It will be found to have the same length and to be continuous with the line representing the equilibrant. It therefore represents the resultant. It should be 7 lb.-wt. (fig. 25).

We have thus arrived at a rule known as the **Parallelogram** of Forces—*If two forces acting at a point are represented in magnitude and direction by two adjacent sides of a parallelogram, then their resultant may be represented in magnitude and direction by the diagonal which passes through the point of application.*

We may look at fig. 25 from two different points of view thus:

(1) OD is the resultant of the forces OA and OB.

(2) OA, OB, OC represent three forces in equilibrium acting at a point.

But the three forces OA, OB, OC can also be represented in magnitude and direction by the triangle OAD if we make the arrows follow round in order (fig. 25).

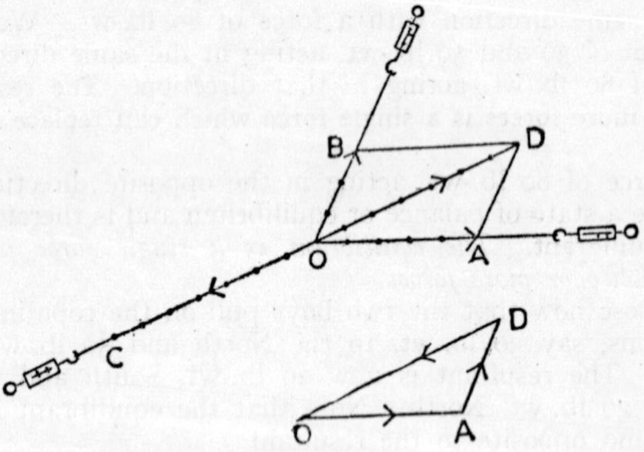

FIG. 25.

This is just a particular case of a general fact, namely, that "*if three forces acting at a point are in equilibrium, then they can be represented in magnitude and direction* (*but not in position*) *by the sides of a triangle taken in order.*"

The converse is also true—"if three forces acting at a point can be represented in magnitude and direction by the sides of a triangle taken in order then the three forces must be in equilibrium."

These two rules are generally known as the **Triangle of Forces.** You will remember from geometry that when we are given three lengths it is only possible to draw a triangle when any two of these lengths are together greater than the third length. For example, you could not draw a triangle having sides of 3,

4 and 8 cm. Correspondingly, forces of 3, 4 and 8 lb.-wt. could not possibly be in equilibrium.

Problem. Forces of 3, 4 and 5 lb.-wt. act at a point and are in equilibrium. Show how they must act and measure the angles between them.

We proceed as follows: Draw a triangle ABC having sides 3, 4 and 5 in. long. Put arrows round the triangle in order. Choose any one of the three angular points and arrange the three forces to act away from that point. The same figure will be obtained whichever angular point is chosen (fig. 26). Measure the angles ECD, ECA and ACD.

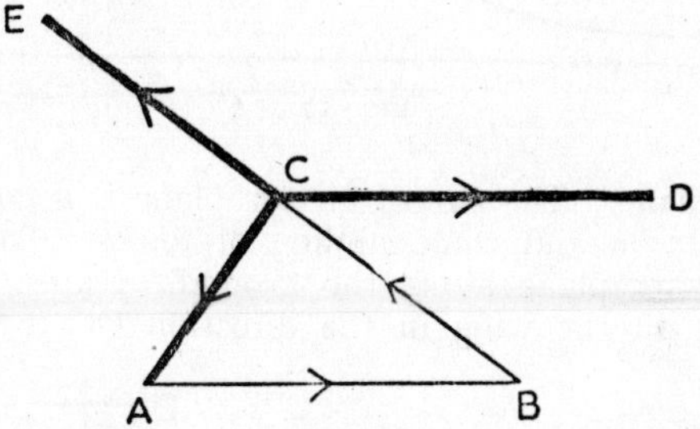

FIG. 26.

Resolution of Forces. Sometimes it is not convenient to apply a force in the direction in which the body is intended to move. Thus a horse walks along a towpath in order to pull a barge along the canal (fig. 27); any other arrangement would certainly be inconvenient. The pull is exerted in a slanting direction and part of the force exerted is wasted.

Problem. A horse pulls a barge along a canal exerting a force of 60 lb.-wt. at an angle of 20° with the direction of motion. Calculate the useful force and the wasted force.

Represent the pull of 60 lb.-wt. to scale (fig. 27). Complete the rectangle and measure OA and OB. You will find that a force of 56 lb.-wt. urges the boat forward and a force of $20\frac{1}{2}$ lb.-wt. pulls it into the side. This latter force is neutralized by the bargeman at the rudder. *N.B.*—The two components do *not* add up to 60 lb.-wt.

You will notice that this problem is the reverse of that known as the parallelogram of forces. There we compounded two forces to form a resultant. Here we **resolve** a single force into its components and the process is known as **resolution** of a force.

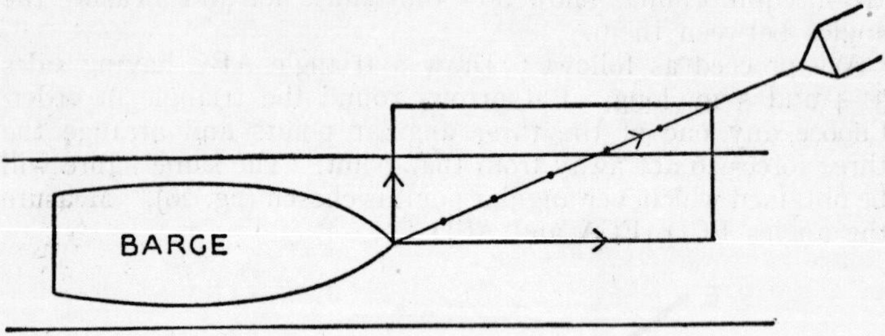

FIG. 27.

The Aeroplane. The rise of an aeroplane is a good example of the resolution and compounding of forces. The engine in driving the aeroplane along the ground, creates an artificial wind acting on the wing in the direction OC (fig. 28). The

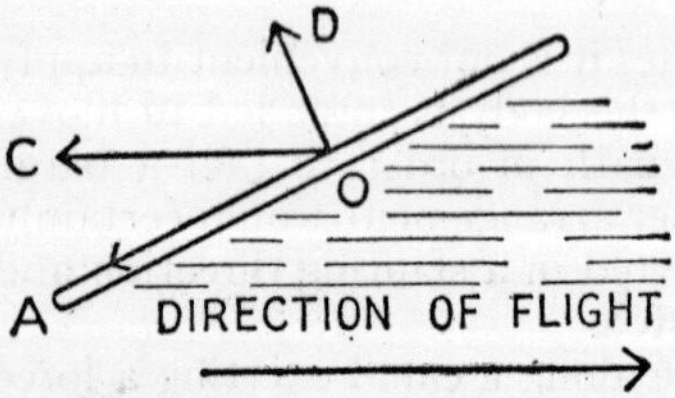

FIG. 28.

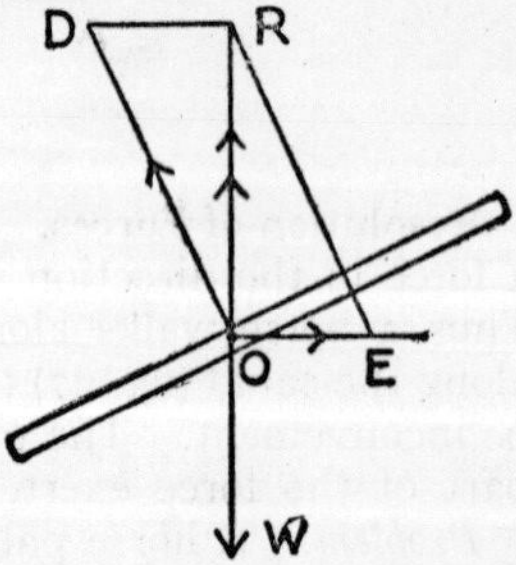

FIG. 29.

force along OC is equal to the components along OD and OA. The component along OA has no effect.

Moreover, there is another force along OD due to suction caused by the formation of a partial vacuum behind the wing. If we now compound the total force along OD with the engine's force along OE (fig. 29) we get a resultant upward force along

OR, and when this is greater than the weight, the aeroplane rises.

Similar reasoning applies to the rise of a kite and to the fact that a sailing ship can have its sails so adjusted that it can travel almost opposite to the wind. The fact to remember is that **the net effect of the wind on a surface is a thrust normal to that surface.**

QUESTIONS

1. How is force measured? Describe with the aid of a diagram an experimental method of finding the resultant of two forces acting at a point. (L.)

2. Three forces act at a point, 2 lb.-wt. N., 7 lb.-wt. W., 4 lb.-wt. NW. Find their resultant.

3. Forces of 1, 3, 5, and 7 lb.-wt. act N, S, E, and W respectively. Find the resultant.

4. A mass of 10 lb. is suspended by a string. It is pulled aside by a force of 10 lb.-wt. Find the direction and tension of the string.

5. *Funicular Polygon.* A string ABCD 107 cm. long is attached to two nails A and D 75 cm. apart in the same horizontal line. A 50-gm. mass is attached at C and x gm. at B. AB = 29 cm., BC = 47 cm., CD = 31 cm., BD = 63 cm. Using the triangle of forces, find graphically the tension in CB, then the mass x.

6. The bob of a pendulum weighs 40 gm. It is pulled out of the vertical by a horizontal force until the string makes an angle of 30° with the horizontal. Using the parallelogram of forces, find the horizontal force and the tension in the string.

7. State the theorem known as the Triangle of Forces. Given string, a frictionless pulley, and a pound weight, how would you determine the approximate weight of a given body? (J.M.B.)

8. A stout thread fastened to a tooth in the upper jaw of a small boy is held at an angle of 30° with the horizontal. Find the horizontal and vertical components when the pull is 10 oz.-wt.

9. A string is attached to a nail in the floor. A pull of 20 lb.-wt. is applied at an angle of 40° with the vertical. Find the force tending to (*a*) pull the nail out, (*b*) bend the nail over.

10. A roller of mass 200 lb. is being hauled up a slope inclined at 30° with the horizontal. What force will just prevent it running back?

CHAPTER V

MOMENTS

It is common knowledge that two boys can play at see-saw although there may be a great difference between their weights; the heavy boy gets nearer the centre or the small boy moves farther away. From the scientific point of view, the see-saw is a **lever** turning about a **fulcrum**. The necessary condition for successful working of the see-saw is not that the weights shall be equal, but that the turning effects shall be equal. The turning effect, or **moment** as it is called, depends partly on the weight and partly on the distance from the fulcrum. More exactly we say *the moment of a force is the turning effect it exerts about a fixed point called the fulcrum. It depends upon* (a) *the magnitude of the force,* (b) *the perpendicular distance from the fulcrum to the line of action of the force.* Thus: *The moment of a force about a point is the product of the force and the perpendicular distance from the point to the line of action of the force.*

Moment = Force × Distance.

To appreciate the importance of "perpendicular" distance, let us consider the opening of a gate (fig. 30). A force of

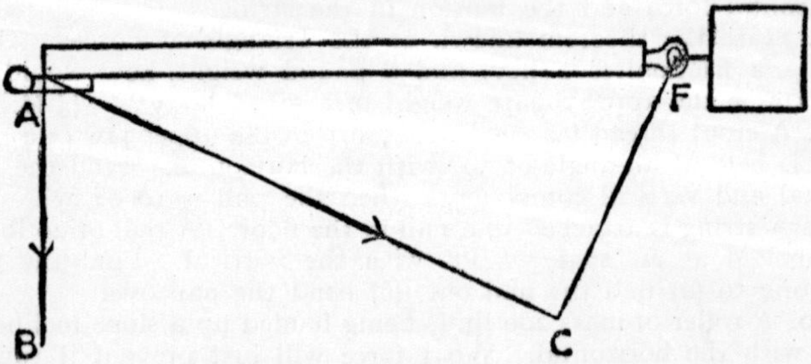

FIG. 30.

5 lb.-wt. has more effect acting along AB than along AC because the perpendicular FA is greater than the perpendicular FC.

Experiment. Take a light stiff rod about 2 ft. long marked off in inches (fig. 31). Suspend it at the mid-point by means

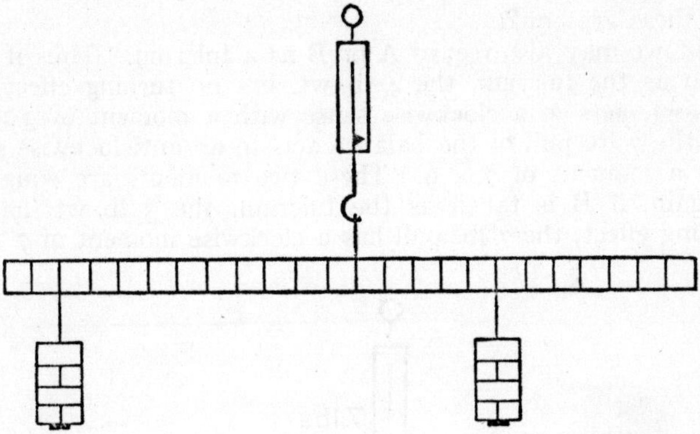

FIG. 31.

of a spring balance. Hang a weight on each side of the bar and adjust for equilibrium. Vary the weights and the distances, then compile a table.

Weight.	*Distance from Fulcrum.*	*Anti-Clockwise Moment.*	*Weight.*	*Distance from Fulcrum.*	*Clockwise Moment.*

The experiment can be varied by using more than two weights, adding the moments on the same side to get the total moment.

You should learn two facts from the experiment :

(1) When the lever is in equilibrium, the sum of the clockwise moments is equal to the sum of the anticlockwise moments.

(2) The upward force registered on the spring balance is equal to the total of the downward forces.

We will now consider the particular case illustrated in fig. 32.

$$\text{Clockwise moment round F} = 3 \times 12$$
$$\text{Anticlockwise moment round F} = 4 \times 9$$

and these are equal.

But we may also regard A or B as a fulcrum. Thus if A is taken as the fulcrum, the 4 lb.-wt. has no turning effect, the 3 lb.-wt. acts in a clockwise sense with a moment of 3×21, and the 7 lb. pull of the balance acts in an anticlockwise sense with a moment of 7×9. These two moments are equal.

Again, if B is taken as the fulcrum, the 3 lb.-wt. has no turning effect, the 7 lb. pull has a clockwise moment of 7×12

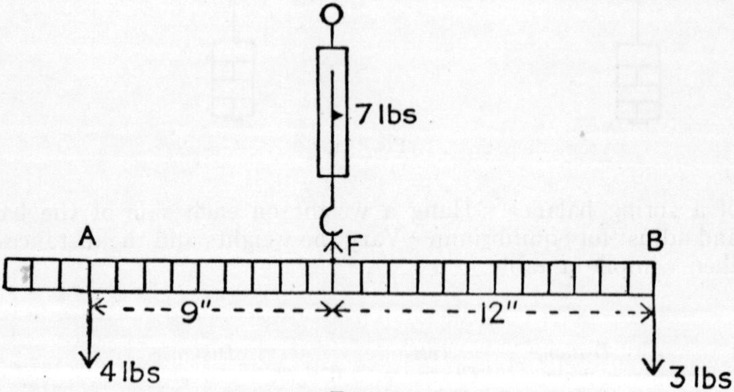

FIG. 32.

and the 4 lb.-wt. an anticlockwise moment of 4×21. These two moments are also equal.

We are now in a position to understand the general statement of the **Law of the Lever** or the **Principle of Moments**—*If a lever is in equilibrium, the sum of the moments tending to turn it clockwise round any point is equal to the sum of the moments tending to turn it anticlockwise round that point.*

We may usefully consider the above example from another point of view. The 7 lb.-wt. pull of the spring balance acting at F can be regarded as the **equilibrant** of the 4 lb.-wt. and the 3 lb.-wt. But the equilibrant is always equal and opposite to the **resultant** or **replacing force,** therefore the 4 and 3 lb.-wt.

could be replaced by a force of 7 lb.-wt. acting down from F. That is, the resultant of the parallel forces 4 lb.-wt. and 3 lb.-wt. is a force of 7 lb.-wt. acting down from F and $4AF = 3BF$.

Centre of Gravity. Balance a metre scale on the flat end of a pencil. The upward force you apply is the equilibrant of all the little parallel forces due to the earth's attraction on the little particles of which the scale is made. All these little forces have a resultant which we call the weight of the body; it is the sum of the particle weights. The equilibrant and resultant both act at a point which is called the **centre of gravity** of the body. It may be thus defined—*The centre of gravity of a body is the point of action of the resultant of all the little parallel forces acting on the particles of the body due to their weight. It is the point where the whole weight of the body may be supposed to act.* When a body is supported at rest, the line of action of the supporting force must pass through the centre of gravity.

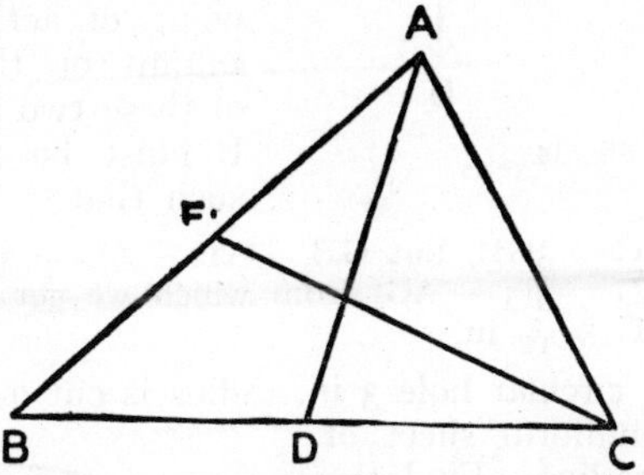

FIG. 33.

Centre of Gravity of a Triangular Lamina. A lamina is a thin flat sheet. Cut out a triangular lamina of cardboard (fig. 33). Suspend it from any point in its area and draw the line of action of the supporting force. This line must contain the C.G. Support the lamina from another point and obtain a second line. The C.G. is at the intersection of these two lines.

On the other side of the cardboard draw medians AD and CF. Pierce the triangle at the intersection of the medians with a pin. The pin will be found to come out at the C.G. already determined.

Similarly the C.G. of any parallelogram will be found to be at the intersection of the diagonals.

Problem. A piece of cardboard consists of a square of side 4 in. and an isosceles triangle erected on one side with an altitude of 3 in. (fig. 34). Find the C.G. of the whole figure.

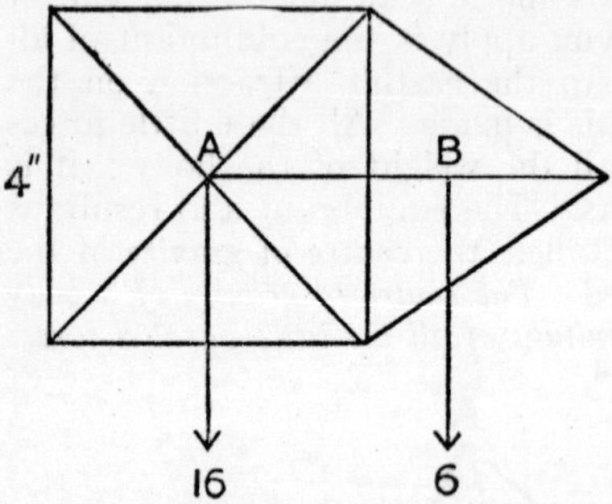

FIG. 34.

The C.G. of the square is at A.

The C.G. of the triangle is at B.

The areas are 16 and 6 sq. in. AB is 3 in. long and is in effect a bar carrying weights of 16 and 6 units or 8 and 3 at the ends. The problem is to find the point of action of the resultant or the equilibrant of these two parallel forces. It must be at a point G such that

$$8AG = 3GB, \text{ but } GB = AB - AG = 3 - AG$$
$$\therefore\ 8AG = 3(3 - AG) \text{ from which we get that}$$
$$AG = \tfrac{9}{11} \text{ in.}$$

Problem. A circular hole 3 in. radius is cut out close to the edge from a uniform sheet of lead of 6 in. radius. Find the C.G. of the remaining portion.

Area of large circle $= 36\pi$
Area of small circle $= 9\pi$
Area of remainder $= 27\pi$

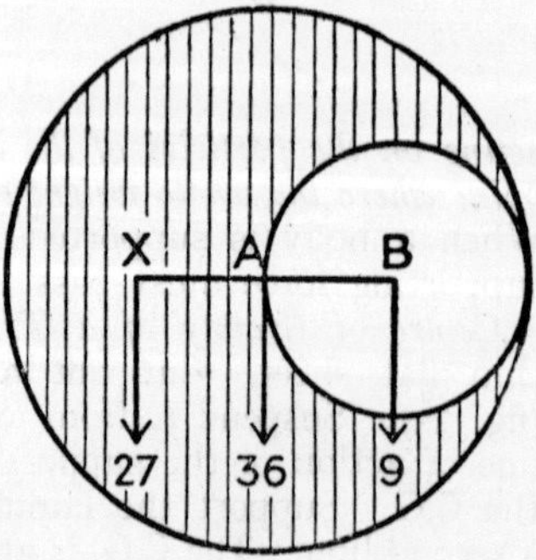

FIG. 35.

The C.G. must be at some point X on the diameter through A and B. We may look upon XAB (fig. 35) as a bar with weights of 27, 36, and 9 units, 36 being the resultant of 27 and 9. Therefore

$$27AX = 9AB = 9 \times 3 = 27$$
$$\therefore\ AX = 1 \text{ in.}$$

C.G. of any Quadrilateral Lamina. We may suspend the lamina from two different points or proceed as follows: Divide the lamina into two triangles by drawing a diagonal BD (fig. 36).

Find the C.G. of each triangle by medians. The C.G. of the lamina must be in the line EF. Draw the other diagonal and repeat the process *or* calculate the areas of triangles ABD and CBD and use these areas as weights on the bar EF.

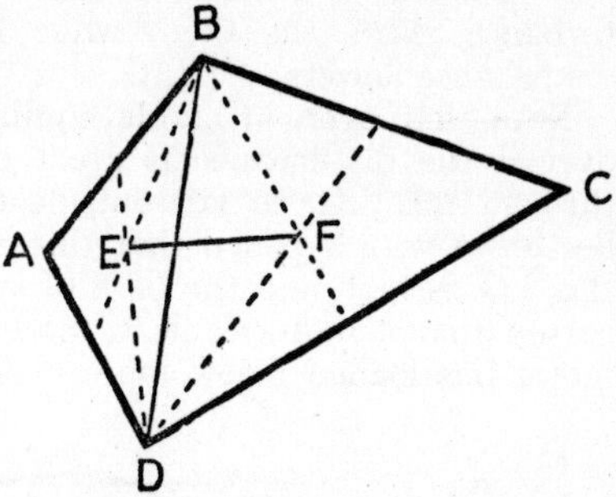

FIG. 36.

Conditions of Stability. We have seen that when a body is supported at rest, the line of action of the supporting force must pass through the C.G. Now the supporting force can be applied (*a*) above the C.G., (*b*) below the C.G., (*c*) at the C.G.

Case (*a*) is well illustrated by a simple pendulum supported at a point F (fig. 37). If the bob is slightly disturbed, it returns to its original position because there is a *restoring moment* $W \times$ AF.

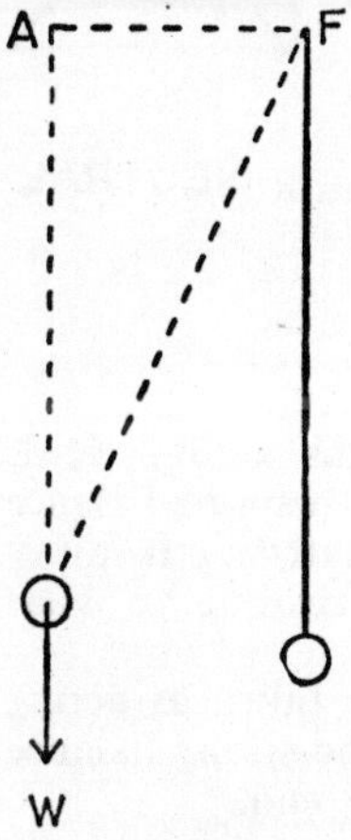

FIG. 37.

Bodies supported above the C.G. are always in **stable equilibrium**, that is, *when slightly disturbed they always return to their original position.*

In Case (*b*) the body is not always in stable equilibrium. Consider a cone supported on its base, on its vertex, then on its side (fig. 38).

In the first position there is a restoring moment $W \times$ AF and the cone is therefore in stable equilibrium. In the second position there is an *upsetting moment* $W \times$ AF and the cone is in **unstable equilibrium**, that is, *when disturbed it tends to move farther still from its original position.* In the third position there is neither an upsetting moment nor a restoring moment, and the cone is said to be in **Neutral Equilibrium**, that is, *when disturbed it neither returns to its original position nor moves farther away from it.*

Case (*c*) can be illustrated by thrusting a compass point

through any lamina at its C.G. Bodies supported in this way are always in neutral equilibrium.

It is useful to remember that in stable equilibrium any disturbance raises the C.G., while in unstable equilibrium any disturbance lowers the C.G.

Note that even in stable equilibrium, the body will topple over if the disturbance is great enough to cause the vertical through the C.G. to fall outside the base of support. It can be shown with a pencil that this can quite easily happen when the C.G. is high and the base of support narrow. It is for this reason that a motor-cycle is more stable than a pedal cycle, a motor-bus loaded below more stable than one loaded above.

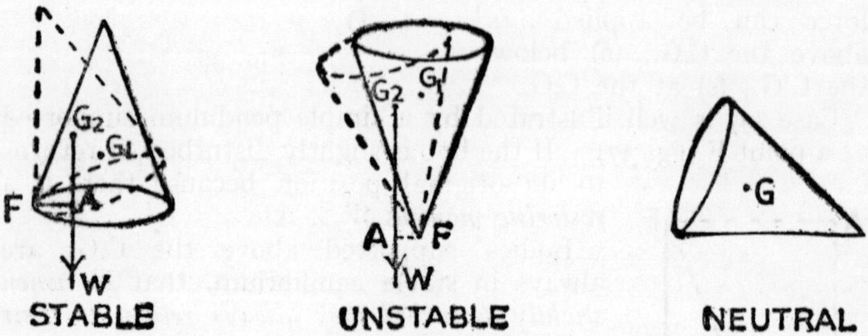

FIG. 38.

More Complex Lever Problems.

Problem. A uniform bar 10 ft. long weighs 20 lb. It is supported at one end by a table, at the other by a spring balance (fig. 39). The bar carries a mass of 18 lb. situated $1\frac{1}{2}$ ft. away from the spring balance. What is the balance reading? What weight is supported by the table?

Since the bar is uniform the weight may be taken as acting from its middle point. Let force exerted by the spring balance be T lb.-wt. Take moments round the table end.

$$(20 \times 5) + (18 \times 8\tfrac{1}{2}) = T \times 10$$
$$100 + 153 = 10T$$
$$\therefore T = 25{\cdot}3 \text{ lb.}$$
$$\text{Wt. supported by the table} = 20 + 18 - 25{\cdot}3$$
$$= 12{\cdot}7 \text{ lb.}$$

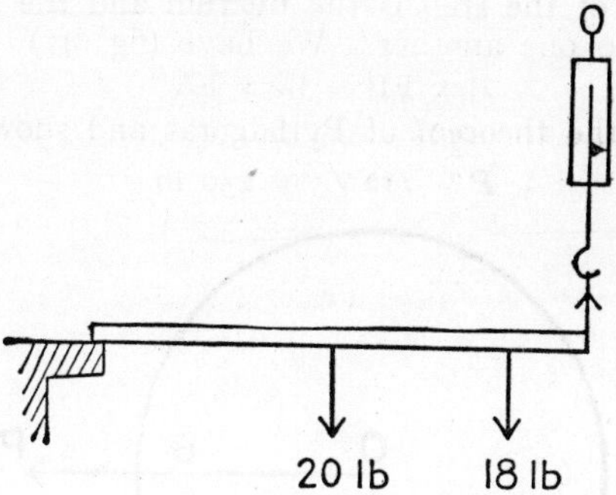

FIG. 39.

Problem. The same bar carries weights of 12 and 16 lb. at the ends (fig. 40). Where must it be supported to balance horizontally?

The upward force = 12 + 20 + 16 = 48 lb.-wt.

Call the point of action X.

Take moments round *any* point, say A.

$$20AB + 16AC = 48AX$$

Hence $$AX = 5 \text{ ft. } 5 \text{ in.}$$

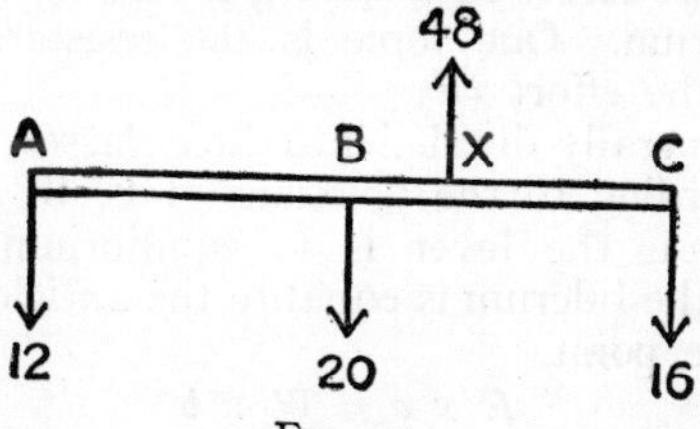

FIG. 40.

It is a very useful exercise to take moments round each of the other points in turn and see if the same result is obtained.

Problem. A garden roller weighing 2 cwt. and 24 in. in diameter rests on a horizontal surface. What horizontal force applied at the axle would be necessary to enable it to surmount a step 4 in. high? (C.W.B.)

The corner of the step is the fulcrum and the acting forces are inclined to one another. We have (fig. 41)

$$P \times \mathrm{FB} = W \times \mathrm{FA}$$

Find FA by the theorem of Pythagoras and show that

$$P = 112\sqrt{5} = 250 \text{ lb.}$$

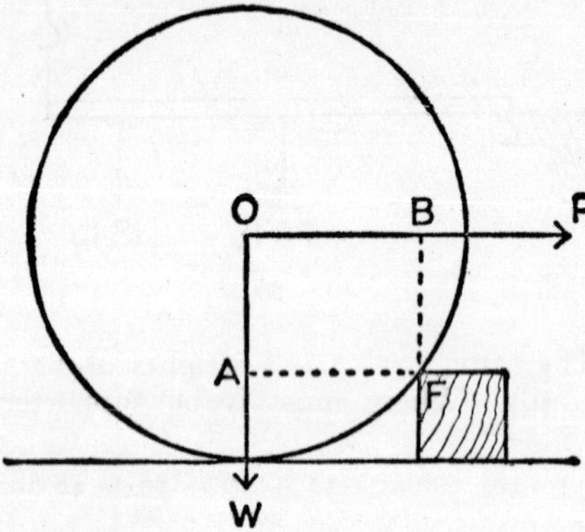

FIG. 41.

The Common Levers. The lever principle is applied in daily life in many different ways. In every common lever we have a fulcrum and two forces each having a turning effect or moment round the fulcrum. One force is the resistance or load (W) and the other the effort (E).

Levers are generally divided into three classes, not according to merit, but according to the positions of F, W and E (fig. 42).

In all cases, if the lever is in equilibrium, the clockwise moment round the fulcrum is equal to the anticlockwise moment round the same point.

$$E \times a = W \times b$$

or

$$\frac{a}{b} = \frac{W}{E}.$$

The ratio $\frac{W}{E}$ is called the mechanical advantage of the lever, while a and b are the effort arm and resistance arm respectively. The mechanical advantage is generally greater than 1 in classes (1) and (2), that is, we overcome a large resistance with a small effort. In class (3) the ratio is always less than 1 and the object of using the lever is just convenience.

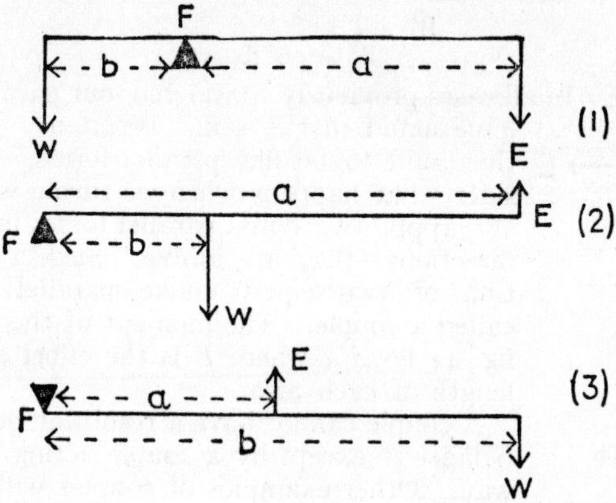

FIG. 42.

Levers may be simple or double. Thus a fire poker used in the usual way is a simple lever of the first class while a pair of scissors is a double lever of the same class.

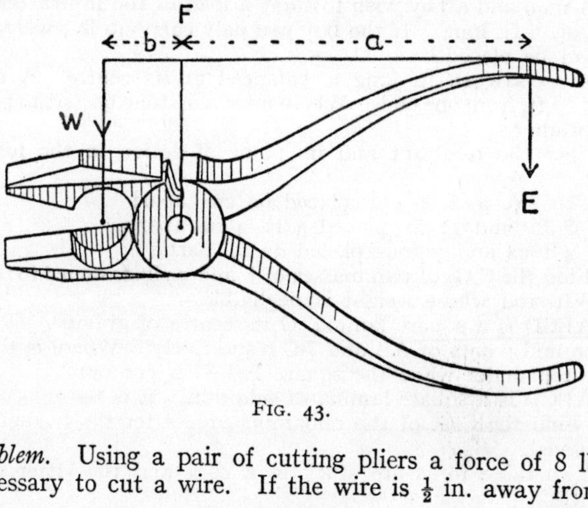

FIG. 43.

Problem. Using a pair of cutting pliers a force of 8 lb.-wt. is necessary to cut a wire. If the wire is $\frac{1}{2}$ in. away from the pivot and the force is applied 6 in. from the pivot, calculate the resistance exerted by the wire (fig. 43).

Taking moments round the pivot, we have

$$W \times \tfrac{1}{2} = 8 \times 6$$
$$\therefore W = 96 \text{ lb.-wt.}$$

Couples. In all cases previously considered, our parallel forces have acted in the same direction. They are then said to be **like** parallel forces. But consider what happens when we turn a water tap. We apply two equal parallel forces in opposite directions—they are **unlike.** Such a combination of two equal unlike parallel forces is called a **couple.** The moment of the couple in fig. 44 is $2Ea$ where E is the effort and a the length of each arm.

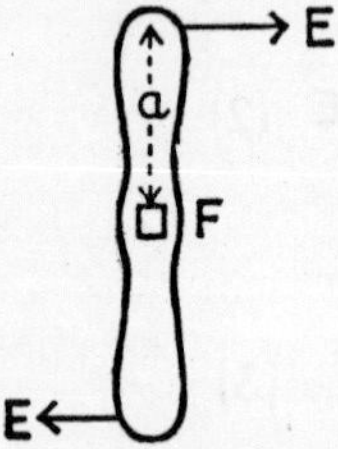

FIG. 44.

A couple cannot have a resultant nor can we balance it except by a couple acting the other way. Other examples of couples will occur to you such as those exerted when winding a watch or clock, spinning a top, and turning a door knob.

QUESTIONS

1. A man and a boy wish to carry a load of 100 lb.-wt. on a stiff light pole 6 ft. long. If the boy can only carry 40 lb., where must the load be placed?

2. A see-saw 16 ft. long is balanced at its centre. A 6-stone boy sits 3 ft. from one end. Where must a 4-stone boy sit to produce equilibrium?

3. Find the resultant and its point of action in the following cases:

20 gm. and 80 gm. placed 60 cm. apart
8 lb. and 12 lb. placed 3 ft. 4 in. apart
4 tons and 7 tons placed 22 ft. part.

4. Find the C.G. of two masses of 8 and 24 lb. fastened to the ends of a 6-ft. rod whose weight is negligible.

5. ABCD is a square lamina, O its centre of gravity. E and F are the mid-points of AB and BC respectively. Where is the C.G. of the remainder when the square EBFO is cut out?

6. ABCD is a square lamina of side 6 in. E is the mid-point of AB. Find the C.G. of the remaining area after the triangle CED is removed.

7. Two table forks are stuck in a cork and the latter is then

balanced on the finger tip. What kind of equilibrium is this? Illustrate your answer by a diagram.

8. What is meant by (*a*) the moment of a force, (*b*) the centre of gravity of a body?

A uniform straight bar 12 in. long, weighing 12 lb., rests on a flat table with 4 in. of its length projecting over the edge of the table. What force is required to make the bar overbalance (1) when applied in a downward direction to the projecting end, (2) when applied in an upward direction to the other end? (L.)

9. Define centre of gravity of a body.

A uniform metal bar 30 in. long is bent so that the two parts 10 in. long and 20 in. long enclose a right angle. Show graphically how such a rod would hang if suspended by the end of the short arm. (C.W.B.)

10. (*a*) Describe the way in which a straight rod may be used as a lever to tilt a heavy solid block.

(*b*) A uniform steel bar is 1 metre long; it is suspended from its centre point; at one end a weight of 400 gm. is hung; at what point must a weight of 1 kg. be suspended to make the rod hang horizontal?

(*c*) If the weight of the bar is 200 gm. and the bar lies on a horizontal table with 40 cm. projecting over the edge, what weight hung on the projecting edge will just cause the bar to overbalance? (L.)

11. Define the moment of a force about a point.

A uniform cylinder 30 in. in diameter and weighing 180 lb. is being rolled up a slope of 30° by means of a tangential force parallel to the slope. What is the least value of this force? (C.W.B.). [This can be solved graphically.]

12. Classify the following and state whether they are single or double levers: nutcrackers, oar, sugar tongs, the human forearm, common balance, pliers, handle of village pump, Roman steelyard (used by butchers for weighing carcasses), wheelbarrow, treadle of sewing machine.

13. A symmetrical circular table 5 ft. in diameter is supported on three upright legs equally spaced round a circle of 2 ft. radius. If the whole table weighs 45 lb., what is the least vertical force applied at the edge of the table that will cause it to tilt? (C.W.B.)

14. Two men are carrying a 20-ft. uniform ladder which weighs 80 lb.; one man is at one end, the other 4 ft. from the opposite end. What weight is supported by each?

15. Two men are carrying a 20-ft. uniform ladder weighing 80 lb. A 40-lb. bag of cement is hung on the ladder 4 ft. from one end. If the men support the load at the ends of the ladder, what force is exerted by each?

16. Work out example 15 in three other ways.

CHAPTER VI

WORK, POWER, MACHINES

THE word "work" has a very special meaning in physics. The physicist is only concerned with mechanical work. When an author dictates a 1200-page novel to his typist, all the "work" is done by the typist!

A force is said to do work when the point of application moves in the direction in which the force acts. If you lift a mass of 1 lb. vertically through a distance of 1 ft., you have done 1 ft.-lb. of work. When a 56-lb. mass is lifted 10 ft. the work done is 560 ft.-lb. If you push against a wall and make it fall over you have done some work, but if the wall is too strong you are only applying force; you are doing no work. If a horse using a force of 80 lb.-wt. pulls a cart half a mile along the road, he has done 80 lb. × 2640 ft. = 211,200 ft.-lb. of work. Work is measured as the product of a force and a distance.

Work Done = *Force applied × Distance moved by the point of application in the direction of the force;* or

Work Done = *Resistance overcome × Distance through which the resistance is overcome.*

Power. Power is a rate of working. We have to consider the *time* taken to do the ft.-lbs. James Watt investigated the rate of working of horses and found that a good horse could do 22,000 ft.-lb. per minute. Watt at this time was making and selling engines and it was necessary to have some method of stating the power of the engines. His customers had been accustomed to using horses, so he decided to call an engine **1 H.P.** if it had a rate of working of **33,000 ft.-lb. per minute.**[1]

Problem. Water collects in a mine shaft 400 yd. deep at the rate of 55 gallons per minute. At what horse-power must the pumping engine work to keep it under control? [1 gallon of water weighs 10 lb.]

Work to be done per minute = (55 × 10) lb. × (400 × 3) ft.

$$\text{Necessary horse-power} = \frac{55 \times 10 \times 400 \times 3}{33{,}000} = 20 \text{ H.P.}$$

[1] i.e. 50% higher than that of a real horse.

The Simple Machines. A machine is a device by which effort can be applied more conveniently than would otherwise be the case.

(*a*) We can use a small effort through a great distance to overcome a great resistance through a small distance, in cases where the resistance is so large that direct action is impossible, *e.g.* crowbars, lifting jacks, block and tackle, wheel and axle.

(*b*) We can use a large effort through a small distance to overcome a small resistance through a great distance, *e.g.* pedalling a bicycle, the human forearm.

(*c*) We can use effort in a more convenient direction, *e.g.* a single fixed pulley for hoisting purposes.

In no case do we get more work out than we put in. There is a rule called the **Principle of Work** which applies to all machines—*If there is no friction, the work got out of a machine is equal to the work put in.* Actually there always is friction, some work is wasted in overcoming this and the work got out is less than the work put in.

$$\text{Efficiency of a Machine} = \frac{\text{Work got out}}{\text{Work put in}}.$$

This ratio is always less than 1.

In dealing with machines there are two other ratios which are also important.

(1) The Mechanical Advantage or Force Ratio

$$= \frac{\text{Resistance or Load}}{\text{Effort}} = \frac{W}{E}.$$

(2) The Velocity Ratio

$$= \frac{\text{Distance effort moves}}{\text{Distance load moves}} \text{ or } \frac{E\text{'s distance}}{W\text{'s distance}}.$$

These ratios are connected with the efficiency ratio thus:

$$\text{Efficiency} = \frac{\text{Work got out}}{\text{Work put in}} = \frac{W \times W\text{'s distance}}{E \times E\text{'s distance}} = \frac{\text{Force Ratio}}{\text{Velocity Ratio}}.$$

The Wheel and Axle. Let us apply these ideas to a simple machine called the Wheel and Axle (fig. 45). It consists of two cylindrical rollers forming one piece and turning on a common axis, the larger roller being the "wheel," the smaller one the "axle." There are two ropes: one round the wheel, the other round the axle.

Applying the Principle of Moments we have $E \times a = W \times b$ where a and b are the radii of the wheel and axle respectively.

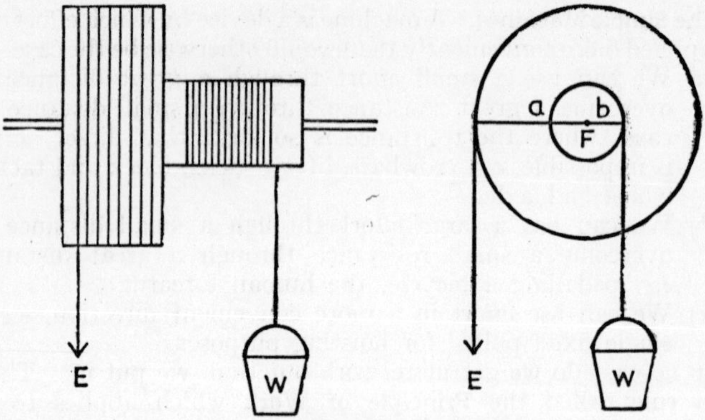

FIG. 45.

Therefore Mechanical Advantage or Force Ratio

$$= \frac{W}{E} = \frac{a}{b}.$$

In one revolution E is applied through a distance of $2\pi a$ while W moves through a distance of $2\pi b$

$$\text{Therefore Velocity Ratio} = \frac{E\text{'s distance}}{W\text{'s distance}} = \frac{2\pi a}{2\pi b} = \frac{a}{b}$$

$$\text{Efficiency} = \frac{\text{Work got out}}{\text{Work put in}} = \frac{W \times W\text{'s distance}}{E \times E\text{'s distance}}$$

$$= \frac{\text{Force Ratio}}{\text{Velocity Ratio}} = \frac{\frac{a}{b}}{\frac{a}{b}} = 1$$

In a perfect machine the force ratio is equal to the velocity ratio and the efficiency is 1 or 100%. In an actual machine the velocity ratio is still the same because it depends solely on the dimensions of the machine. It is the force ratio or $\frac{W}{E}$ which suffers, for E has to be increased to overcome the friction which can never be entirely eliminated.

To find the real efficiency of a given wheel and axle we proceed as follows : Measure the circumferences of the wheel and axle to get the velocity ratio which will of course be constant throughout the experiment. Using various loads, note the effort necessary in each case to maintain motion when given a gentle start. Draw up a table and find the efficiency at different loads.

Load.	*Effort.*	*Force Ratio.*	*Velocity Ratio.*	*Efficiency.*

Pulleys. (*a*) Single fixed pulley (fig. 46). The tension E in the string will be the same throughout its length. If there were no friction, W would be equal to E and the Force Ratio would be 1. But actually E has to be greater than W.

If the effort moves through 1 ft. the load moves 1 ft. ∴ Velocity Ratio is 1.

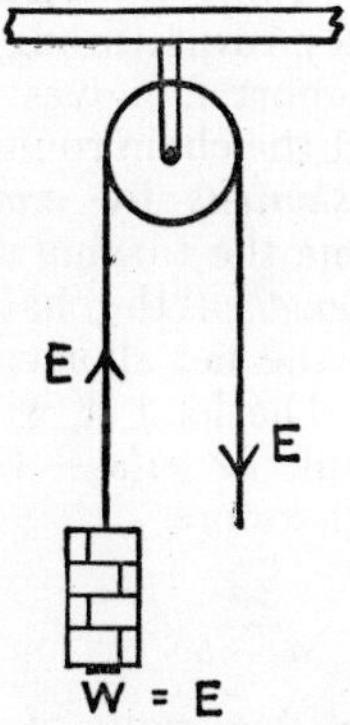

FIG. 46.

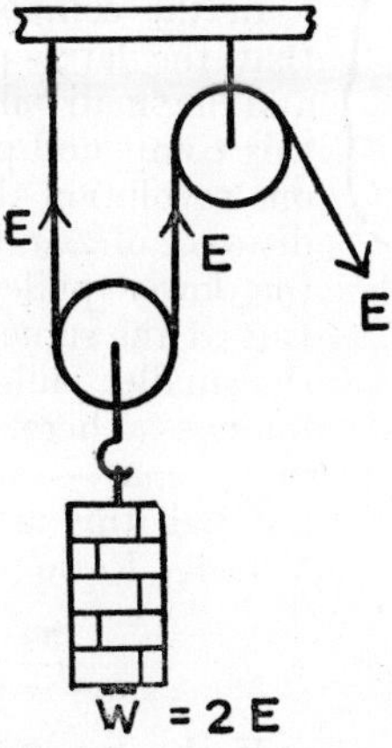

FIG. 47.

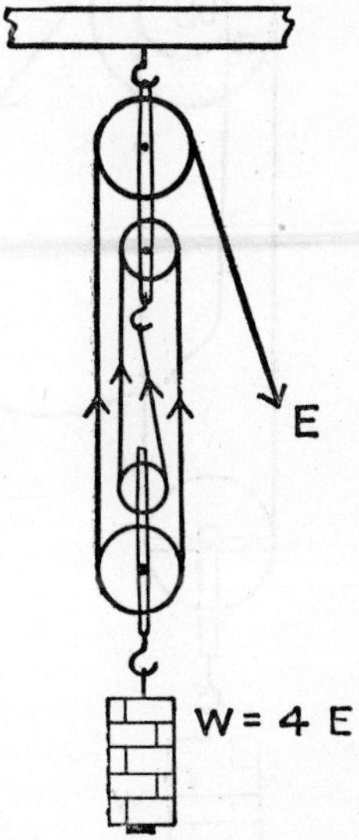

FIG. 48.

(*b*) Single movable pulley (fig. 47).

If E moves 1 ft., W moves 6 in.

∴ Velocity Ratio is 2.

$$\text{Actual Efficiency} = \frac{W \times W\text{'s distance}}{E \times E\text{'s distance}} = \frac{W}{E} \times \frac{1}{2} = \frac{W}{2E}.$$

(*c*) The block and tackle (fig. 48).

If E moves 1 ft., W moves 3 in.

∴ Velocity Ratio is 4.

$$\text{Actual Efficiency} = \frac{W}{E} \times \frac{1}{4} = \frac{W}{4E}.$$

In this scheme there are two pulley blocks and in each block the separate pulleys are parallel to one another, but in diagrams they are generally drawn one above the other to show the position of the string more clearly.

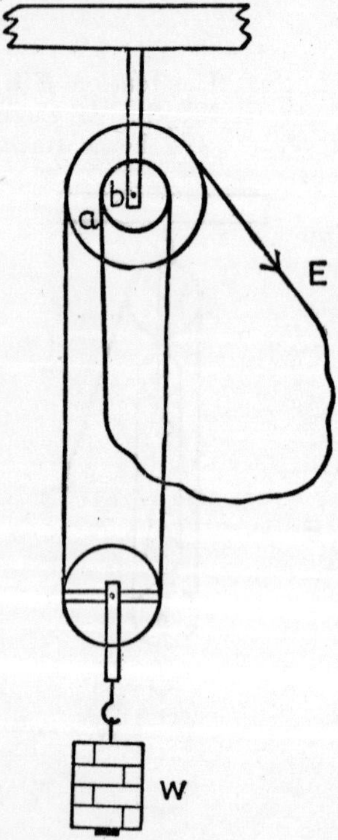

FIG. 49.

(*d*) The Weston Differential Pulley. This machine, illustrated diagrammatically in fig. 49, consists of an endless chain, two pulleys of different radii cast in one piece and a single movable pulley.

In the compound pulley suppose that the large pulley has radius a and the small pulley radius b. When this compound pulley turns through one revolution the effort E moves a distance of $2\pi a$, and the chain round the lower pulley *shortens* by $2\pi a$. But at the same time the turning of the smaller pulley *lengthens* the chain by $2\pi b$. Therefore the net shortening is $2\pi a - 2\pi b$. The load W will rise half this amount, *i.e.* $\pi(a - b)$. Velocity Ratio is therefore

$$\frac{2\pi a}{\pi(a-b)} = \frac{2a}{a-b}$$

If the top pulley has radii of 8 and $7\frac{1}{2}$ in., the Velocity Ratio (and Theoretical Mechanical Advantage) will be 32, and a pull of 70 lb.-wt. should lift a ton! But in practice, friction is purposely introduced into this machine to bring the efficiency down, since it is found that with all machines of efficiency less than 50%, the load will not run back when released.

The Inclined Plane. When we climb a hill we do not often think of it as a machine, but it certainly satisfies the definition of a machine as a device whereby we can use a small effort through a great distance to overcome a great resistance through a small distance. The hill has a "velocity ratio," a "mechanical advantage" and we can speak of its efficiency. When you see a horse "tacking" up a steep hill, he is trying to increase the velocity ratio.

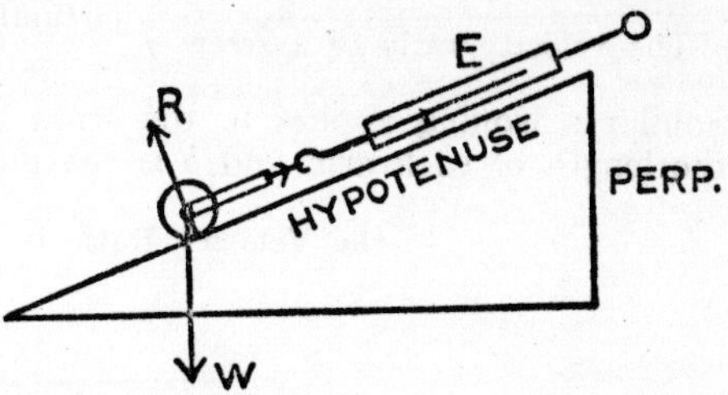

FIG. 50.

Let us now consider a laboratory inclined plane (fig. 50). We may pull a heavy roller up the hypotenuse by means of effort applied with a spring balance.

While the effort E moves along the hypotenuse the weight W is lifted a height equal to the perpendicular.

$$\therefore \text{ Velocity Ratio} = \frac{\text{Hypotenuse}}{\text{Perpendicular}}$$

and as in other machines

$$\text{Actual Efficiency} = \frac{W}{E} \div \text{Velocity Ratio} = \frac{W}{E} \times \frac{\text{perp.}}{\text{hyp.}}$$

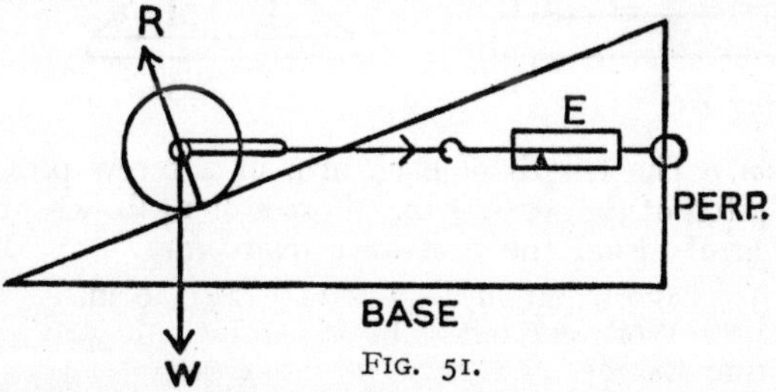

FIG. 51.

Next suppose that the effort is applied parallel to the base (fig. 51). For this purpose a stirrup is used which will pass round the plane. In this case

$$\text{Velocity Ratio} = \frac{\text{base.}}{\text{perp.}}$$

This method of applying the effort is not usual, but it has an important application in the ordinary screw; a screw is approximately an inclined plane wrapped round a cylinder. You can illustrate this by wrapping a piece of paper, cut to shape, round a pencil.

$$\text{The velocity ratio of a screw} = \frac{\text{circumference}}{\text{pitch}}.$$

Similar reasoning applies to the screw press (fig. 52). If a is the length of each arm and b is the pitch of the screw

$$\text{the Velocity Ratio is } \frac{2\pi a}{b}.$$

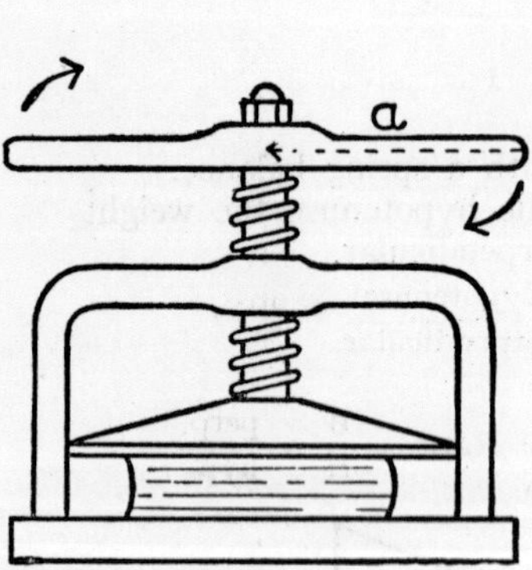

FIG. 52.

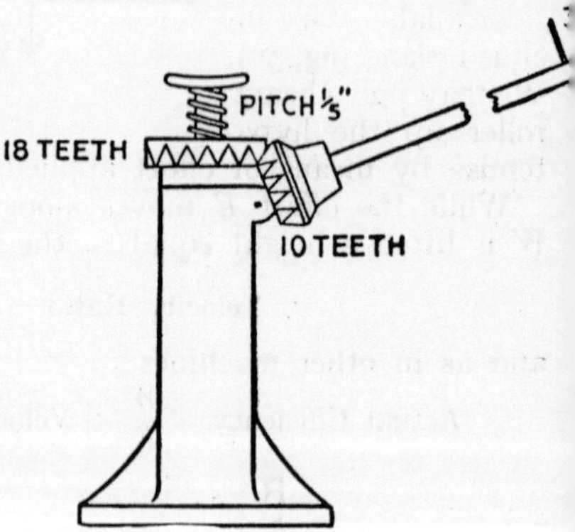

FIG. 53.

Problem. The length of each arm of a screw press is 6 in. and the pitch of the screw $\frac{1}{4}$ in. Forces of 14 lb.-wt. are applied to each arm. Find the resistance overcome.

$$\text{Work put in} = 2 \times 14 \times 2\pi \times 6 \text{ in.}$$
$$\text{Work got out} = W \times \tfrac{1}{4} \text{ in.}$$

Neglecting friction,

$$2 \times 14 \times 2\pi \times 6 = W \times \tfrac{1}{4}$$
$$\therefore W = 4224 \text{ lb.-wt.}$$

Problem. In the screw jack shown (fig. 53) the crossbar is 7 in. long, the bevelled wheel has 10 teeth engaging with a wheel of 18 teeth which raises a screw of pitch $\frac{1}{5}$ in. Show that the velocity ratio is 198.

QUESTIONS

1. A man weighing 9 stone 6 lb. climbs to the top of a "skyscraper" 1000 ft. high in 40 min. At what horse-power was he working?

2. If 1 inch = 2·54 cm. and 1 lb. = 454 gm., express 10 ft.-lb. in cm. gm.

3. An engine raises 2 tons from the bottom of a shaft 440 yd. deep in 72 sec. At what horse-power is the engine working?

4. An aeroplane climbs 6000 ft. in 5 minutes. If its total weight is 5500 lb., at what horse-power is it working against gravity?

5. Describe with a diagram a simple pulley system in which the effort moves four times as fast as the load. What effort will be required to lift 72 lb. if the system is 60 per cent. efficient? (C.)

6. Define a Unit of Work.

A cyclist weighing, with his machine, 150 lb. rides up a gradient of 1 in 12 at 5 miles per hour. What work does he do per second if friction resistance is equal to 10 lb.-wt.? (C.W.B.)

7. A car travelling at 25 miles per hour comes to a slope of 1 in 20. What extra horse-power must it develop to maintain the same speed up the slope, if the weight of the car is 2200 lb.? [One horse-power = 550 ft.-lb. per second.] (C.W.B.)

8. A man capable of exerting a force of 150 lb. requires to raise a weight of 700 lb. vertically for some distance. Describe and explain the action of a mechanical device that will enable him to do so. (C.W.B.)

9. Describe, with explanation and diagrams, the working of (*a*) a block and tackle, (*b*) a differential pulley.

10. Explain exactly how you could find the *efficiency* of an inclined plane.

11. A man wishes to pull a 2-cwt. roller up the garden steps a vertical distance of 3 ft. He uses a plank 12 ft. long. What force does he exert?

12. A railway porter pulls a trolley up a 15° slope from the "metals" to the platform. What fraction of the load will his applied force need to be?

13. A horse holds a load on a 10° down slope. With what force is he pushing back if the load weighs 1 ton?

14. The arm of a screw jack is 2 ft. long and engages directly with the screw whose pitch is $\frac{1}{2}$ in. What force applied at the end of the arm will lift a weight of 1 ton?

15. A cyclist travelling at 12 m.p.h. finds that he has to work harder by one-tenth of a horse-power on account of the wind. Calculate the force exerted by the wind on the cyclist. (J.M.B.)

CHAPTER VII

MOTION

Velocity. There is an important difference in meaning between the word "speed" and the word "velocity." Suppose a man running round a track does 10 miles in an hour. It is very unlikely that he will do 5 miles in each half-hour, 1 mile every 6 minutes, half a mile every 3 minutes and so on down to the smallest interval of time. His speed will not be **uniform.** *The speed of a body is said to be uniform when the body travels equal distances in equal intervals of time, however small the intervals may be.*

Now, although speed is rarely absolutely uniform, we frequently meet cases where it is approximately so. It is worth remembering that a speed of **60 miles per hour is the same as 88 ft. per second.**

When we speak of "velocity," the *direction* is taken into account. We speak of a velocity 10 m.p.h. due N. A velocity can be represented by a straight line drawn to scale just like a force. Moreover, we have a rule called the Parallelogram of Velocities by which velocities can be compounded into a resultant velocity. The speed of the runner on the track may be approximately uniform, but his velocity is certainly not uniform since the direction is changing all the time. At one instant his velocity will be 10 m.p.h. due N., a quarter of the way round it will be 10 m.p.h. E. or W., half-way round it will be 10 m.p.h. due S. and so on.

Acceleration. You will sometimes hear motorists speaking of "smooth and rapid acceleration." It will be instructive to consider the meaning of this phrase. "Acceleration" generally means an increase of velocity. Suppose the car in 11 sec. got up a speed of 88 ft. per second. Most people would call this "rapid" acceleration. Further, if the car put on 8 ft. per second in each of the 11 sec., the acceleration might also be truly called "smooth." But would the scientist call it uniform acceleration? Not unless the car gained a speed of 4 ft. per second in each half-second, 2 ft. per second in every quarter-second, and so on. Thus *acceleration is said to be uniform when the body receives equal changes of velocity in equal intervals of time, however small the intervals may be.*

In the case mentioned above, the acceleration would be called 8 ft. per sec. per sec. or 8 ft./sec.^{2}, which means that the speed increases by 8 ft. per second every second. When the car is slowing down, the scientist still considers it as a case of acceleration—*negative acceleration.*

Formulæ. By the use of very elementary algebra we can deduce several very important formulæ concerning the motion of a body moving with uniformly accelerated velocity.

(*a*) A body starting from rest moves with an acceleration of a ft./sec.^{2} To find the velocity v at the end of t sec.

Velocity at the end of 1 sec. $= a$ ft./sec.
Velocity at the end of 2 sec. $= a \times 2$ ft./sec.
Velocity at the end of t sec. $= at$

$$\therefore v = at.$$

(*b*) A body starting from rest has an acceleration of a ft./sec.^{2} To find the distance s travelled in t sec.

$$\text{Distance} = \text{average velocity} \times \text{time}$$

$$= \frac{0 + v}{2} \times t$$

but

$$v = at$$

$$\therefore \text{Distance} = \frac{0 + at}{2} \times t$$

$$\therefore s = \tfrac{1}{2}at^2.$$

(*c*) A body starting from rest has an acceleration of a ft./sec.^{2} To find the distance the body must travel to pick up a velocity of v ft./sec.

$$v = at \quad \ldots \quad (1)$$

$$s = \tfrac{1}{2}at^2 \quad \ldots \quad (2)$$

$$v^2 = a^2t^2 \quad \ldots \quad (3)$$

From (2) $t^2 = \dfrac{2s}{a}$ and from (3) $t^2 = \dfrac{v^2}{a^2}$

$$\therefore \frac{v^2}{a^2} = \frac{2s}{a} \text{ or } v^2 = 2as$$

We have now obtained three useful formulæ relating to the

motion of a body which starts off from rest and travels with uniform acceleration. The most important example of such motion is that of a falling body. The whole question was first investigated by Galileo (1564–1642) and he it was who first derived the above formulæ by experiment and mathematical reasoning. Perhaps his most important experiment was that in which he showed that the motion did not depend upon the weight of the body. Before his time it was generally thought that a heavy body would fall faster than a light one. Galileo climbed the leaning tower of Pisa and from the top dropped

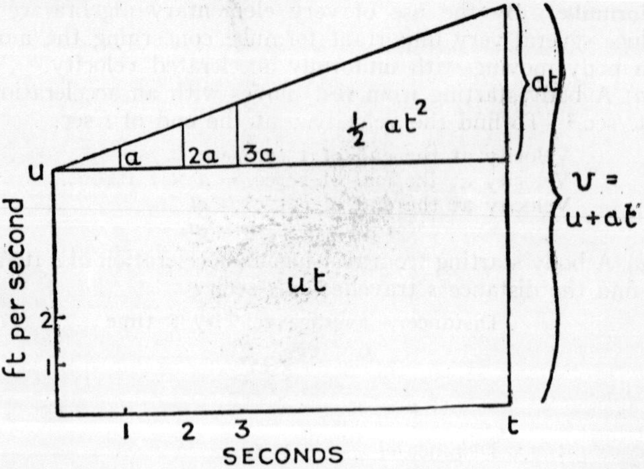

FIG. 54.

simultaneously a cannon ball and a musket bullet. Both reached the ground at the same time.

Later on, Newton (1642–1727) showed that even a coin and a feather would fall at the same rate in a vacuum. You may yourself do a simple experiment which illustrates the same fact. Place a small piece of paper on the middle of a penny and allow the penny to fall. The penny and paper reach the ground together.

The acceleration due to gravity is roughly 32 ft. per sec. per sec. It is generally referred to as g and we may rewrite our formulæ with g in place of a.

If a body instead of starting from rest has an initial velocity of, say, *u* ft. per second, the formulæ will be slightly different, but they can easily be derived by the same methods. For convenience they are brought together here, their proof being left as a simple mathematical exercise.

Starting from rest	*Starting with initial vel.* u *ft. per sec.*
$v = at$ $s = \frac{1}{2}at^2$ $v^2 = 2as$	$v = u + at$ $s = ut + \frac{1}{2}at^2$ $v^2 = u^2 + 2as$

The formulæ can all be illustrated graphically, marking *time* on the *x*-axis and *velocity* on the *y*-axis. The distance travelled will then be represented by areas. Fig. 54 illustrates the formula $s = ut + \frac{1}{2}at^2$.

To Compound Velocities. When a body has two velocities simultaneously, they can be compounded to form a resultant velocity just like forces.

EXAMPLE. A boy swims from one boat to another anchored 100 yd. due north of the former (fig. 55). The current is flowing eastwards at $1\frac{1}{2}$ miles per hour, and the boy can swim at 2 miles per hour in still water. Show graphically the direction in which he must swim, and calculate the time he will take to get from one boat to the other. (C.W.B.)

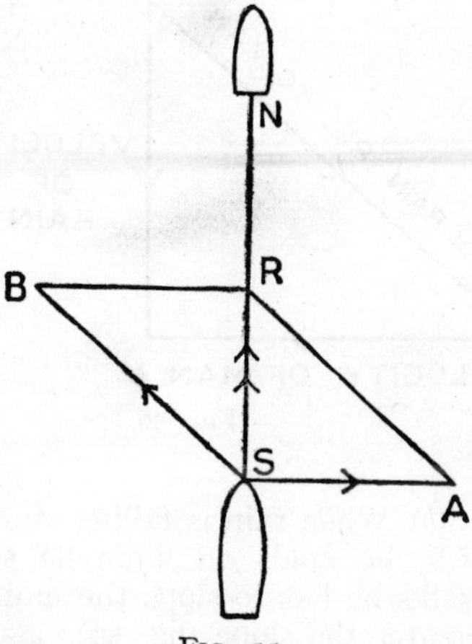

FIG. 55.

Draw SA due east $1\frac{1}{2}$ units long. With centre A and radius 2 units cut the SN line at R. Complete the parallelogram. The boy must swim in the direction SB. Show that the resultant velocity is 1·3 miles per hour and that he will take 157 sec.

Relative Velocity. Sometimes two bodies are in motion and it is important to find the velocity of one *relative* to the other.

(*a*) When we are sitting in a train A there may be another train B on our left going in the same direction. If B happens to be travelling at the same speed, it seems for a moment that both trains are at rest, until we look out of the opposite window. Then suddenly a train C flashes by in the opposite direction. Suppose all three trains are doing 50 m.p.h. Then

Velocity of B relative to A

= 50 miles an hour − 50 miles an hour = 0

or **Actual Velocity of B** compounded with **Reversed Velocity of A.**

Velocity of C relative to A

= − 50 miles an hour − 50 miles an hour = − 100

or **Actual Velocity of C** compounded with **Reversed Velocity of A.**

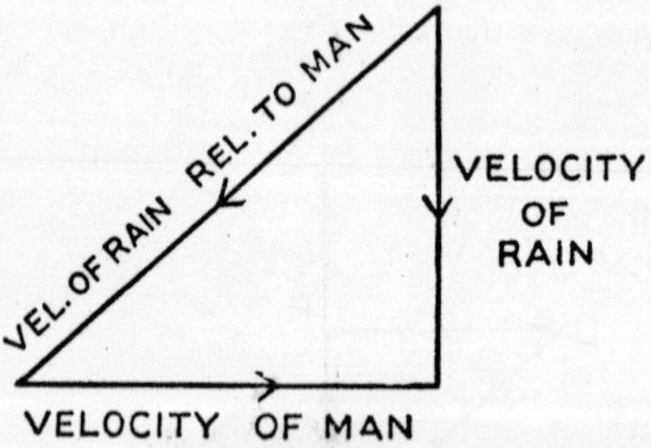

Fig. 56.

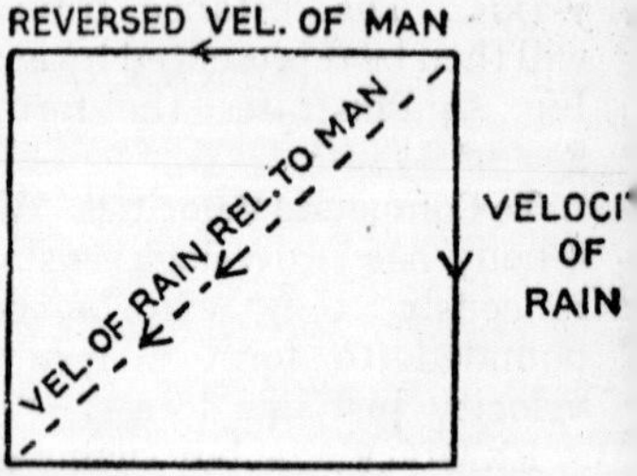

Fig. 57.

(*b*) When rain is falling straight down and a man is standing still, he holds an umbrella straight up. But as soon as he walks he has to slope the umbrella and the faster he walks the greater the slope (fig. 56).

The same rule again holds good

Velocity of rain relative to man

= **Actual Velocity of rain** compounded with **Reversed Velocity of man** (fig. 57).

(*c*) Spin a globe from west to east and attempt to draw a chalk line from the north towards the equator. The line will come from the north-east. This explains the north-east trade winds.

Velocity of wind relative to earth

= Actual Velocity of wind compounded with **Reversed Velocity of earth.**

The south-east trade winds arise in a similar way.

(*d*) Wind blowing at right angles to the course of a cyclist may become almost a head-on wind in either direction. Try to explain this on similar lines.

The Pendulum. Galileo may be said to have invented the pendulum as an instrument for measuring time. He discovered that the period or time of swing does not depend on the weight of the bob, or on the extent of the swing provided this is not extremely wide, but that the period is proportional to the square root of the length.

These facts can be verified with a long thread attached to a lead bob. The length of the pendulum is measured from the bottom of the supporting clamp to the middle of the bob. The period or time of swing is the time taken for a double journey, that is, two vibrations or beats. The time for 20 to 40 vibrations is taken with a stop-watch. The effect of altering the length can easily be investigated by making the length 16, 25, 36, 49, 64, 81, 100, 121 and 144 cm. A table should then be drawn up thus:

Length.	*No. of Swings.*	*Time.*	*Period.*	$\sqrt{\textit{Length.}}$
16 cm. etc.	40			

It will be convenient to take 20 swings when the pendulum is long and 40 when short.

The final result should show that when the length is increased four times the period is doubled, when the length is increased nine times the period is trebled. That is, *the period is proportional to the square root of the length.* It should also be noticed that when the pendulum is 100 cm. long, the period is 2 sec. This is called the *seconds pendulum* because it " beats " seconds.

It is shown in more advanced mechanics that T the period is equal to $2\pi\sqrt{\frac{l}{g}}$. Can you offer any suggestions as to why

π and g should occur in the formula? The formula provides an excellent method of determining the value of g, and if l is measured in feet then g should in our latitudes work out to 32.

Newton's Second Law of Motion. The product of the mass m of a body and its velocity v is called the *momentum* of the body. Thus momentum $= mv$. The momentum of a motor-coach travelling at 10 miles per hour would be considerably greater than a sports car travelling at the same speed. But if the sports car is travelling at 80 the momenta might easily be equal.

Newton's second law of motion states that *the rate of change of momentum is proportional to the acting force and takes place in the direction in which the force acts.* Suppose that the velocity of a body of mass m increases from u to v during a time t. The change of momentum is $mv - mu$. The *rate* of change of momentum is

$$\frac{mv - mu}{t} \text{ or } \frac{m(v - u)}{t} \text{ or } ma \text{ (since } v = u + at\text{).}$$

That is, rate of change of momentum is ma.

Now Newton's law means that F the acting force and ma are proportional to one another. On these ideas scientists founded a new unit of force. They agreed that this unit of force should be the force which causes unit mass to move with unit acceleration. In the British system of units the new unit was called the *poundal*. *A poundal is that force which acting on a mass of 1 lb. will give it an acceleration of 1 ft./sec.*^{2} Thus to give

1 lb. mass an accel. of	1 ft./sec.^{2}	requires a force of	1 pdl.
m lb. ,, ,, ,, ,,	1 ft./sec.^{2}	,, ,, ,,	m pdls.
m lb. ,, ,, ,, ,,	a ft./sec.^{2}	,, ,, ,,	ma pdls.

Calling this force F we have

$$\mathbf{F} \text{ poundals} = \mathbf{m} \text{ lb.} \times \boldsymbol{a} \text{ ft./sec.}^2$$

In the metric system the new unit was called the dyne and is that force which acting on a mass of 1 gm. gives it an acceleration of 1 cm./sec.^{2}. Again

$$\mathbf{F} \text{ dynes} = \mathbf{m} \text{ gm.} \times \boldsymbol{a} \text{ cm./sec.}^2$$

The poundal and dyne are the **absolute** units of force; they are the same everywhere, whereas the **gravitational** units, the lb.-wt. and the gm.-wt., depending as they do on the pull of the earth, must vary slightly from place to place. But since the acceleration due to gravity all over the earth may be taken as 32 ft./sec.^{2} approximately, we may say that the earth's pull produces in 1 lb. mass an acceleration of 32 ft./sec.^{2}

Hence a force of 1 lb.-wt. = 32 poundals.
In the Metric System g is 980 cm./sec.^{2}
Therefore 1 gm.-wt. = 980 dynes.

Absolute Units of Work. We saw in an earlier chapter that when a force of 1 lb.-wt. moves its point of application through a distance of 1 ft., the work done is 1 *ft.-lb.* The corresponding metric unit of work is the *cm. gm.* These are the gravitational units of work. The absolute units of work are the foot-poundal and the erg which are thus defined:

The *foot-poundal* is the amount of work done when a force of one poundal moves its point of application through a distance of 1 ft.

The *erg* is the amount of work done when a force of one dyne moves its point of application through a distance of 1 cm.

Energy. Energy is the capacity for doing work. Any living thing has energy, but in mechanics we are mainly concerned with the energy possessed by inanimate bodies. A body may have **kinetic or motion energy** or it may have **potential energy.** Energy is measured in work units—ft.-lb., cm. gm., foot-poundals or ergs.

The kinetic energy of a moving body is the amount of work it will do in being brought to rest.

The potential energy of a body is the amount of work it will do by reason of its position or because it is in a state of tension or compression, e.g. a mass poised above the ground, stretched rubber, coiled springs, stretched springs, compressed springs, a bent ruler.

A body thrown upwards has kinetic energy when it starts. This is gradually transformed into potential energy as the body rises, until at the highest point the body possesses only potential energy. On the down journey the potential energy is again transformed into kinetic energy. This transformation of energy is also well illustrated in swings and pendulums. At the highest point the energy is all potential, at the lowest all kinetic. A pendulum finally comes to rest because the energy is gradually dissipated as heat produced by friction with the air or at the support.

Problem. A cricket ball of mass m is travelling with velocity v. To find the amount of work it does in being brought to rest, that is, to find its kinetic energy.

Suppose that the fielder applies a constant resistance F while he is drawing his hands back through a distance s and suppose that the time taken is t. Work done by the ball against $F = Fs$.

The average velocity over this distance $= \frac{v}{2}$

$\therefore s = \frac{1}{2}vt$, but $F = ma = m\frac{v}{t}$

$\therefore$ Work done $= Fs = \frac{mv}{t} \times \frac{vt}{2} = \frac{1}{2}mv^2$.

Note that if m is in lb. and v in ft./sec. then the kinetic energy $\frac{1}{2}mv^2$ is in foot-poundals. This is also the amount of work that would have to be done on the cricket ball to *give* it this kinetic energy.

Potential Energy. We have seen that when a mass of 10 lb. is lifted 5 ft. the work done is 50 ft.-lb. In foot-poundals this will be 50×32, and generally we may say that the work done in lifting m lb. through h ft. against gravity is mgh ft.-pdls. This is also the work which the body would do in falling. We say then that the potential energy of the body is $\boldsymbol{mgh}$ **ft.-pdls.**

Transformation of Energy. Suppose that a mass of m lb. falls from a height h ft. through a distance s ft. We can show that **Potential Energy lost = Kinetic Energy gained.**

Potential Energy lost $= \boldsymbol{mgs}$ **ft.-pdls.**

Suppose that in falling a distance s the velocity gained is v.

Then in the formula $v^2 - u^2 = 2as$ we have $u = 0$ and $a = g$

$\therefore v^2 = 2gs$.

Kinetic Energy gained $= \frac{1}{2}mv^2 = \frac{1}{2}m \times 2gs$

$= \boldsymbol{mgs}$ ft.-pdls.

This is a particular example of a general law—the **Law of Conservation of Energy** which says that **energy cannot be created or destroyed.** It may seem at first sight that the kinetic energy of the moving cricket ball was lost when caught by the fielder, but in this case the mechanical energy is converted into heat energy ; the ball and the hands will all be a little warmer. In fact this law may be regarded as the *fundamental law of physics ; there are no exceptions.*

Friction. When dealing with machines, we saw that there

was always a certain amount of work lost in overcoming friction. Let us consider a simple example of friction from the point of view of energy. Suppose a table to be dragged along the floor. Work has to be done in the process, but the table in its new position has no more potential energy than before, nor has it kinetic energy. The energy has been changed into useless heat energy and sound energy.

We may define *friction* as *a force brought into play when two surfaces slide or tend to slide over each other. It always opposes motion.* It is important to find out what this force called friction depends upon.

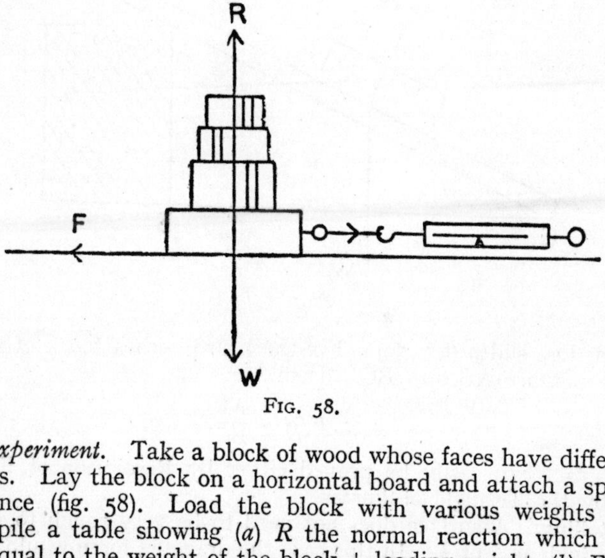

FIG. 58.

Experiment. Take a block of wood whose faces have different areas. Lay the block on a horizontal board and attach a spring balance (fig. 58). Load the block with various weights and compile a table showing (*a*) *R* the normal reaction which will be equal to the weight of the block + loading weight, (*b*) *F* the force required to keep the block moving slowly with uniform velocity, (*c*) the ratio of *F* to *R*.

R lb.-wt.	*F* lb.-wt.	*F/R*

It will be found that $\dfrac{\text{Frictional Force}}{\text{Normal Reaction}}$ is a constant. This constant is called the *coefficient of friction* for those surfaces and is denoted by the letter μ. The frictional force is therefore proportional to the normal reaction.

The experiment should now be repeated, putting one of the other faces in contact with the board. It should be found that **the frictional force does not depend on the area of the surfaces in contact.** We can find the ratio μ in another way.

Experiment. Place the block on the board and tilt until the

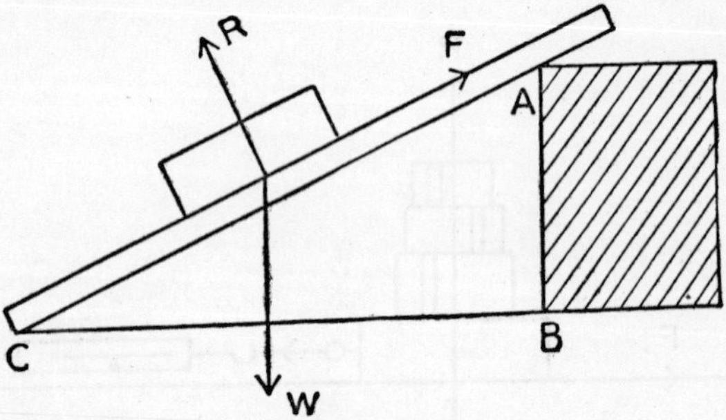

FIG. 59.

block just slides (fig. 59). Fix the board with a block of wood and measure AB and BC. Then

$$\mu \text{ or } F/R = \frac{AB}{BC}.$$

This fact can easily be proved either by Resolution of Forces or by the Triangle of Forces.

Rolling. A surface does not need to be very rough to make μ as high as $\frac{1}{3}$ or $\frac{1}{2}$. In this case the dragging force would have to be $\frac{1}{3}$ or $\frac{1}{2}$ the weight. Let us imagine our prehistoric ancestors faced with the problem of transporting a cubical block of granite of side 20 in. It is quite possible that they will find it more convenient to roll it by pushing at A (fig. 60). Taking moments round C we have

$$P \times AC = W \times EC$$

or

$$P \times 28 = W \times 10$$

$$\therefore P \text{ is roughly } \tfrac{1}{3} \text{ of } W.$$

This is the *maximum* value of P because the moment of W becomes less as the block turns round C. In this case rolling is certainly as easy as dragging.

Consider next a block of roughly hexagonal shape again assuming a 20-in side (fig. 61). We now have

$$P \times 40 = W \times 10$$

and the maximum value of P is $\frac{1}{4}W$.

It is now easy to see that the more sides there are to the block, the more advantageous does rolling become as opposed

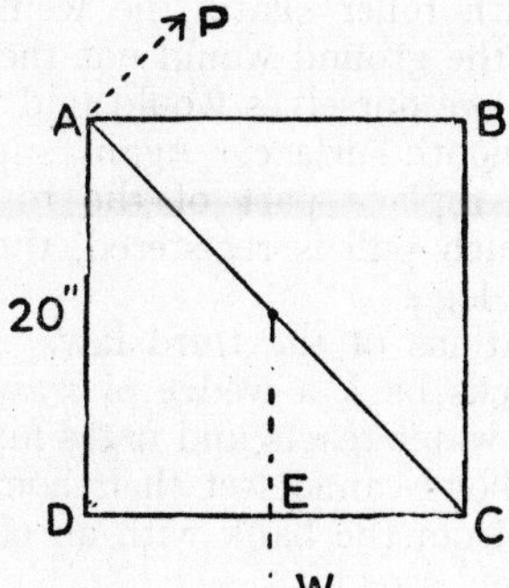

FIG. 60.

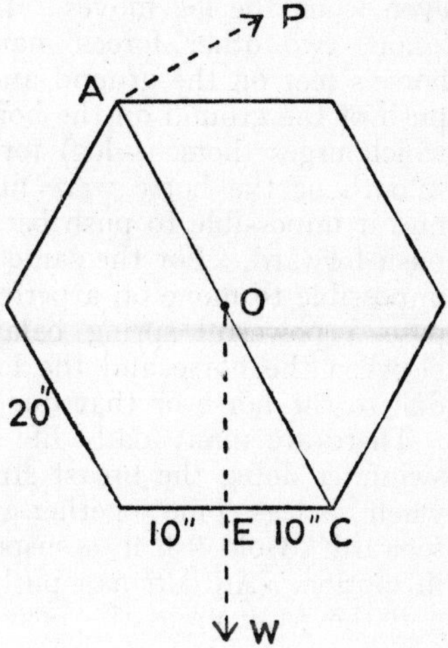

FIG. 61.

to dragging or sliding. It was probably by some such practical experience that our remote ancestors first discovered the wheel. We must not of course assume that they reasoned it out from the Principle of Moments! Nowadays we have advanced a step further and we overcome the disadvantages of sliding friction by applying the rolling idea in ball and roller bearings.

Now although we use considerable ingenuity in overcoming friction, we should be in a very bad way if it were entirely abolished from nature. We should be unable to tie a knot, spin yarn, weave cloth, use nails or screws or even to move about on the surface of the earth ; life as we know it would be absolutely impossible.

The Third Law of Motion states that "action and reaction are equal and opposite." In other words, whenever a force is in action there is always an equal force in opposition. The law is readily accepted by students when no motion occurs ; they quite believe that the two forces acting between the ground and any object resting on it are equal. But the law also holds good when a horse pulls a log along the ground. The horse pulls forward and the log pulls back and the pulls are equal even when the log moves. The difficulty only arises when we ignore two other forces, namely, the backward push of the horse's feet on the ground and the equal and opposite forward push of the ground on the horse's feet. It is this forward push which urges (horse + log) forward. If the ground were very smooth or the horse were fitted with roller skates, he would find it impossible to push back and the ground would not then push forward. For the same reason we ourselves would find it impossible to move on a perfectly smooth surface. Again, suppose a powerful spring balance to replace part of the rope between the horse and the log ; which pull is registered, that due to the horse or that due to the log ?

There are many daily life illustrations of the third law. A swimmer doing the breast stroke kicks back a wedge of water when his legs come together and the water reacts and urges him forward. Gold fish in a suspended bowl cannot set their home in motion. An oarsman pushes off from the bank with an oar and the bank urges the boat into mid-stream.

QUESTIONS

1. Explain the terms velocity and acceleration.

A body starting from rest moves with an acceleration of 5 ft. per sec. per sec. In what time will it acquire a velocity of 50 ft. per second, and what distance will it have travelled in that time ? (L.)

2. What is the difference between velocity and acceleration ? How long will a stone take in falling from rest a distance of 200 ft. to the ground ? [$g = 32$ f.s.s.] (L.)

3. A shot is projected vertically upwards with a velocity of 160 ft. per second ; how high will it travel and what will be its

position and its velocity at the end of the fourth and of the eighth second? (L.)

4. A motor-car can attain a speed of 60 miles per hour in 14 sec. from a standstill. Calculate the acceleration.

5. Illustrate graphically the formulæ relating to the motion of a body starting from rest and travelling with uniform acceleration.

6. A car travelling at 40 miles per hour has its speed reduced in 2·5 sec. to 10 miles per hour. Assuming the retardation to be uniform, what distance was covered in the time? (C.W.B.)

7. Illustrate graphically the formulæ relating to the motion of a body starting with an initial velocity and moving with uniform acceleration.

8. A motor-car with an initial speed of 40 miles per hour has its speed reduced by a uniform retardation to 10 miles per hour in travelling 400 yd. What was the time occupied? What was the average velocity?

9. State the formulæ relating to the motion of a body which has an initial velocity and moves with uniform acceleration. Show how these formulæ may be proved algebraically.

10. The following table gives speeds of a car and corresponding braking distances (distance in which speed is reduced to 0).

Speed .	20 m.p.h.	30	40	50	60	70	80
Distance .	17 ft.	$37\frac{1}{2}$	66	105	150	213	266

Calculate the retardation in each case.

11. Obtain an expression for the distance traversed by a uniformly accelerated body in terms of its initial and final velocities and its acceleration.

A train moves from rest with a uniform acceleration of 1·5 ft. per sec. per sec. After what time and distance will its speed be 30 miles per hour? (C.W.B.)

12. A car, starting from rest, with uniform acceleration, attains a speed of 30 miles per hour in 8 sec. It then runs with uniform speed for 2 min., after which the brakes are applied and it is brought to rest in 4 sec. What is the total distance covered? (D.)

13. A stone is projected vertically upwards with a velocity of 160 ft. per second. Indicate its subsequent behaviour by completing the table shown.

Time.	*Velocity.*	*Distance in each sec.*	*Total Distance from ground.*
0	+ 160 ft./sec.	—	—
1 sec.	+ 128 ft./sec.	144 ft.	144 ft.

14. Use the results of (13) to plot a space-time curve and a velocity-time curve. From the graphs find when the body is 320 ft. from the ground, and the velocity at that instant.

15. In a series of experiments with simple pendulums the following numbers were obtained :—

Length in ft.	1	2	3	4	5
Time in sec. . . .	1·10	1·57	1·92	2·21	2·48

Plot a graph showing the relation between the length of a pendulum and the square of its time of swing. (D.)

16. How far will a body fall from rest in half a second?

17. Define a unit of force on the foot-pound-second system.

A body of mass 10 lb. acted on by a constant force for one minute acquires thereby a velocity of 1000 yd. per minute. Determine the value of the force. (C.W.B.)

18. A body of mass 50 gm. acquires a velocity of 14·7 metres in 10 sec. Find the force acting on it in dynes and gm.-wt.

19. If the bob of a simple pendulum is drawn aside and let go when the string is taut so that its vertical fall is 3 in., what is its velocity at the lower position? Neglect air resistance. (C.W.B.)

20. Calculate the momentum and the kinetic energy of a mass of 30 lb. which has fallen from a height of 16 ft.

21. Explain clearly the difference between kinetic and potential energy. Show, with the aid of examples from everyday life, how potential energy may be transformed into kinetic energy, and *vice versa*. (L.)

22. A stone projected with a velocity of 10 ft. per second along a horizontal sheet of ice comes to rest in 25 sec. What is the ratio between the frictional force and the weight of the body? (D.)

23. A motor-car weighing 2500 lb. and travelling at 20 miles per hour comes to a slope of 1 in 30 down which it travels for 200 yd., with the engine disconnected, without diminution of speed. What is the resisting force due to friction? Which of the data can be altered without affecting the result? (C.W.B.)

HEAT

CHAPTER VIII

THERMOMETERS

It has been said that *man is an animal which cooks its food.* Fire is certainly not used by any other animals, so the definition is logically sound. The earliest known means of obtaining fire was by rubbing together two pieces of dry stick. Now although this demands considerable skill and experience, there are many other cases known to all of us where we produce considerable heat by the rubbing of two surfaces together; in cold weather we rub our hands together, a brass button rubbed on wood becomes very hot, if we rub the rim of a bicycle wheel with emery cloth with sufficient vigour we get burnt. The effect is very striking when using the kind of saw which is adapted for cutting a hole in wood; the narrow blade of such a saw becomes unbearably hot. If a nail is hammered repeatedly both nail and hammer get hot.

There is one fact which is common to all these operations—we are doing work or using up motion energy. This fact is so striking that scientists have come to the conclusion that heat is a form of motion energy. Heat is certainly not a form of matter, otherwise a body would be heavier when hot. Yet the hot body is strikingly different in its behaviour, and it was difficult at first to explain why. The modern explanation is that in rubbing, the motion energy is passed on to the molecules of the bodies rubbed; the hotter the body, the faster its molecules are vibrating. As a body cools, its molecules slow down until finally they come to a standstill at the absolute zero of temperature! Further knowledge will convince you of the reasonableness of this mental picture of vibrating molecules.

Heat and Temperature. If we have a large flask and a small flask both full of boiling water, the large flask contains more "heat," but both flasks are at the same temperature. Again, suppose that a red-hot poker is plunged into a bucket of tepid water. Heat will pass from the poker to the water because the former is at a higher temperature, but it is quite likely that the bucket of water contained more heat.

Temperature may be compared with water-level. Thus if a burette and an inverted bell-jar are joined up as shown (fig. 62), water will flow from the burette if the level is higher. Similarly, if two bodies A and B are placed in contact and heat passes from A to B, it is because A was at a higher temperature than B.

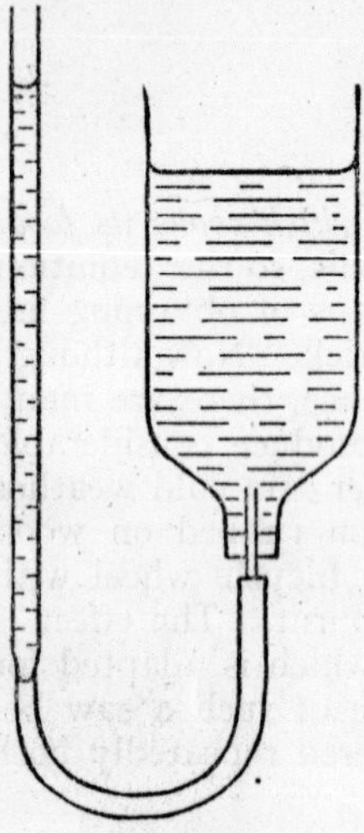

FIG. 62.

We are accustomed to judging the temperature of bodies by feeling them, but a little thought will show that the sense of touch is not always reliable. Thus in summer sunshine a corrugated roof would feel hotter than the neighbouring woodwork although both would be at the same temperature. In winter the opposite would be the case. The metal part of a workman's shovel feels very cold in winter and the grips on the handlebars of a bicycle feel warmer than the adjoining metal work.

A more reliable method of judging temperature is to use some kind of thermometer. Most thermometers depend on the fact that matter expands on heating.

Expansion. There are many simple experiments designed to show that solids expand on heating. In fig. 63 the metal bar

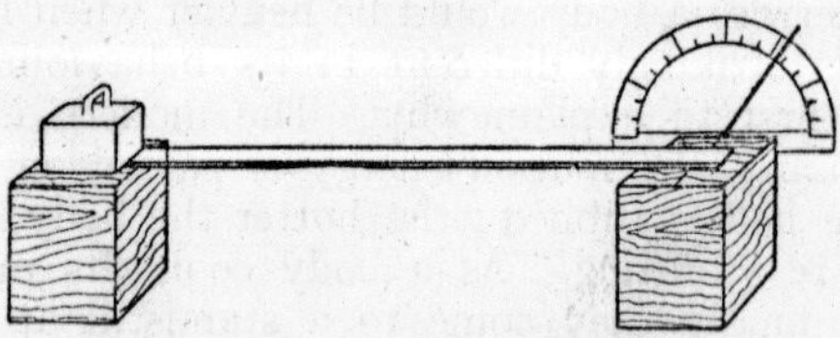

FIG. 63.

is fixed at one end against a weight while the other end rests on a needle pushed into a straw pointer. When the bar is heated, it can only move at the needle end. The needle rolls and causes the straw to travel round the graduated scale.

We often meet examples of this expansion of solids in daily life. On railway lines a gap is left between the ends of the rails; the "fish-plate" which connects the ends have bolt holes which are longer than they are wide. Without these precautions the rails would buckle either upwards or outwards. The glass for windows and picture frames has to be cut a little smaller than the frame. In the summer of 1934 the metal of a drawbridge over the river in New York expanded so much that it was impossible to close it.

It can be shown that different metals do not expand at the same rate; a compound bar of iron and brass riveted together, when heated in a bunsen flame, forms a curve with the brass on the outside.

The expansion of a liquid can be shown with the apparatus illustrated in fig. 64 A. A flask full of coloured water is fitted with a stopper and capillary tube. On immersing the flask in hot water, the thread of coloured liquid drops a little, then rises considerably. The initial drop is caused by expansion of the glass before the heat reaches the liquid. If the flask is filled with alcohol, it can be shown that this liquid expands more than water for the same rise in temperature.

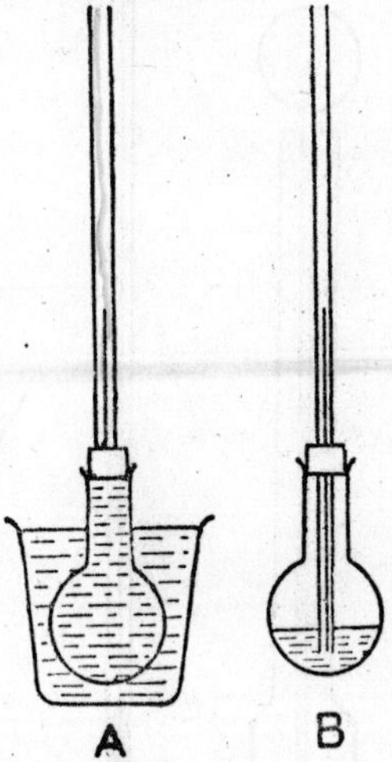

FIG. 64.

The expansion of a gas (air) can be shown with the same flask fitted up as shown at fig. 64 B. On warming the flask with the hands the air expands and forces the coloured liquid up the capillary tube. It can be shown, though not conveniently with the present apparatus, that all gases expand at the same rate, a fact which lends support to an important hypothesis in chemistry.

The first thermometer (fig. 65) was made by Galileo. This, an air thermometer, consisted of a long glass tube of fine bore with a bulb at the top. The bulb was warmed a little and the end of the tube was then dipped into coloured water in the small bottle. When the bulb cooled the water ran a little way up the tube.

The instrument was very sensitive to small changes in temperature but had the disadvantage that air pressure also affected the height.

FIG. 65.

FIG. 66.

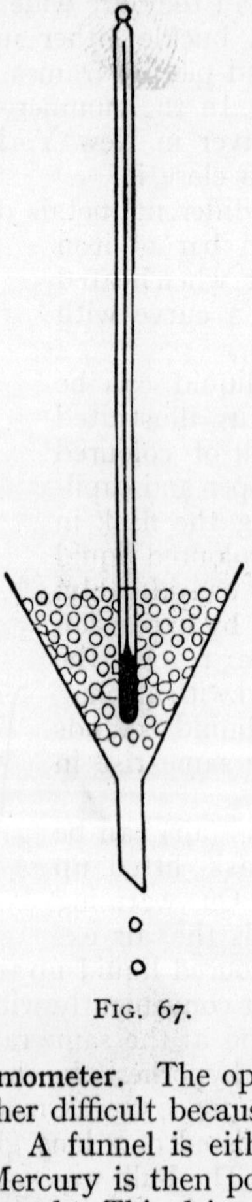

FIG. 67.

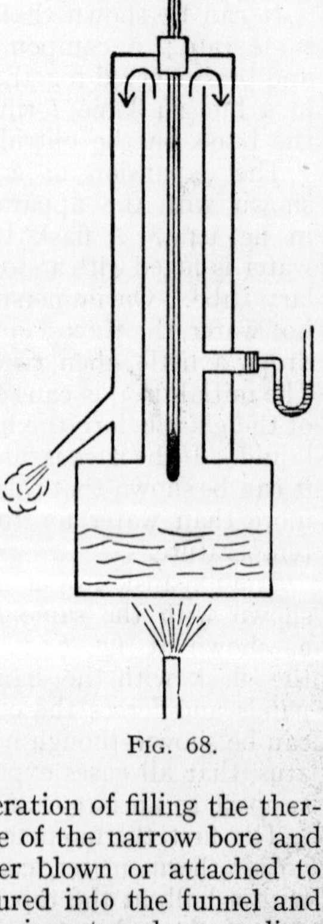

FIG. 68.

The Mercury Thermometer. The operation of filling the thermometer bulb is rather difficult because of the narrow bore and the presence of air. A funnel is either blown or attached to the end (fig. 66). Mercury is then poured into the funnel and the bulb gently warmed. This drives air out and, on cooling, mercury passes down into the bulb. After repeating this a few times, the bulb and part of the stem will be full of mercury.

The mercury is now boiled to get rid of air which tends to cling to the walls of the tube. After cooling down, the tube is again heated up to a temperature a little higher than the thermometer is intended to read. The tube is now drawn off with a small blowpipe flame, while it is still full of mercury. This prevents the presence of air in the finished thermometer.

Marking the Fixed Points. The bulb of the thermometer is immersed in small pieces of pure melting ice (fig. 67). A mark is made on the glass where the mercury is just visible above the ice. Pure ice must be used because dissolved solids have the effect of lowering the freezing-point of a liquid.

The thermometer is next placed in a "hypsometer" (see p. 104) in order to mark the upper fixed point (fig. 68). But here there are some precautions to take. If the water is not pure the boiling-point will be a little higher than the steam which comes off, therefore the bulb must not be even within splashing distance of the water. The boiling-point also alters with the pressure, so inside the hypsometer the pressure must be 760 mm. To ensure this we must see that both arms of the water gauge are equal by adjusting the burner, and also read the barometer. If the barometer is not at 760 mm. we must use vapour pressure tables and apply a correction before making a scratch on the tube.

If the thermometer is to be marked according to the Centigrade scale, the higher point is called 100° and the lower point 0°, the space between being divided into 100 equal parts called degrees.

If the thermometer is to be of the Fahrenheit type the corresponding points are marked 212° and 32°, the space between being divided into 180 equal parts.

Thus **100 C.** degrees = **180 F.** degrees.

Mercury as a thermometric substance has the following advantages:

1. It is easily seen.
2. It does not wet the tube.
3. It is a good conductor of heat.
4. It has a low specific heat. (See Chap. X.)
5. Its expansion is very uniform.
6. It has a long range of usefulness because its freezing-point is − 39° C. and its boiling-point 357° C. By filling the tube

above the liquid with compressed nitrogen to raise its boiling-point, it can be used even above 357° C.

The Alcohol Thermometer. Alcohol as a thermometric substance has the following advantages:

1. It can be used in cold countries since its freezing-point is − 112° C.

2. It expands about six times as much as mercury for the same rise of temperature.

The disadvantages compared with mercury are:

1. It boils at 78° C.

2. Its expansion is not so uniform.

3. It wets the tube—a distinct disadvantage when the temperature is falling.

4. It does not conduct heat so readily as mercury.

In marking an alcohol thermometer it is usual to fix the lower point by means of melting ice and obtain the other graduations by comparison with a standard mercury thermometer. This procedure is necessary because of disadvantages (1) and (2).

Water as a thermometric substance would combine the disadvantages of mercury and alcohol besides doing strange tricks round about 4° C. which absolutely disqualify it. We shall learn later that the best substance is hydrogen; very accurate mercury thermometers are graduated by comparison with a thermometer filled with this gas but having a different shape from the ordinary thermometer.

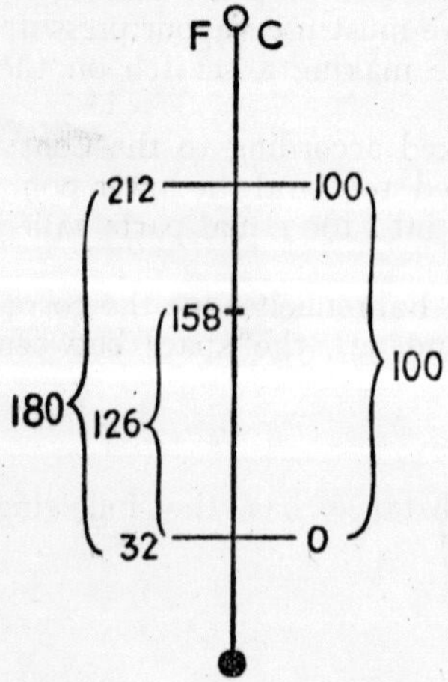

Fig. 69.

Conversion of Readings from one Scale to Another.

Example. What Centigrade reading corresponds to 158° F.?

The frequent blunders committed with such examples can be avoided by following two rules:

(*a*) Draw a rough diagram (fig. 69) showing freezing-point and boiling-point on the two scales.

(*b*) Ask the question—" How many divisions is the given

temperature above or below freezing-point?" 158° F. is 126 F. divisions above freezing-point.

But 180 F. divisions above f.p. = 100 C. divisions above f.p.

$$\therefore 126 \quad ,, \quad ,, \quad ,, \quad = \frac{100 \times 126}{180} \quad ,, \quad ,, \quad ,,$$

= 70 C. divisions above f.p.

but freezing-point is 0° on the Centigrade scale

∴ actual reading is 70° C.

EXAMPLE. What Fahrenheit reading corresponds to 70° C.?

100 C. divisions above f.p. = 180 F. divisions above f.p.

$$\therefore 70 \quad ,, \quad ,, \quad ,, \quad ,, \quad = \frac{180}{100} \times 70 \quad ,, \quad ,, \quad ,,$$

= 126 F. divisions above f.p.

But freezing-point is 32° on the Fahrenheit scale

∴ actual reading is 158° F.

The Maximum and Minimum Thermometer. There are many cases where it is important to know the highest and lowest

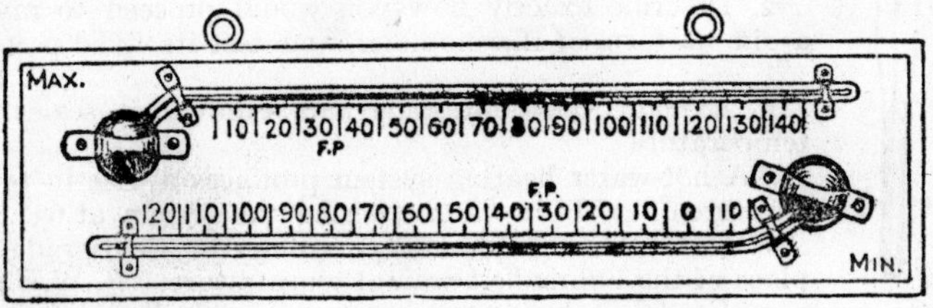

FIG. 70.

temperatures reached during a certain time. For this purpose a "maximum and minimum" thermometer is used (fig. 70.).

In the type shown the maximum thermometer contains a thread of mercury separated from the main body of liquid by a small air bubble. When the temperature rises, the thread is driven along the tube and stays there even when the temperature falls. The end distant from the bulb then indicates the maximum temperature.

The minimum thermometer contains alcohol with a steel or glass index inside the liquid. As the temperature falls, the index is pulled back by the meniscus and the distant end shows the minimum temperature.

FIG. 71.

Both indexes can be brought back by shaking.

The Clinical Thermometer is a maximum thermometer used by doctors (fig. 71). It has a limited range and must never be washed in hot water. Before taking the temperature of a patient the mercury is shaken down well below the normal blood temperature. When the thermometer is taken from the patient and the mercury cools, the thread breaks at a constriction in the bore and the main body of mercury runs back into the bulb. The more expensive clinical thermometers carry the sign NP showing that they have been tested at the National Physical Laboratory.

QUESTIONS

1. Describe simple experiments showing that solids, liquids, and gases expand on heating. Mention some common examples of practical precautions necessary on account of expansion. (L.)

2. Describe exactly how you would proceed to make a simple form of thermometer, and test its fixed points. (L.)

3. Explain the Centigrade and Fahrenheit scales of temperature.

"A hot-water heating system produces a rise in temperature of 41° F. in water entering the system at 63° F."

Rewrite the above sentence using the Centigrade in place of the Fahrenheit scale of temperature. (C.W.B.)

4. Explain why water is not a suitable liquid for use in thermometers. How are the upper and lower fixed points of a thermometer determined? What reading on a Centigrade thermometer corresponds to 77 on the Fahrenheit scale? (O.)

5. Draw a graph showing Fahrenheit readings on the x-axis and Centigrade readings on the y-axis. From the graph determine the C. reading corresponding to $-40°$ F.

6. Explain the need for fixed points on a thermometer scale.

7. Describe how you would construct an alcohol thermometer to read from 0° F. to 110° F. and state all the precautions you would take. What advantages and disadvantages would such a thermometer have compared with a similar mercury one? (L.)

8. Draw and explain the working of a maximum, a minimum, and a clinical thermometer.

9. Define the fixed points on the Centigrade temperature scale.

A mercury thermometer with uniform bore has a millimetre scale marked on it. The fixed points correspond to readings of 25 mm. and 210 mm. What is the temperature (*a*) in degrees Centigrade, (*b*) in degrees Fahrenheit, when the reading is 54 mm.?

(C.W.B.)

10. If C and F are corresponding readings on a Centigrade thermometer and a Fahrenheit thermometer respectively, prove that $\frac{F - 32}{9} = \frac{C}{5}$.

CHAPTER IX

THE MEASUREMENT OF EXPANSION

WHEN measuring the expansion of solids we deal with the *linear expansion* or increase in length, the *superficial expansion* or increase in area and the *cubical expansion* or increase in volume.

Linear Expansion. *The coefficient of linear expansion of a substance is the increase in length when unit length is heated*

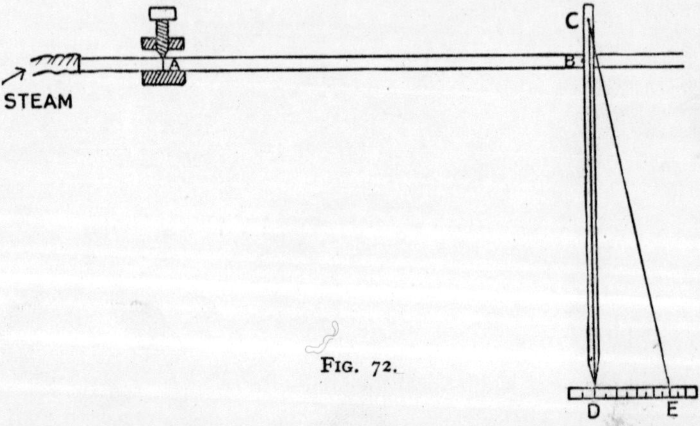

FIG. 72.

through 1° C. If the unit length is a centimetre, it will obviously be very difficult to measure such a small increase. We get over the difficulty by using a long bar, warming it through a fairly long temperature range and employing some multiplying device.

One of the many multiplying devices is illustrated in fig. 72. AB is a brass tube clamped at a mark A and free to move at the B end. Since its internal diameter is only $\frac{1}{4}$ in., it will take ordinary rubber tubing by which steam may be sent in. At B a steel needle is firmly fixed in a drilled hole. The tube and scale DE are set up horizontally. CD is a lath 70 cm. long with a centre line marked along its length and a hole drilled at C to carry a supporting pivot. The initial and final temperatures are taken by slipping a thermometer into the tube. As the rod expands the needle B pushes the lath out of the vertical. AB is 100 cm., CB is 1 cm. and CD is 70 cm. The coefficient of linear expansion is given by

$$\frac{DE \times CB}{CD \times AB \times \text{Range}};$$

for a brass tube this should come to about 0·0000189 per 1° C.

This means that 1 cm. of brass heated 1° C. expands by 0·0000189 cm. Similarly, 1 mile of brass heated 1° C. expands by 0·0000189 mile. Changing the unit of length makes no difference to the coefficient, but if we adopt the Fahrenheit scale the coefficient will be $\frac{5}{9}$ of the ordinary coefficient.

Superficial and Cubical Expansion. *The coefficient of superficial expansion of a substance is the increase in area when unit area is heated through* 1° C.

Suppose we have a square of brass 1 cm. side. When heated through 1° C. the new length of each side will be 1 + 0·0000189. Since the coefficient of linear expansion is generally indicated by the letter α we may say the new area is

$$\begin{aligned}(1 + \alpha)^2 &= 1 + 2\alpha + \alpha^2 \\ &= 1 + 2 \times 0{\cdot}0000189 + 0{\cdot}0000189^2\end{aligned}$$

The third term is evidently negligible compared with the other terms. Therefore the increase in area of unit area is 2α. In other words, the coefficient of superficial expansion is twice the coefficient of linear expansion. By similar reasoning we arrive at the conclusion that the coefficient of cubical expansion or the increase in volume when unit volume is warmed through 1° C. is equal to 3α.

Further Consequences of Expansion. In the last chapter mention was made of the precautions necessary in laying railway lines and fitting glass to windows and picture-frames. Expansion has also to be allowed for in the case of clocks controlled by pendulums ; during warm weather the pendulum gets longer and the clock loses. One interesting way of overcoming the difficulty is shown in fig. 73. The expansion of the iron rod tends to lower the C.G., but this is cancelled by the expansion of a *short* column of mercury because the coefficient for mercury is about five times greater than that for iron. A more modern method is to use an alloy of nickel and iron; an alloy containing 36% nickel is found to have practically a zero coefficient over a wide range of temperature. It has therefore been given the name "Invar."

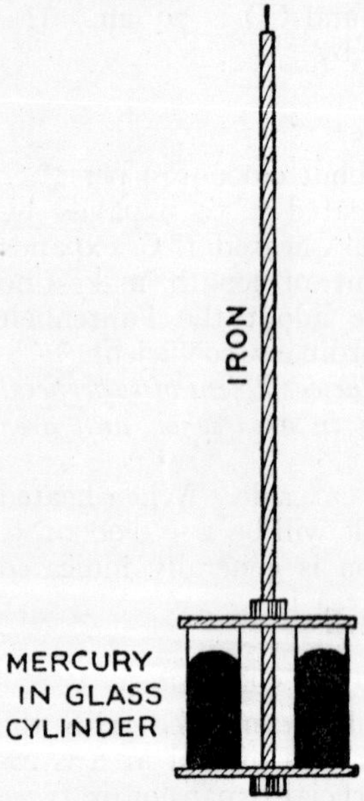

Fig. 73.

In science and industry it is often necessary to make a gas-tight joint between a metal and glass. Now platinum and glass have the same coefficient of expansion, so the joint between these two does not break on cooling. For many years this was the only known method, but in recent times another alloy of nickel and iron (not Invar) has been made which has the same coefficient as glass. It contains 45% nickel and is now used in electric lamps to conduct the current through the glass seal. It is found an advantage to plate this alloy with copper. This gives it a reddish colour and in the trade it is sometimes known as "red platinum."

Boiler-makers use red-hot rivets because on cooling they pull the plates tightly together. For the same reason the wheelwright heats up an iron tyre which is slightly small, slips it over the woodwork and cools the job with buckets of water.

The well-known tendency of glass to crack under extremes of temperature is due to its bad conductivity; the heated surface tries to expand before the heat reaches all parts. A vessel made of fused silica does not crack so readily because its coefficient of expansion is about one seventeenth as great.

Expansion of Liquids. In measuring the expansion of liquids we are only concerned with cubical expansion, but the question is complicated by the fact that, unless the vessel is of fused silica, we must take into account the expansion of the containing vessel. We thus have a *real coefficient of expansion* and an *apparent* coefficient of expansion. To obtain the real coefficient we add the apparent coefficient and the coefficient of cubical expansion of glass or whatever material the containing vessel is made of. In dealing with this problem you will need to remember the fact that

$$\text{Density} = \frac{\text{Mass}}{\text{Volume}} \text{ or Volume} = \frac{\text{Mass}}{\text{Density}}.$$

Experiment. To find the coefficient of apparent expansion of turpentine.

A suitable apparatus is shown in fig. 74. The bottle is weighed empty and dry. It is then filled with turpentine and immersed in *ice-cold* water for ten minutes. The volume of turpentine is adjusted to the mark A by adding more or drawing some off with a small pipette. The bottle is taken out, dried and weighed, then again immersed. The water is now gently heated to boiling-point, drawing off turpentine when necessary. After boiling for about five minutes the turpentine is adjusted to the mark and the bottle dried, cooled, and weighed.

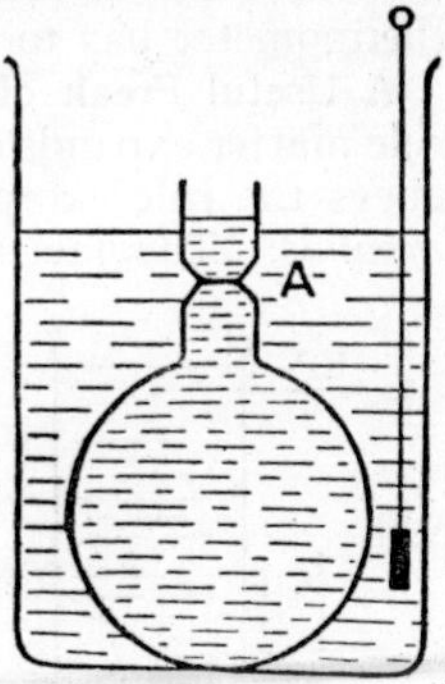

FIG. 74.

Wt. of bottle	= 9·21 gm.
Wt. of bottle + turpentine	= 31·05 gm.
Original wt. of turpentine	= 21·84 gm.
Initial temperature	= 0° C.
Final temperature	= 100° C.
Wt. of bottle + turpentine finally	= 29·21 gm.
Final wt. of turpentine	= 20·00 gm.
Wt. of turpentine drawn off	= 1·84 gm.
Let density of turpentine	= d gm./c.c.

then $\frac{20\cdot00}{d}$ c.c. heated through 100° C. expand $\frac{1\cdot84}{d}$ c.c.

$\therefore$ 1 c.c. " " " " $\frac{1\cdot84}{d} \times \frac{d}{20\cdot00}$ c.c.

$\therefore$ 1 c.c. heated through 1° C. expands $\frac{1\cdot84}{20 \times 100}$.

∴ Coefficient of app. expansion of turpentine = 0·00092 per ° C.
Coefficient of cubical expansion of glass = 0·000026 per ° C.
∴ Coefficient of real expansion of turpentine = 0·00095. per ° C.

Since alcohol and mercury are used in thermometers, it is worth noticing their coefficients of real expansion which are 0·00110 and 0·00018 per ° C. respectively. It is because the coefficient for mercury is small that the bore of a mercury thermometer has to be so narrow.

A Useful Freak of Nature. We have seen that as a general rule matter expands on heating and contracts on cooling. Water obeys the rule except when cooled from 4° C. to 0° C. when it *expands*. This fact is illustrated in Hope's experiment (fig. 75).

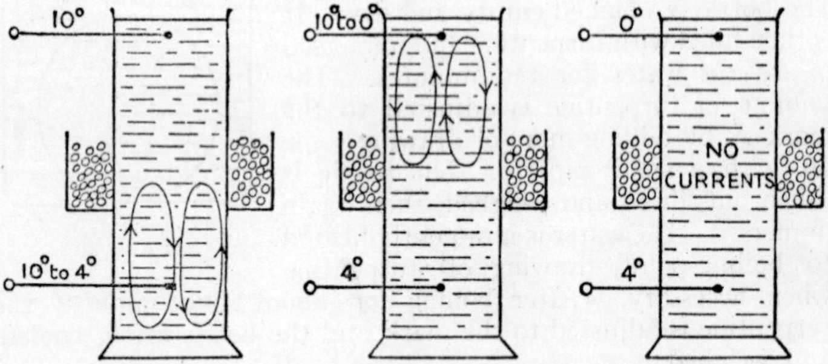

FIG. 75.

A glass jar containing pure water is surrounded at the middle by a mixture of ice and salt. If readings are taken on the thermometers at short intervals we shall observe:

(1) The lower thermometer sinks to 4° C. and remains stationary.

(2) The upper one now sinks to 0° C. and the surface water freezes.

The explanation is simple. As the water in the middle cools, it gets denser and falls until the lower half of the water is all at 4° C. Any further cooling at the middle causes expansion and the cold water rises, thus cooling the upper half. Water has its maximum density at 4° C.

The experiment explains what takes place in winter in a lake or any large body of water. No ice can form on the surface until the whole mass of water has cooled to 4° C. When this temperature is reached, there are no further convection currents and since water is a very bad conductor of heat, the main bulk of the water remains at 4° C. If the surface layer gets any cooler, it expands, gets lighter, and stays there. If it freezes it also stays there because freezing causes further expansion and the ice floats at the top. If ice were denser than water each layer would sink as it formed until the whole lake became a solid block of ice.

The peculiar behaviour of water from 4° C. to the solid state enables aquatic life to survive the hardest winter in temperate zones. The thick line in fig. 76 might well be termed the "fish's life-line."

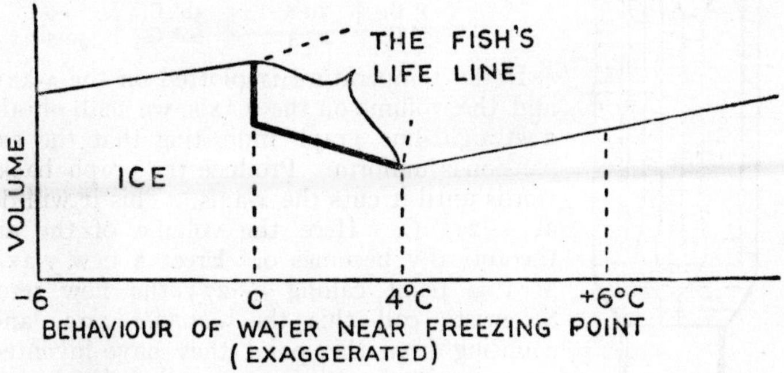

FIG. 76.

The expansion of water during freezing is also the cause of the bursting of water pipes in winter. That the burst only becomes evident during the thaw is due to the fact that the crack was nicely sealed with ice.

Expansion of Gases. When studying the expansion of solids and liquids there was no need to consider the pressure, but when dealing with the effect of temperature on the volume of a gas we must obviously keep the pressure constant.

The coefficient of expansion of air is conveniently found by means of the apparatus shown in fig. 77. The bulb A contains air enclosed and kept dry by strong sulphuric acid. The inverted bell-jar contains ice and water initially. The acid levels are adjusted by means of the tap B. The volume and temperature are read. Steam is now sent in for half a minute, then stopped by opening clip C. The water is well stirred, the acid levels adjusted and the volume and temperature again read. The process may be repeated until the water boils if time allows. By constantly adjusting the acid levels, the pressure is kept equal to atmospheric pressure.

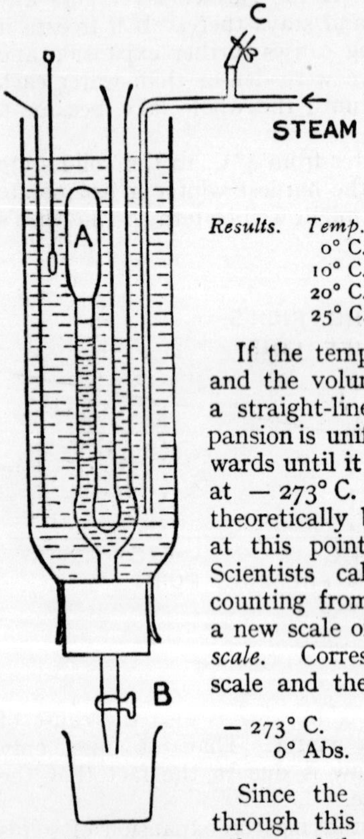

FIG. 77.

Results.

Temp.	*Volume*	*Temp.*	*Volume.*
0° C.	25 c.c.	30° C.	27·8 c.c.
10° C.	25·9	40° C.	28·7
20° C.	26·8	50° C.	29·6
25° C.	27·3	60° C.	30·5

If the temperature is plotted on the *x*-axis and the volume on the *y*-axis, we shall obtain a straight-line graph indicating that the expansion is uniform. Produce the graph backwards until it cuts the *x*-axis. This it will do at − 273° C. Here the volume of the air theoretically becomes 0. Erect a new *y*-axis at this point calling − 273 the new zero. Scientists call this the *absolute zero*, and counting from this point they have invented a new scale of temperatures called *the absolute scale*. Corresponding temperatures on this scale and the Centigrade scale are:

− 273° C.	− 173° C.	0° C.	100° C.
0° Abs.	100° A.	273° A.	373° A.

Since the graph is a straight line going through this new zero, we can say that *the volume of the air is directly proportional to the absolute temperature.* The French scientist Charles found that other gases behaved in the same way and made the general statement that **the volume of a given mass of gas is directly proportional to the absolute temperature provided that the pressure remains constant** (Charles's Law).

Now we have made an assumption above that requires a

little more investigation. Our experiment only gave us information concerning the behaviour of air between 0° C. and 60° C. and we assumed that it would "keep to the straight path" when cooled below 0° C. As a matter of fact it does until about − 184° C., when it starts liquefying. Hydrogen keeps to the straight line down to about − 253° C., while helium goes to − 269° C. By causing liquid helium to evaporate rapidly, it has been found possible to reach a temperature between − 272 and − 273° C., but the absolute zero has never yet been reached. It is thought that at this temperature the molecules stop moving, they have no kinetic energy and there is no heat left in the substance.

Let us now consider our experimental results from another point of view. We found that

25 c.c. of air heated from 0° to 60° C. expanded by 5·5 c.c.

∴ 1 c.c. " " " **0° to 1° C.** " " $\frac{5 \cdot 5}{25 \times 60}$

$= 0 \cdot 00367$ or $\frac{1}{273}$.

The expression *0° to 1° C.* is very necessary and important. It will be remembered that we defined the coefficient of cubical expansion of a solid as the increase in volume when unit volume is warmed *through 1° C.* Strictly speaking, we should say from *0° to 1° C.*, but in the case of solids it does not make much difference on what part of the temperature scale we are working. But consider the following facts:

1 c.c. of gas warmed from 0° to 1° C. expands by $\frac{1}{273}$ c.c.
∴ 273 c.c. " " " " " " 1 c.c.
∴ 273 c.c. at 0° C. become
274 c.c. at 1° C.
323 c.c. at 50° C.
324 c.c. at 51° C., and so on.

From this we see that if we take the coefficient at 50° C. we get $\frac{1}{323}$ not $\frac{1}{273}$. We must therefore be more precise with gases and define the *coefficient of expansion of a gas as the increase in volume when unit volume is warmed from 0° to 1° C.*

From the above reasoning we can get another statement of Charles's Law, namely, **a gas expands $\frac{1}{273}$ of its volume at 0° C. for each rise in temperature of 1° C. provided that the pressure remains constant.**

The Gas Thermometer. What will happen if we heat a gas and prevent it expanding? Obviously the pressure will increase; and here is a striking fact—*If the gas is heated through* $1°$ *C. its pressure increases by* $\frac{1}{273}$ *of its pressure at* $0°$ *C.* In other words, the "pressure coefficient" and the "volume coefficient" are both equal to $\frac{1}{273}$. This fact can be deduced from Boyle's Law and Charles's Law or it can be proved by experiment using the apparatus shown in fig. 78.

The bulb is filled with dry gas by exhausting it several times and allowing the gas to enter through a drying tube after each exhaustion. The bulb is now immersed in a vessel containing ice and distilled water. After stirring well, the volume is adjusted by bringing the mercury to the zero index at A. The height AB is read and added to the atmospheric pressure, or taken away if B happens to be lower than A. The water is now raised to the boiling-point, the volume again adjusted to the zero index and the pressure read.

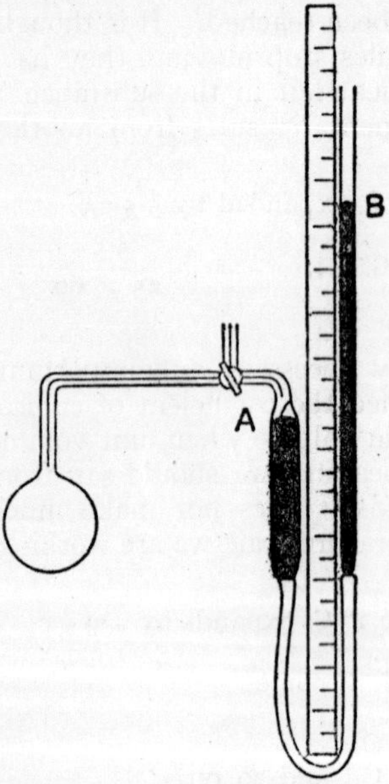

Fig. 78.

These two readings will suffice to enable us to calculate the pressure coefficient, but if time allows we may let the water cool and take various readings during the cooling. A graph may then be drawn, plotting temperature on the *x*-axis and pressure on the *y*-axis. With care we should again obtain a straight-line graph cutting the *x*-axis at $-273°$ C.

Using the readings obtained at freezing-point and boiling-point we proceed thus

Initial Pressure at 0° C. = 760 + 6 = 766 mm.
Final Pressure at 100° C. = 760 + 287 = 1047 mm.
Increase of pressure for 100° C. = 281 mm.
" " " " 1° C. = 2·81 mm.

$$\text{and } \frac{2{\cdot}81}{766} = \frac{1}{273} \text{ approx.}$$

Our apparatus could evidently be used as a gas thermometer, every rise or fall of 2·81 mm. in the pressure representing 1° C. It would not of course be very suitable for domestic use or for a doctor's waistcoat pocket, but it has some very important scientific uses. The gas thermometer has a very long range, thus with helium in the bulb it can be used almost to the absolute zero, while with a non-fusible bulb temperatures even above 1000° C. can be measured. It is also very sensitive and the expansion of a gas is uniform. For these reasons it is much used for standardizing mercury thermometers.

The Gas Equation. Suppose that we have a vessel full of gas and that the volume is v_1, the pressure p_1 and the temperature T_1 absolute. Next suppose that the pressure alters to p_2 and the temperature to T_2 absolute. Call the new volume v_2. Then it is easy to prove that

$$\text{new volume } v_2 = \frac{v_1 p_1 T_2}{p_2 T_1}$$

$$\therefore \frac{p_1 v_1}{T_1} = \frac{p_2 v_2}{T_2}.$$

In other words $\frac{pv}{T}$ is a constant.

This combination of Boyle's Law and Charles's Law is known as the *Gas Equation.*

The gas equation is very useful in chemistry, for there we frequently need to find what the volume of a certain mass of gas would be under standard conditions of temperature and pressure. The Standard or Normal Temperature and Pressure are regarded as 0° C. and 760 mm. pressure, and these are generally referred to as S.T.P. or N.T.P.

EXAMPLE. Convert 350 c.c. of oxygen at 17° C. and 740 mm. pressure to N.T.P.

17° C. = 273 + 17 = 290° Absolute
0° C. = 273° Absolute

then $p_1 = 740$ mm., $v_1 = 350$ c.c., $T_1 = 290°$ A.
and $p_2 = 760$ mm., v_2 is required, $T_2 = 273°$ A.

$$\text{but} \quad \frac{p_1 v_1}{T_1} = \frac{p_2 v_2}{T_2}, \quad \therefore \frac{740 \times 350}{290} = \frac{760 \times v_2}{273}$$

from which we can obtain the value of v_2.

QUESTIONS

1. Define the coefficient of linear expansion of a solid.

Show how the coefficient of cubical expansion is related to the coefficient of linear expansion.

Describe the experiment you would make to determine the coefficient of linear expansion of a metal. (C.W.B.)

2. The coefficient of linear expansion of aluminium is 0·000024 for 1° C. What will its value be in terms of the Fahrenheit scale and why is it unnecessary to consider the unit of length used?

At 0° C. a bar of aluminium is 2 in. long and a bar of iron 2·01 in. in length. At what temperature will they be of equal length? [Coeff. of Linear Expan. for iron, 0·000012.] (D.)

3. If the length of a bar is L_0 at 0° C., L_t at t° C. and α is the coefficient of linear expansion, show that $L_t = L_0(1 + \alpha t)$.

An iron bar is 15 ft. long at 60° C. What will be its length at 10° C.? [$\alpha = 11{\cdot}9 \times 10^{-6}$.]

4. A square sheet of steel has a 15-ft. side at 0° C. What will be its area at 40° C.? [$\alpha = 0{\cdot}000011$.]

5. Answer Question 1, p. 78, using the additional facts learnt in this chapter.

6. Explain clearly what is meant by the statement that the coefficient of linear expansion of brass is 0·0000185 per degree C. Deduce the value of the coefficient of cubical expansion.

A glass bulb at 0° C. contains 544 gm. of mercury when full. What weight of mercury will flow out when the bulb is heated to 90° C.? [Coeff. of cub. expansion of mercury in glass = 0·000180 per degree C.] (O. and C.).

7. "Water is not a good thermometric substance." Quote some facts which support the truth of this statement.

Explain why ice forms on the *surface* of a lake. What is the temperature of the water at the bottom of the lake when its surface is coated with ice? Give a reason for your answer. (L.)

8. In an experiment on the expansion of air at constant pressure, the following results were obtained:

Volume .	26·5 c.c.	27·5	28·4	29	29·5	29·9
Temp. .	17° C.	27°	37·3°	44°	49°	53°

From a graph find the volume at 0° C. Then calculate the *volume coefficient*.

9. Describe the constant-volume air thermometer. Explain one purpose for which it may be used. (C.W.B.)

10. Distinguish between real and apparent expansion as applied to liquids, and show what is the relation between them.

A specific gravity bottle weighs 15·44 gm. empty, and 59·64 gm. when full of a certain liquid at 15° C. It is heated in a bath at 60° C., after which it is found that exactly 1 gm. of liquid has been expelled. Calculate the coefficient of apparent expansion of the liquid.

If the coefficient of linear expansion of the glass is 0·000009 per ° C., find the coefficient of real expansion of the liquid. (B.)

11. State the relation connecting the pressure, volume, and temperature of a gas like air.

A quantity of air occupies 250 c.c. at 15° C. when the pressure is 76 cm. of mercury. At what temperature will its volume be 230 c.c. if the pressure is 85 cm.? (C.W.B.)

12. The volume of a gas is 500 c.c. at a pressure of 28 in. and a temperature of 10° C. Find the volume at N.T.P.

13. How would you determine by experiment the increase of pressure needed to keep a mass of gas at constant volume as the temperature is raised?

A given volume of air has a pressure of 850 mm. at a temperature of 50° C. What will the new pressure be if the temperature is lowered to 12° C. but the volume remains unchanged? (L.)

14. Five cubic feet of air are measured at 750 mm. pressure and 15° C. What will be the volume at N.T.P.?

15. A quantity of air is at atmospheric pressure in a closed vessel at a temperature of 15° C. The vessel is heated until the pressure of the air is two atmospheres; what is its temperature? [Assume that the vessel does not expand and that 0° C. is 273 Absolute.] (C. part question.)

16. On a gas thermometer the mercury in the long arm stands 5 cm. below the mark when the bulb is in ice-cold water and 20 cm. above the mark when the bulb is in boiling water. What will be the Centigrade temperature when the mercury stands 8 cm. above the mark? [Atmospheric pressure = 76 cm.]

CHAPTER X

CALORIMETRY

THE title of this chapter indicates that we are about to deal with the *measurement of calories*. A *calorie* is the quantity of heat required to raise the temperature of 1 gm. of water through 1° C. It is sometimes called the gram-degree Centigrade. This is the unit most frequently used in science, but there are also two important practical units met with in gas bills and in engineering. The *British Thermal Unit* is the quantity of heat required to raise the temperature of 1 lb. of water through 1° F. It is sometimes called the pound-degree Fahrenheit. It may help the memory to notice that a *British* unit would naturally refer to pounds and degrees Fahrenheit. A *Therm* is 100,000 of these small units.

1 Therm = 100,000 B.Th.U.

In Chapter VIII we referred to two flasks of boiling water. Both flasks are at the same temperature, but the large one has absorbed more calories or more B.Th.U. If they were both started from cold on equal burners the large one would take longer to boil because of the greater mass of water to be warmed.

Experiment. Place a beaker of water on a balance and with a pipette adjust the total weight to 200 gm. Heat the beaker of water on a tripod and gauze over a flame of medium size, noting the *time* necessary to arrive at boiling-point.

Pour away the water and put lead shot in the beaker to a depth of about $\frac{1}{4}$ in. Add water and again adjust the total weight to 200 gm. Raise to boiling-point over the *same* flame and note the time. The time will be much less, showing that much less heat was necessary.

Here we have a very striking fact—when part of the water was replaced by an equal mass of lead, much less heat was required to warm the total mass through the same temperature range. We may vary the experiment by finding the times taken to heat two equal masses of alcohol and water up to 60° C. Here again the water will require more time and therefore more heat, but the fact is not so striking as in the case of lead.

You will soon find by experiment that 1 gm. of lead heated through 1° C. only takes in 0·03 calorie. This number, 0·03, is known as the *specific heat* of lead.

The Specific Heat of a substance =

$$\frac{\text{Heat required to raise the temperature of the substance } 1^\circ}{\text{Heat required to raise the temp. of the same mass of water } 1^\circ}.$$

The specific heat is a *number* and will be the same no matter what units of heat, mass, and temperature we take. Since we generally use the calorie, the gram, and the degree Centigrade, the specific heat of a substance is sometimes defined as the number of calories required to raise the temperature of 1 gm. of the substance through 1° C.

With very few exceptions water has the highest specific heat, namely, 1. The specific heats of other substances are decimal fractions. Here are a few well-known substances with their specific heats. Aluminium 0·21, mercury 0·033, turpentine 0·42, alcohol 0·55. The high specific heat of water makes it an excellent substance for storing heat, hence its use in warming houses and buildings generally. For the same reason the sea warms up more slowly than the land in early summer and cools more slowly on the approach of winter.

Problem. How many calories are required to heat 50 gm. of lead from 10° to 40° C.?

1 gm. of lead heated	1° C.	requires	0·03 cal.
50 ,, ,, ,,	1° C.	,,	50 × 0·03 cals.
50 ,, ,, ,,	30° C.	,,	50 × 0·03 × 30 cals.
			= 45 cals.

Note that in calculating calories, we multiply three quantities together, the *mass*, the *specific heat*, and the *temperature range*. Generally, M gm. of any substance of specific heat S when heated from t_1 *to* t_2 will require $MS(t_2 - t_1)$ cals., and when allowed to cool will give out the same number of calories. The quantity MS is known as the *heat capacity* or *thermal capacity* of the substance and may be defined as *the quantity of heat required to raise its temperature 1°*. Thus in the above example the thermal capacity of the lead is 50 × 0·03 = 1·5 cals. We see therefore that 50 gm. of lead has only the same thermal capacity as 1·5 gm. of water! In other words, the water equivalent of 50 gm. of lead is 1·5 gm. *The water equivalent of a body is that weight of water which has the same thermal capacity.*

N.B.—Thermal Capacity of 50 gm. of lead = 1·5 cals.
Water Equivalent of 50 gm. of lead = 1·5 gm.

What will be the thermal capacity and water equivalent of a hollow cylinder of copper weighing 50 gm. if the specific heat of copper is 0·095? The thermal capacity is $MS = 50 \times 0{\cdot}095 = 4{\cdot}75$ cals., while the water equivalent is 4·75 gm.

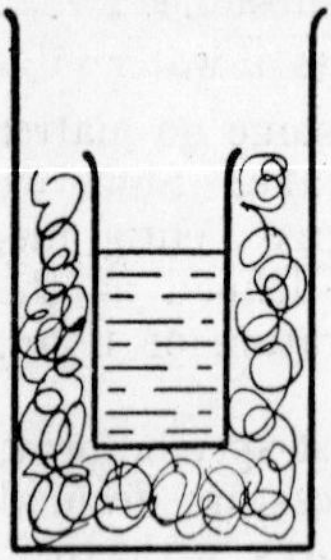

FIG. 79.

Experiment. To find the specific heat of marble.

Weigh a *calorimeter* which is generally a hollow cylinder polished on the outside. Half-fill with water and weigh again. Place the calorimeter in a larger vessel which is generally polished on the inside and packed loosely with cotton-wool (fig. 79). Suspend the weighed piece of marble in boiling water. Read the temperature of the boiling water, then the cold water, transfer the marble to the cold water, stir and take the temperature of the "mixture."

Wt. of marble	=	60·3 gm.
Wt. of calorimeter	=	50·4 gm.
Wt. of calorimeter and water	=	120·6 gm.
Wt. of water	=	70·2 gm.
Water equivalent of calorimeter	=	50·4 × 0·095 = 4·8 gm.
"Total water"	=	75·0 gm.
Temp. of marble	=	99·5° C.
Temp. of cold water	=	12·4° C.
Temp. of mixture	=	24·4° C.

Heat lost by marble = Heat gained by "Total water"

$$m \times s \times \text{temp. fall} = M \times S \times \text{temp. rise}$$

$$60{\cdot}3 \times s \times 75{\cdot}1 = 75 \times 1 \times 12$$

$$\therefore s = 0{\cdot}20.$$

In the above experiment we have calculated the water equivalent from the mass and the known specific heat of copper, but it is possible to determine the water equivalent by experiment.

Experiment. To find the water equivalent of a calorimeter weigh the calorimeter empty, then one-third full of water. Take the temperature. Add hot water at a known temperature, stir, read the temperature of the mixture, then weigh calorimeter and mixture.

Wt. of calorimeter	= 50·4 gm.
Wt. of calorimeter + cold water	= 90·6 gm.
Wt. of cold water	= 40·2 gm.
Wt. of calorimeter + mixture	= 138·8 gm.
∴ Wt. of hot water	= 48·2 gm.
Temp. of hot water	= 62·0° C.
Temp. of cold water	= 20·0° C.
Temp. of mixture	= 41·7° C.

Call the water equivalent E gm.

Heat lost = Heat gained

$$48{\cdot}2 \times 1 \times 20{\cdot}3 = (40{\cdot}2 \times 1 \times 21{\cdot}7) + (E \times 1 \times 21{\cdot}7)$$

$$\therefore E = 4{\cdot}9 \text{ grams.}$$

A Fuel Calorimeter. In industry it is frequently necessary to find the number of calories obtainable from 1 gm. of fuel. An apparatus designed for this purpose by C. R. Darling is illustrated in fig. 80.

One gram of coal is put in a nickel crucible C and ignited by an electric current carried by the copper wires W into a thin iron wire embedded in the coal. Oxygen is driven in by the tube O. The crucible is held in position by three brass clips forming part of a brass tube A. The hot gases pass down the inside of the brass tube into a shallow chamber formed of two recessed plates, the upper one having fine perforations through which the gases escape into the water. It is found that when the gas is thus broken up into tiny bubbles they are more likely to give up all their heat to the water in the outer vessel.

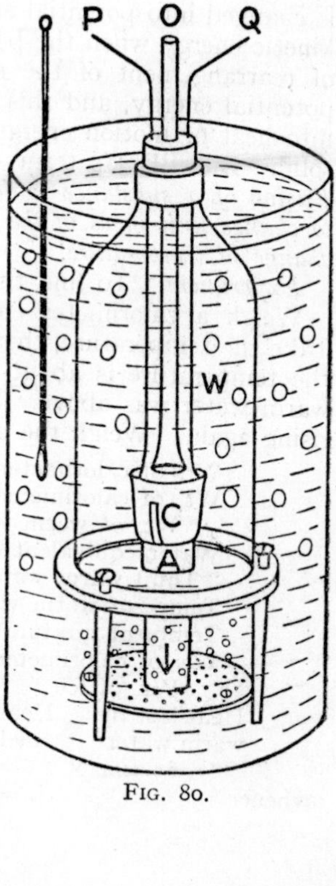

FIG. 80.

Knowing the weight of water, the water equivalent of the apparatus and the rise in temperature, the calories evolved can easily be calculated. The apparatus can be adapted for use with a liquid or gaseous fuel.

Latent Heat of Fusion. When a beaker of ice and water is stirred, the temperature remains at 0° C. until all the ice has melted. This absorption of heat without rise of temperature during the melting of a solid is not peculiar to ice but is a general phenomenon discovered in 1762 by Joseph Black. At that time it was thought that heat was a weightless fluid. Black got the idea that some of this fluid had become "hidden" amongst the molecules. He therefore referred to the heat so absorbed as "latent heat." The modern idea is that the kinetic energy of the flame has been converted into potential energy. When a body is thrown upwards, say on to a shelf, kinetic energy is changed into potential energy which again changes back into kinetic energy when the body falls. So here there is some sort of rearrangement of the molecules in which they have more potential energy, and this energy will once again be converted into heat or motion energy when the liquid changes back to a solid. But Black's term still survives and the *Latent Heat of Fusion of a substance is defined as the quantity of heat required to change unit mass of the substance from solid to liquid without change of temperature.*

Experiment. To find the Latent Heat of Fusion of ice.

Weigh a calorimeter empty, then half-full of warm water. Take the temperature, then add ice dried with filter paper until the temperature is about as far below air temperature as the warm water was above. Read the temperature when it starts rising again. Weigh the calorimeter and mixture.

Wt. of calorimeter	= 50·4 gm.
Wt. of calorimeter + warm water	= 110·6 gm.
∴ Wt. of warm water	= 60·2 gm.
Water equivalent of calorimeter	= 4·8 gm.
"Total warm water"	= 65·0 gm.
Temp. of warm water	= 25·0° C.
Temp. of mixture	= 5·0° C.
Wt. of calorimeter + mixture	= 126·1 gm.
∴ Wt. of ice	= 15·5 gm.

Heat lost by warm water = Heat used in melting ice + Heat used in warming ice-cold water

$$65 \times 1 \times 20 = 15{\cdot}5L + (15{\cdot}5 \times 1 \times 5)$$

whence $L = 79$ The accepted value is 80 cals.

Latent Heat of Vaporization. It is common experience that when once water is boiling, the temperature does not rise any further provided the steam can escape. The heat sent in is now used in changing water into steam and not in raising the temperature. As in the case of fusion, this heat is referred to as " Latent Heat " and is recovered when the steam changes back into water. *The Latent Heat of Vaporization of a liquid is defined as the quantity of heat required to change unit mass of the liquid into vapour without change of temperature.*

Experiment. To find the Latent Heat of Vaporization of water.

Weigh a calorimeter empty, then half-full of cold water. Take the temperature, then pass *dry* steam by way of the water trap (fig. 81) into the cold water until the temperature has risen about 15° C. Read this temperature, then weigh calorimeter and mixture. During the passing of steam into the calorimeter, the latter should be carefully screened from the boiler.

Wt. of calorimeter	=	50·40 gm.
Wt. of calorimeter + cold water	=	128·61 gm.
Wt. of cold water	=	78·21 gm.
Water equivalent of calorimeter	=	4·8 gm.
" Total cold water "	=	83·01 gm.
Temp. of boiling water	=	100° C.
Temp. of cold water	=	12·2° C.
Temp. of mixture	=	28·4° C.
Wt. of calorimeter + mixture	=	130·82 gm.
Wt. of steam	=	2·21 gm.

Heat lost by steam + Heat lost by boiling water = Heat gained by cold water

$$2{\cdot}21L + 2{\cdot}21 \times 1 \times 71{\cdot}6 = 83{\cdot}01 \times 1 \times 16{\cdot}2$$

whence $L = 537$. Accepted value = 540 cals. when the water boils at 100° C.

FIG. 81.

The higher the boiling-point, the smaller does the latent heat of steam become.

QUESTIONS

1. A piece of copper is heated to 100° C., then immersed in an equal mass of water at 10° C. The final temperature is 18° C What do you infer from this?

E G.S.P.

2. The following quantities of water are mixed. Neglecting the effect of the containing vessel, calculate the final temperatures.

80 gm. at 70° C. with 140 gm. at 30° C.
20 gm. at 90° C. with 120 gm. at 10° C.
40 gallons at 72° F. with 70 gallons at 50° F.
21 litres at 120° F. with 48 litres at 43° F.

3. Calculate the thermal capacity and water equivalent of the following:

160 gm. of mercury S.H. 0·033, 500 gm. of copper S.H. 0·095
150 gm. of aluminium S.H. 0·21, 200 gm. of alcohol S.H. 0·55.

In each case find also the quantity of heat necessary to raise the temperature from 16° to 70° C.

4. Define the calorie and the B.Th.U. How many calories are there in one B.Th.U.? [1 lb. = 454 gm.]

Describe how you would find the specific heat of German silver wire in your laboratory: state the experimental precautions to be taken, show in tabular form how you would record your readings, and explain how you would work the result. (O.)

5. A piece of iron weighing 50 gm. is heated to 90° C. and immersed in 100 gm. of water at 15° C. The final temperature is 19° C. Calculate the specific heat of iron.

6. 100 gm. of water at 80° C. are added to 90 gm. of water at 20° C. in a calorimeter weighing 100 gm. The final temperature is 50° C. Calculate the water equivalent of the calorimeter.

7. 4 gm. of steam at 100° C. raised the temperature of 96 gm. of water from 15° to 40° C. Calculate the latent heat of steam.

8. In a Darling Calorimeter 1 gm. of coal heated 1400 gm. of water from 20·1° C. to 25·0° C. If the water equivalent of the apparatus was 250 gm., calculate the calorific value of the coal.

9. A "tin can" containing water at 10° C. was placed on a gas stove. It boiled in 3 min. and the water had disappeared in another 18 min. Calculate the latent heat of vaporization of water.

10. What do you understand by the term Latent Heat? A block of ice whose temperature is − 4° C. is heated continuously until it is all converted into steam. Describe and explain all the changes that will take place, paying regard to state, volume and temperature. (L.)

11. Why is water used in hot-water bottles? Which produces the worse scalding effect, boiling water or steam?

Explain the physical causes producing an insular climate.

12. Explain each of the following:

(*a*) The *specific heat* of brass is 0·1.

(*b*) The *latent heat of steam*, at normal atmospheric pressure, is 540 Centigrade units.

5 gm. of steam at 100° are passed into 200 gm. of water at 10°

in a brass calorimeter of mass 40 gm. Calculate the resulting temperature.

13. Define *latent heat of fusion of ice*, and describe an experiment whereby you could determine its value.

A copper calorimeter weighing 130 gm. contains 240 gm. of water at 25° C. After adding a piece of dry ice the temperature becomes steady at 8° C. What was the weight of ice added?

[Latent heat of fusion of ice = 80 cals. per gm. S.H. of copper = 0·1.] (C.W.B.)

14. What are the effects usually observed on supplying heat to a substance? Can heat be supplied to a substance without raising its temperature? Give an explanation and describe an experiment in which the heat can be recovered.

What is the final result if 150 gm. of water at 50° C. are added to a mixture of 100 gm. of ice and 400 gm. of water at 0° C. [Latent heat of fusion of ice = 80 cals. per gm.] (D.)

15. Explain the terms *specific heat, water equivalent*. Describe how you would measure the specific heat of brine. A sample of brine was found to have a specific heat of 0·8, and 50 gm. of water were added to 100 gm. of the brine. Find the specific heat of the resulting liquid. (B.)

16. Define *latent heat of steam*.

Steam at normal atmospheric pressure is blown into 300 lb. of water contained in a vessel of water equivalent 20 lb. When the temperature has risen from 40° F. to 104° F. the steam supply is removed and the increase in weight is found to be 19 lb. Calculate the latent heat of steam. (L.)

17. Explain what is meant by temperature, and describe the Fahrenheit and Centigrade scales of temperature.

Equal weights of water at 17° C. and 59° F. respectively are mixed together. What will be the final temperature of the mixture in degrees Centigrade? (O. and C.)

18. A piece of iron is heated to 212° F. and is then dropped into 6 lb. of water at 44° F.; the temperature rises to 72° F. Calculate the thermal capacity of the piece of iron. (C. part question.)

19. What do you understand by the statements (*a*) that the temperature of a certain body is 50 C., (*b*) that the thermal capacity of a given brass weight is 20 cals.?

How would you find out which of two metal balls of the same weight had the greater thermal capacity? (O.)

20. Boiling water is poured into a "heavy calorimeter" weighing 725 gm. A steady temperature of 66° C. is reached. The calorimeter and water weigh 840 gm. If the original temperature of the calorimeter was 19° C., find its thermal capacity and the specific heat of the material.

CHAPTER XI

CHANGE OF STATE

FROM the point of view of physical properties, matter can be classified into *solids, liquids* and *gases.* It will be convenient here to sum up our knowledge of the distinctive properties of these three physical states of matter.

	Solids.	*Liquids.*	*Gases.*
1	Definite volume and definite shape.	Definite volume but indefinite shape.	Indefinite volume and shape.
2	Specific gravity generally high.	Specific gravity generally less than unity. *N.B.*—Mercury 13·6.	Specific gravity very low.
3	Force of cohesion very great, *i.e.* particles resist separation.	Force of cohesion much less. Drops easily formed. Surface horizontal.	Force of cohesion practically negligible.
4	Transmit pressure in straight lines.	Transmit pressure equally in all directions.	Transmit pressure equally in all directions.
5	Generally incompressible.	Incompressible.	Can be compressed in accordance with Boyle's Law.
6	Small expansion on heating. Coeff. of cubical expansion of iron 0·0000351. per 1° C.	Greater expansion on heating. Coeff. of water 0·000476. per 1° C.	Still greater expansion on heating. Coeff. for all gases 0·00366. per 1° C.

General Effects of Heat on Matter.

1. Increase in volume. What exceptions do you know?
2. Rise in temperature or

3. Change of state.

4. Increase in electrical resistance. This fact is used in the construction of platinum resistance thermometers for measuring very high or very low temperatures.

5. If two different metals are joined end to end and the free ends connected through a galvanometer, an electric current flows round the circuit when the junction is heated. This fact is used in the measurement of temperature and radiation.

The Lower Change of State.

Experiment. To find the melting-point of a solid.

(*a*) The direct method. Draw out a piece of small glass tubing and seal off. Put a few tiny bits of naphthalene in the tube and strap it to the bulb of a thermometer with small rings cut from rubber tubing. Heat slowly in a beaker of water with constant stirring. Note the temperature at which the solid melts and remove the heat. Note the temperature at which the liquid solidifies. The average of these two temperatures should be the true melting-point (79° C.).

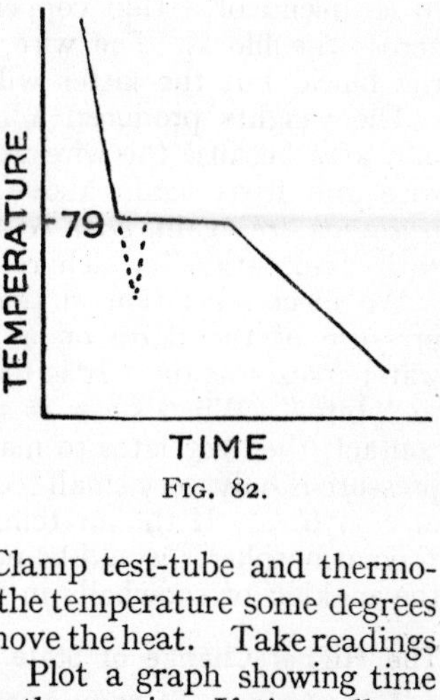

FIG. 82.

(*b*) The cooling-curve method. Put enough naphthalene in a test-tube to cover the thermometer bulb when the solid has melted. Clamp test-tube and thermometer in a beaker of water. Raise the temperature some degrees above the melting-point. Then remove the heat. Take readings of temperature every half-minute. Plot a graph showing time on the *x*-axis and temperatures on the *y*-axis. If time allows, it is interesting to do the experiment twice, once with constant stirring and once without touching the apparatus during cooling. In both cases there should be a well-marked horizontal portion where the liquid stops cooling because the latent heat given out just balances the cooling losses and the temperature remains constant (fig. 82). In the second case "supercooling" may also occur (fig. 82, dotted line). In the case of mixtures two horizontal portions may show on the graph indicating two definite melting-points. This sometimes occurs with paraffir wax.

The freezing-point of a solution is lower than the freezing point of the pure solvent. For this reason a solution of common salt or of calcium chloride is used as the circulating liquid in cold stores. This *depression of the freezing-point* is also used in chemistry in the determination of molecular weights.

Experiment. To show the effect of pressure on the melting-point of ice.

Most substances contract on freezing and their melting-points are raised by pressure. Water, as we have seen, expands on freezing; the melting-point of ice is lowered by pressure.

Support a block of ice on two retort stands. Attach a weight to each end of a thin copper or iron wire and place the wire across the block. The wire will steadily cut its way through the block, but the latter will still be in one piece.

The weights produced a considerable pressure or force per unit area because the wire was thin. The ice melted under the wire and froze again above the wire. This process is called *regelation* (*re* again, *geler* to freeze). Do not confuse the term with "relegation" which refers to league football teams!

We meet regelation in skating and making snowballs. The pressure of the skate on a small area melts the ice and the water freezes again. It is for this reason that the skate is able to "bite." When snow is squeezed it melts at the points of contact, then regelates to make a firm mass. But the effect of pressure is only very small; one atmosphere produces a lowering of 0·0076° C. If the air temperature is − 7·6° C. a pressure of 1000 atmospheres would be necessary to produce melting. Thus the making of snowballs in very cold weather is impossible.

The Higher Change of State.

Experiment. To show that the boiling-point of a solution is higher than that of the pure solvent.

Boil some distilled water in a flask and take the temperature of the boiling liquid. Add some salt or some calcium chloride and again find the boiling-point, making sure that the thermometer bulb is in the liquid. Also read the temperature of the steam.

Experiment. To show the effect of pressure on the boiling-point.

Boil some water in a round-bottomed flask. At the same moment remove the burner and cork the flask. Invert the flask under a running tap. The water now boils vigorously under reduced pressure.

The effect of pressure can be shown in more detail with the apparatus shown in fig. 83. To study the effect of *increased* pressure boil the water with the screw clip open and take the temperature. Then close the clip and find the boiling-point

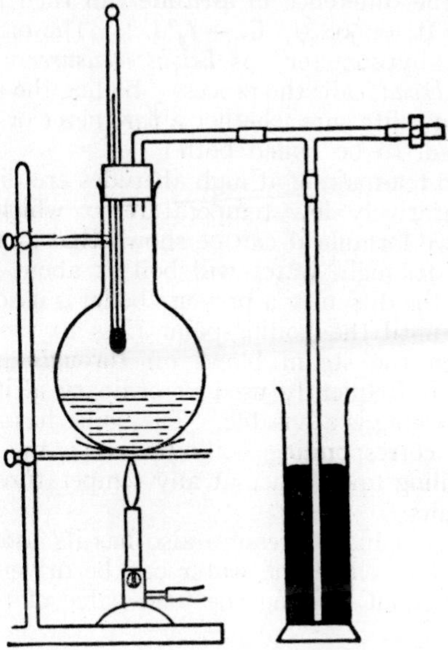

FIG. 83.

when there are varying depths of mercury in the gas jar. The total pressure is found in each case by adding the mercury depth to the height of the barometer.

To study the effect of *reduced* pressure, lower the burner, attach a filter pump and open the clip. Mercury then rises in the long tube.

The reason why the boiling-point rises and falls with the pressure will be understood when the question of vapour pressure is studied. We now understand why, when using a hypsometer to mark the upper fixed point on a thermometer, the water is not allowed to touch the bulb and why the point is not marked 100° C. unless the pressure is normal.

When dealing with barometers we saw that the greater the altitude the less the air pressure. We have just learnt that the less the air pressure the lower the boiling-point. For this reason a hypsometer (page 74) is, on account of its portability, used to measure altitudes. The boiling-point of water is determined at two stations and the difference in altitude can then be found from the formula h ft. = 968 (t_1° C. − t_2° C.). The original meaning of the word "hypsometer" is *height measurer*. Mark Twain, in *A Tramp Abroad*, calls the process "boiling the thermometer," but he was not quite sure whether a *baro*meter or a *thermo*meter had to be used, so he boiled both!

Cooking and tea-making at high altitudes are difficult because of the comparatively low temperature at which water boils. From the above formula it can be shown that at the top of Mt. Blanc, 16,000 ft. high, water will boil at about 84° C.

To get over the difficulty a pressure boiler is used. This keeps the steam in until the boiling-point rises to the desired temperature, when the steam blows off through a safety-valve. Such a boiler is frequently used at ordinary altitudes in cases where rapid cooking is advisable. The boiler has a dial showing pressures and corresponding boiling-points; the valve can be set so that boiling takes place at any temperature and pressure within the limits.

Boiling under reduced pressure also has its uses; in making condensed milk much of the water can be driven off at a low temperature without altering the food value of the milk.

Solid to Gas.

As a general rule, we may say that any substance can exist in all three physical states. But in some cases a solid decomposes before it reaches the gaseous state. Some substances jump over the liquid state and are then said to *sublime*. Iodine almost does this, while sal-ammoniac does it perfectly. These substances can be liquefied by heating under pressure. In this way the great expansion necessary to form the gaseous state is prevented and the heated solid can only become liquid. Again in other cases we are not able to produce a high enough temperature to change the solid into a gas.

All known gases show a perfect agreement with the rule; they have all been liquefied and even solidified. This is accomplished by the joint effect of cooling and pressure. The former is more important and there is in fact for every gas a certain temperature to which it must be cooled before pressure, however great, can effect liquefaction. This temperature is called the *critical temperature* and the corresponding pressure which will just liquefy the gas at this temperature is called the *critical pressure*. Thus the critical temperature of carbon dioxide is 31° C. and its critical pressure 73 atmospheres. Above 31° C. carbon dioxide is a true gas, below it is a vapour. Water is a gas above 365° C. and a vapour below that temperature. For the facts about critical temperature science is indebted to Thomas Andrews of Belfast (1813–85).

Evaporation. It is well known that a liquid need not be boiled to change it into vapour. We constantly find that water disappears at ordinary temperatures and we say that it has *evaporated*. As in boiling so also in evaporation, latent heat has to be supplied to change the liquid into a vapour. A gram of water at 15° C. would require considerably more than 540 cals. to change it into vapour at that temperature. If this heat is not supplied the general temperature of the water drops.

This fact is applied in tropical countries to keep water cool. The water is stored in porous vessels, evaporation takes place and the necessary latent heat is taken from the main body of water. Again, during hot weather we perspire and the evaporation of this moisture keeps the temperature down. The simple fact that evaporation at ordinary temperature requires latent heat can be illustrated by a well-known experiment.

Experiment. Place a beaker containing ether in a pool of water on a block of wood. Bubble air through with a foot bellows. The water freezes because the forced evaporation has lowered the general temperature of the ether and the water.

Vapour Pressure. It can be shown that when a liquid evaporates, the vapour so formed exerts a definite pressure.

Experiment. By means of a curved pipette (fig. 84) a few drops of ether are sent up into the vacuum of a Torricelli barometer. The liquid vaporizes almost immediately and the mercury is forced down. In the "vacuum" we have an *unsaturated vapour*. Pass up a few more drops of ether until a layer is seen on the top of the mercury. We have now a *saturated vapour* exerting its *maximum vapour pressure* for the existing temperature. At 10° C. this will be 291 mm. Wring out a duster after immersion in warm water and wrap it round the upper part of the tube, passing up more ether if necessary. **The vapour pressure increases with the temperature.** At 20° C. it is 440 mm. There is for any given liquid a definite vapour pressure corresponding to each temperature. At 35° C., the boiling-point of ether, the vapour pressure will be equal to the atmospheric pressure and the mercury will be at the same level inside and outside the tube.

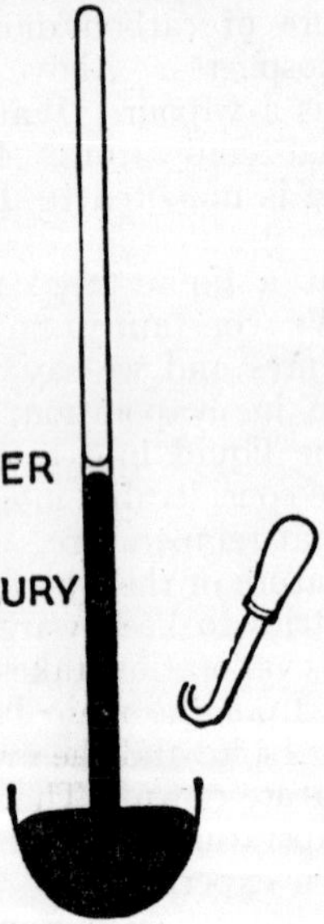

FIG. 84.

The experiment can be repeated with water in place of ether, using a steam jacket instead of a warm duster. It will be noticed that for the same temperature the vapour pressure is considerably less than in the case of ether. At 10° C. it is 9 mm., at 20° C. it is 17 mm. At 100° C., the boiling-point of water, the vapour pressure is equal to the atmospheric pressure. We may now define the *boiling-point of a liquid* as *that temperature at which its vapour pressure becomes equal to the normal atmospheric pressure.* If the external pressure becomes greater than this, either naturally or by design, then the vapour pressure has to rise to some value corresponding to a higher temperature. In other words, the boiling-point rises. In the same way, if the external pressure is diminished the boiling-point drops.

Our knowledge of vapour pressure is mainly due to the English scientist Dalton (1766–1844) and the French physicist Regnault (1810–78). In chemistry you will have need to use a table called " Maximum Pressure of Aqueous Vapour." This table is due to Regnault. His method was based on the fact arrived at above, namely, that the vapour pressure at the boiling-point is equal to the external pressure. Regnault's apparatus was similar to that shown in fig. 85. The air pressure in B was adjusted to some definite value by pumping air in or drawing air out. The water (or other liquid under investigation) was heated in A. It boiled when its vapour pressure was equal to the pressure in B as registered on the open manometer M.

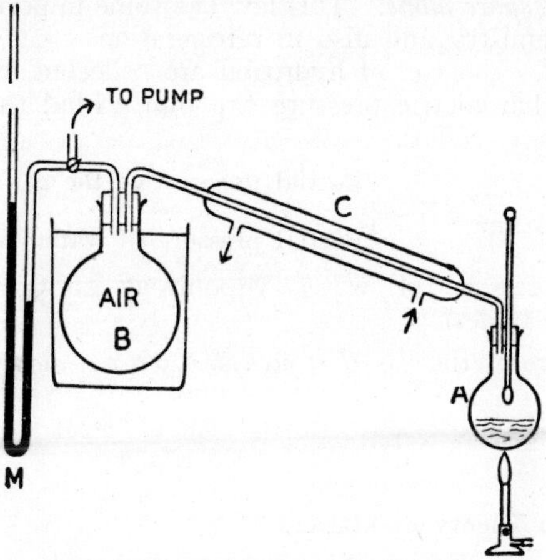

Fig. 85.

The vapour condensed in C and flowed back into the flask. When the temperature and pressure were steady these were read. Then a new adjustment of pressure was made and the corresponding temperature found. The reservoir B was immersed in water and served as a buffer to steady the pressure.

With this apparatus, using metal vessels for the higher pressures, Regnault worked up to a pressure of 28 atmospheres. A few of his results for low temperatures and pressures are given here.

Temp. .	4° C.	6° C.	8° C.	10° C.	12° C.	14° C.	16° C.	18° C.	20° C.	22° C.
Pressure	6·1 mm.	7·0	8·0	9·2	10·5	12·0	13·6	15·5	17·5	19·8

John Dalton, besides doing a good deal of pioneer work which paved the way for Regnault, discovered that even if a closed space is already occupied by a gas, another liquid will still evaporate into it until it sets up its own vapour pressure appropriate to the existing temperature. His **law of partial pressures** states that *If two or more gases which do not react chemically are mixed together in a closed vessel, then the pressure will be the sum of the pressures which each would exert if it occupied the space alone.* This law has some important applications in chemistry and also in refrigeration.

EXAMPLE. 500 c.c. of hydrogen are collected over water at 20° C. and barometric pressure 770 mm. Find the volume of the dry gas at N.T.P.

$$\begin{matrix}\text{Total pressure}\\ \text{(770 mm.)}\end{matrix} = \begin{cases}\text{Partial pressure of the gas}\\ \qquad + \\ \text{Partial pressure of water vapour}\end{cases}$$

But the pressure of water vapour at 20° C. = 17·5 mm. (Regnault's tables).

∴ pressure of the gas *if it occupied 500 c.c. alone* would be

$$770 - 17{\cdot}5 = 752{\cdot}5 \text{ mm.}$$

$$\therefore \text{ Volume at N.T.P.} = \frac{500 \times 752{\cdot}5 \times 273}{760 \times 293} = 461 \text{ c.c.}$$

The Kinetic Theory of Matter.

Scientists have found that many of the observed facts of physics and chemistry can best be explained on the supposition that *matter consists of molecules in motion and attracted by each other with a force called cohesion.* So far no facts have been discovered which contradict that supposition. Moreover, the theory has enabled us to predict new facts. The idea of molecular motion may therefore be regarded as well established.

Each molecule of a solid is supposed to oscillate about some fixed position and the force of cohesion is strong. When the solid is heated the molecules move faster and farther from their average positions—the solid expands. Metal workers find the force of cohesion is then less.

In a liquid there is more freedom, but the force of cohesion is still strong. Consider a water molecule well inside the liquid. It is attracted by all the molecules round it within a short range. These attractions balance out and the molecule is not urged in any special direction. But molecules at the surface are only pulled inwards, the surface tends to decrease in area and acts like a stretched sheet of rubber. This is the phenomenon known as **surface tension.** It is used by gnat larvæ and " pond skaters " and may easily be demonstrated by lowering a clean needle on to the surface of water. Surface tension is also evident in soap films.

Allied to surface tension is an effect known as **capillarity.** Here we have a struggle between cohesion and adhesion. The

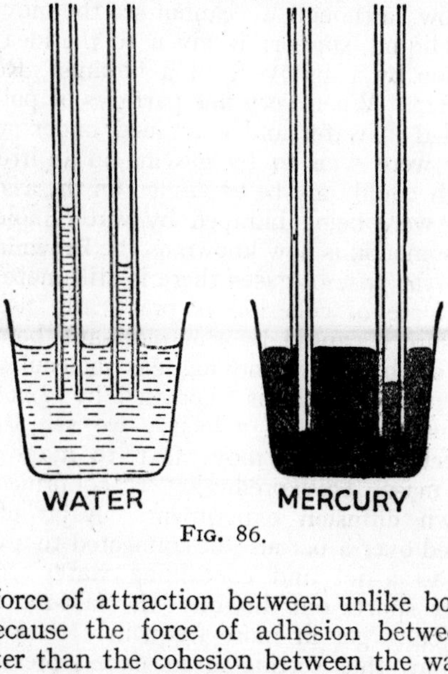

FIG. 86.

latter is the force of attraction between unlike bodies. Water wets glass because the force of adhesion between glass and water is greater than the cohesion between the water particles. When a narrow glass tube is dipped into water, the surface of contact tends to increase and the water rises until the adhesive dragging force is just equal to the weight of the water supported (fig. 86). The liquid naturally sags in the middle, making the surface concave because the drag is greatest round the circle of contact. The liquid rises higher in a narrow tube because the weight to be supported increases faster than the internal circumference along which the pull is exerted. If the diameter is halved the height is doubled.

The force of cohesion in mercury is greater than the force of adhesion between mercury and glass, therefore mercury does not wet glass, the contact area tends to decrease, and the surface is depressed in a narrow glass tube dipped in that liquid. The name "capillarity" comes from the fact that the effect only occurs with tubes of fine bore (Lat. *capillus*, a hair). Blotting-paper and lamp wicks depend on capillarity, but more important is the part it plays in the transport of liquid along root and stem in the plant world.

FIG. 87.

Now, although we cannot see the moving molecules of a liquid, support is given to the idea of molecular motion by a discovery of a botanist, Robert Brown, in 1827. When very fine particles of pollen were suspended in water and examined under a microscope, they were seen to be moving in an irregular fashion which could only be explained on the assumption that they were being bumped by water molecules. This phenomenon is now known as the **Brownian movement.**

In the case of gases there is still more freedom and the force of cohesion is practically negligible. Gas pressure is caused by the incessant bombardment of the enclosure by moving gas molecules. Since the energy of a body is expressed by $\frac{1}{2}mv^2$ where m is its mass and v its velocity, we see that hydrogen molecules should move fast to make up for their low mass. This prediction is confirmed by a well-known **diffusion** experiment. A jar of hydrogen is placed over a porous pot connected to a **J**-tube drawn out to a jet and containing water (fig. 87). The water spurts out because the fast-moving hydrogen molecules get in more frequently than air molecules get out, thus setting up an excess pressure.

In more advanced work it is shown that Boyle's Law, Charles's Law and Avogadro's Law all follow directly from the simple assumptions of the Kinetic Theory.

The mental picture of moving molecules is also valuable in explaining evaporation. Owing to frequent collisions, the molecules of a liquid will not all be moving at the same speed. When a molecule near the surface happens to have a speed higher than the average, it may be able to overcome the attraction of the molecules underneath. It then escapes through the surface; this is **evaporation.** Since it is the average speed which determines the temperature, the loss of a large number of the faster-moving molecules will cause the temperature to fall unless energy is received from outside. This is cooling by evaporation. If the temperature rises, the average kinetic energy of the molecules will increase and more molecules will have the speed necessary for escape. But if the liquid is in an enclosed space, the vapour will finally set up its appropriate vapour pressure corresponding to the existing temperature. There is now a condition of equilibrium, equal numbers of molecules escaping and returning.

But consider again the case of the liquid in an open vessel. When the boiling-point is reached, we have a different state of affairs. Bubbles of air or of vapour form *inside* the liquid and into these the liquid vaporizes. When the vapour pressure in these bubbles is equal to the external pressure they are able to grow and rise through the liquid; this is **ebullition or boiling.**

Refrigeration. Refrigerating machines depend on *cooling by evaporation*, an evaporating liquid taking its latent heat from the bath or enclosed space which has to be cooled. Two systems will be described—the Compressor System and the Absorption System.

The Compressor System. Ammonia gas is compressed by a pump into coils immersed in cold water (fig. 88). The work done in the compression is partly converted into heat as in a bicycle pump. This heat of compression is removed by the cold water of the *condenser* and the ammonia liquefies under pressure, about 170 lb. per square inch being sufficient at 30° C. Once this pressure is removed, the liquid cannot remain liquid but rapidly vaporizes and this is arranged by letting the liquid leak through a regulating valve. The latent heat is taken from a bath containing a 20% calcium chloride solution. The suction stroke of the pump causes the low pressure and on the next compression stroke the ammonia again starts the cycle. To obtain blocks of ice, cans of water are suspended in the bath. To do cold-store work or freeze a skating rink, the brine is circulated by another pump.

Carbon dioxide is sometimes used instead of ammonia, but it requires higher pressures.

The Absorption System. The Electrolux refrigerator is a well-known example of this system, but it has an additional feature of its own in the fact that there are no moving mechanical parts to make a noise. Fig. 89 shows a diagrammatic sketch of the apparatus stripped, for simplicity, of some details not essential except for optimum working.

The cycle of operation starts with the heating of a strong aqueous solution of ammonia. This solution is lighter than water and becomes denser as the ammonia is driven off. The ammonia therefore travels up and the water down. Let us follow the ammonia. Since the aqueous solution gives off about

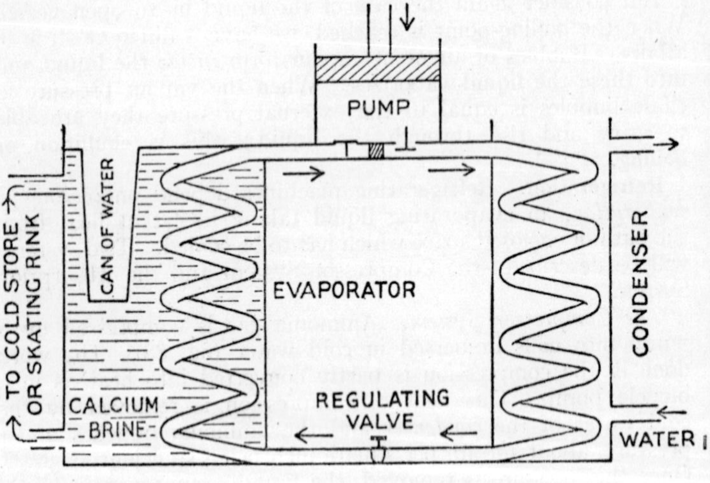

FIG. 88.

700 times its own volume of gas, a sufficient pressure will be set up to liquefy this gas on its way through a tube where it is cooled, sometimes by air and sometimes by water. The *liquid* ammonia now passes into the *evaporator* where it trickles over baffle plates and meets a stream of hydrogen gas. Here it vaporizes, setting up its own partial pressure in accordance with Dalton's law. Here the cooling takes place, latent heat being taken from the surroundings. The mixture of hydrogen and ammonia now travels to the *absorber* which it enters near the bottom. Here it meets the water coming from the boiler. The

water trickling over baffle plates dissolves the ammonia and carries it down while the lighter gas, hydrogen, continues its

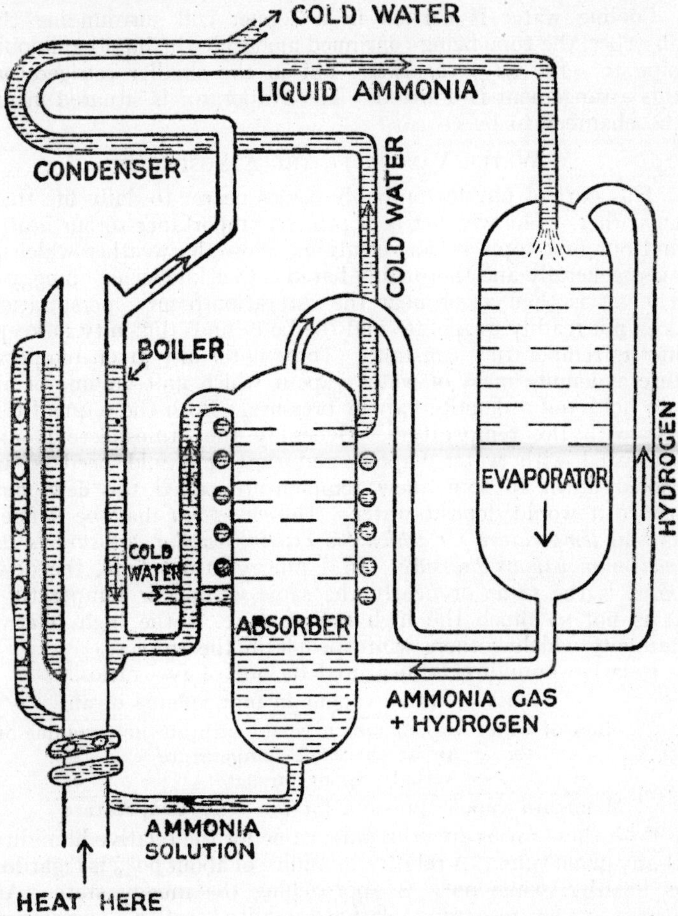

Fig. 89.

upward course and wends its way back to the evaporator. The ammonia solution now passes through a spiral pipe wound round the source of heat. Bubbles of ammonia gas are formed in the liquid and these push the liquid up over the top into the boiler ready to start the cycle again.

Cooling water is carried in a copper coil surrounding the absorber, the tube being continued alongside the liquid ammonia pipe to serve as a *condenser*, but in the smaller refrigerators this arrangement is omitted. The evaporator is situated inside the chamber to be cooled.

Water Vapour in the Atmosphere

This part of physics probably comes nearer to daily life than any other. The weather is of primary importance to our health and our first topic in conversation. Now the weather which is most generally and thoroughly hated is that known as "muggy." The air is then at or near the saturation-point; perspiration does not readily evaporate and the body finds difficulty in keeping its temperature constant. There is for any given temperature a definite mass of water vapour which unit volume of air can hold and a definite vapour pressure. Both these quantities rise with the temperature. Generally the atmosphere is unsaturated with water vapour and the air would need to be cooled down to some new temperature called **the dew-point** before it would deposit water. The *dew-point* may be defined as *that temperature for which the existing vapour pressure is the maximum vapour pressure.* In a muggy atmosphere, the dew-point is the same or nearly the same as the air temperature. It is not so much the high temperature as the high **relative humidity** which bothers white people in the tropics.

Relative humidity is measured by one of two ratios.

$$(a)\quad \frac{\text{Mass of water vapour in unit volume of air}}{\text{Mass of water vapour which would saturate unit volume of air at the same temperature}}$$

$$(b)\quad \frac{\text{Actual vapour pressure}}{\text{Maximum vapour pressure for the same temperature}}.$$

Both these ratios give the same value for the relative humidity at any given time. A relative humidity of about 60% is regarded as healthy, while 90% is approaching the muggy state. An instrument for measuring relative humidity is called a *hygrometer*.

The Chemical Hygrometer uses ratio (*a*). A large measured volume of air is aspirated through **U**-tubes containing calcium chloride in lumps, and the increase in weight for 1 cubic metre

(1000 litres) of air is found. The denominator of the ratio is found from tables.

Regnault's Hygrometer makes use of ratio (*b*) and a little thought will show that this can be written as

$$\frac{\text{Maximum vapour pressure at the dew-point}}{\text{Maximum vapour pressure at the existing temperature}}.$$

Ether is placed in a glass tube terminating in a silver thimble (fig. 90). Air is drawn through the ether by means of an aspirator. Rapid evaporation of the ether cools the air in contact with the thimble. When the dew-point is reached, water vapour condenses on the thimble. The aspirator is immediately stopped and the thermometer read. This "appearance" temperature is generally too low, so we allow the temperature to rise and take the "disappearance" temperature. The mean of these two will be the dew-point. The corresponding vapour pressures for the dew-point and the air temperature are found from Regnault's vapour pressure tables and the relative humidity calculated.

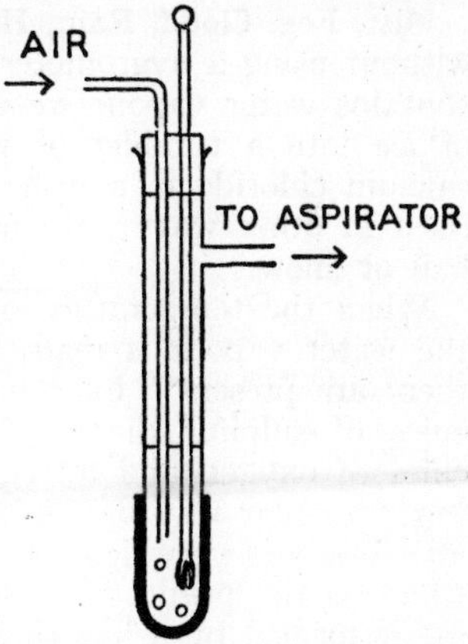

FIG. 90.

The Wet and Dry Bulb Hygrometer consists of two identical thermometers, the bulb of one being covered by a muslin bag dipping in a small bottle of water. If the air around is saturated with water vapour, both will read the same temperature and the relative humidity will be 100%. But if the air is not saturated, the wet bulb will be cooled by evaporation to an extent depending on the dryness of the air. The dry bulb reading and the difference are noted. From a table giving dry bulb readings and differences, the actual vapour pressure and maximum vapour pressure can be found and the relative humidity calculated. Thus

Dry bulb 17° C. Wet bulb 13° C. Difference 4° C.

$$\left.\begin{array}{ll}\text{Max. vapour pressure at } 17^\circ \text{ C.} & = 14{\cdot}4 \text{ mm.}\\ \text{Actual vapour pressure} & = 9{\cdot}1 \text{ mm.}\end{array}\right\}\text{From the table.}$$

$$\text{Relative humidity} = \frac{9{\cdot}1}{14{\cdot}4} = 63\%.$$

N.B.—The wet bulb reading does *not* give the dew-point. If desired, the dew-point can be obtained by finding from the table what temperature corresponds to a maximum vapour pressure of 9·1 mm. In this case it will be found to be approximately 10° C.

Determination of relative humidity is important in meteorology, greenhouses, cold stores, hospitals and certain factories such as cotton mills.

Mist, Fog, Cloud, Rain, Hail, Snow. If we wish to illustrate, without using a hygrometer, the bare fact that the atmosphere contains water vapour we can do so either by dropping pieces of ice into a tumbler of water or by leaving recently fused calcium chloride in a dish. But the water vapour also shows itself in other ways; we frequently see mist, fog, cloud, rain, hail or snow.

When the temperature of the air falls below the dew-point the water vapour is ready to condense but can only do so if there are present "hygroscopic nuclei." These may be molecules of sulphur dioxide, particles of sea-salt or even molecules of oxygen and nitrogen which have been acted upon in some peculiar way by sunlight. We then have a **mist.** If the mist becomes very dense it is called a **fog.** It is not the smoke which is the prime cause of the notorious London fogs; the fog is formed by a lowering of temperature due to radiation of heat from the lower layers of air into a cloudless sky above. The fog then prevents the escape of the smoke and the smoke colours the fog.

Clouds are formed by rising air. Air charged with water vapour, being less dense than dry air, rises into regions of lower pressure. The air then expands, doing work at the expense of its heat. The temperature then falls below the dew-point and vapour condenses on hygroscopic nuclei, forming a **cloud.** But this condensation liberates latent heat which may be sufficient to prevent further condensation. If, at the time or subsequently, further condensation does take place, then the drops may become large enough to fall as **rain.**

On p. 101 we saw the possibility of "super-cooling" naphthalene. *Pure* liquids often do this but immediately solidify when touched by a particle of the solid. Drops of pure water have been supercooled to − 20° C.! The same thing is thought to take place high up in the atmosphere. Here the temperature has dropped below $-20°$ C., and ice particles have formed which then fall through clouds containing supercooled water drops. These freeze on to the ice particles which now grow to **hailstones.**

Snow results when water vapour changes direct to the solid state without liquefying. Just as snow can change into vapour and disappear without melting, so the opposite change produces the snow in the higher reaches of the atmosphere by a kind of reversed sublimation.

During the night it frequently happens that solid bodies on or near the ground radiate their heat so rapidly that their temperature falls below the dew-point, although the temperature of the air is still above the dew-point. Drops of water are then formed from the *vapour* in the air in contact with these bodies. This is regarded as true **dew,** and it is formed in the same way as on the tumbler of iced water.

The conditions favouring the formation of dew are a clear sky, no wind and a good radiating surface not in good thermal contact with other bodies.

During the day a plant gives off water vapour and during the early evening water still rises to the leaf pores, but now instead of passing off as vapour it may condense on the leaf. This is also sometimes referred to as dew.

The formation of **hoar-frost** is similar to that of snow. It is a direct change from vapour to solid.[1]

QUESTIONS

1. Name the *distinctive* properties of solids, liquids, and gases respectively.

What physical conditions are necessary in order that a gas may be converted into a liquid? (L.)

2. What are the effects likely to be observed when heat is applied to a solid? Describe how you would investigate *one* of these effects. (D.)

3. What do you understand by the *boiling-point* and *melting-point* of a substance? Explain the effect of pressure on the boiling-point and melting-point and describe experiments to illustrate your answer. (O. and C.)

[1] The topics of "Water in the Atmosphere" and "Dew" are fully dealt with by Dr. G. C. Simpson, F.R.S., in *Nature,* April 14, 1923, and October 12, 1929.

4. A weight is suspended by a loop of copper wire passing round a block of ice. Describe and explain carefully what happens. (O. and C.)

5. Distinguish between evaporation and boiling. Explain clearly any experiments you have seen showing the effect of increased pressure and of decreased pressure on the boiling-point of water. (L.)

6. The dial of a pressure cooker gives corresponding temperatures and pressures as follows:

° F. . .	212	228	240	250	259	267	274	281
lb./sq. in. .	0	5	10	15	20	25	30	35

Plot temperature and pressure on a graph and explain what the graph means.

7. Plot the given maximum pressures of aqueous vapour against temperature.

Pressure	4·58 mm.	9·20	17·5	31·7	55·1	92·3	149	234	355	526	760
Temperature	0° C.	10° C.	20° C.	30° C.	40° C.	50° C.	60° C.	70° C.	80° C.	90° C.	100° C.

What use can be made of the graph?

8. 100 c.c. of oxygen at 600 mm. pressure and 500 c.c. of nitrogen at 700 mm. are passed into a vacuous litre globe. Find the final pressure.

Hint: Find the new pressures by Boyle's Law, then add these *partial pressures.*

9. Two vessels connected by a tap contain respectively 500 c.c. of hydrogen at 700 mm. pressure and 2000 c.c. of oxygen at 100 mm. pressure. What will be the final pressure when the tap is opened?

10. How does the volume of a gas vary with the pressure if its temperature remains constant? Describe the experiment you would make to verify your statement.

A reservoir A has a volume of 1000 c.c., while B has a volume of 1500 c.c. Both reservoirs are filled with the same gas, but while the pressure in A is 80 cm. of mercury, that in B is 60 cm. If the reservoirs are connected by an open pipe, what does the pressure become in each reservoir? (D.)

11. 254 c.c. of hydrogen are collected over water when the pressure is 775·5 mm. and the temperature 18° C. Find the volume of the dry gas at N.T.P.

12. Explain the phenomenon of surface tension, illustrating your answer with *three* examples. (O. and C.)

13. What do you understand by the term "dew-point"? De-

scribe an experimental way of finding the dew-point. Explain why dew sometimes forms in the evening on the ground. (L.)

14. Liquid ammonia has a latent heat of evaporation of 340 calories per gram and ice has a latent heat of fusion of 80 calories per gram. How many grams of ice can theoretically be formed from water at 10° C. by the evaporation of 500 grams of liquid ammonia?

(J.M.B. part question.)

15. Describe two different methods by which the presence of water vapour in the atmosphere may be detected.

What effect has the presence of this vapour on the height of the barometer? Give a reason for your answer. (L.)

16. On a certain day the relative humidity was 40 per cent. The temperature of the air was 12° C., at which temperature the pressure of saturated water vapour is 10·5 mm. of mercury. Find the pressure exerted by the water vapour in the air on the day in question.

(O. part question.)

CHAPTER XII

THE NATURE OF HEAT

It was mentioned in Chapter VIII that heat is now regarded as a form of *motion energy*. The old idea held by Joseph Black (p. 96) and his contemporaries was that heat was a weightless fluid which they called *caloric*. The advocates of this caloric theory are sometimes referred to as "materialists" since they thought of heat as a form of matter rather than a form of energy.

But we must not look upon the calorists or materialists as stupid. This they certainly were not. Their theory explained all the facts then known and proved quite useful at the time. It is our business now to look carefully into the caloric theory and to learn what new facts were discovered which it could not explain.

The calorists knew that different substances had different heat capacities. They knew for example that the heat capacity of water was 30 times that of mercury. It was they in fact who first used the word capacity in that sense. They thought of water as "putting more out of the way" than mercury, just as we might say of a boy eating cakes. They also knew that solid water (ice) had only half the capacity of liquid water.

They thought that there was in the universe a constant quantity of heat. When heat was produced by rubbing and grinding metals together they said the heat was there already but that the filings produced had a smaller capacity for heat; these filings did not need so much heat to maintain the former temperature, so the temperature of the filings and the rubbed solids went up.

The first fact which made trouble for the calorists was discovered by Count Rumford (1753–1814), one of the founders of the Royal Institution, since made famous by the work of Davy, Faraday, Dewar and Bragg. Rumford showed that the filings had the same thermal capacity as the rubbed solids! He further arranged that a *blunt* drill should be revolved by horse-power in a hole in a metal cylinder weighing 113 lb. The temperature went up 70° F. and the weight of the metallic dust was less than 2 ounces! He next surrounded his cylinder with $2\frac{1}{2}$ gallons of water and repeated the experiment. He managed to make the water boil! He thus showed the weakness of supposing that such a small quantity of filings could liberate such a large quantity of heat by a mere change in thermal capacity. The fact that with a blunt drill one could go on producing heat indefinitely showed that the filings had nothing to do with the

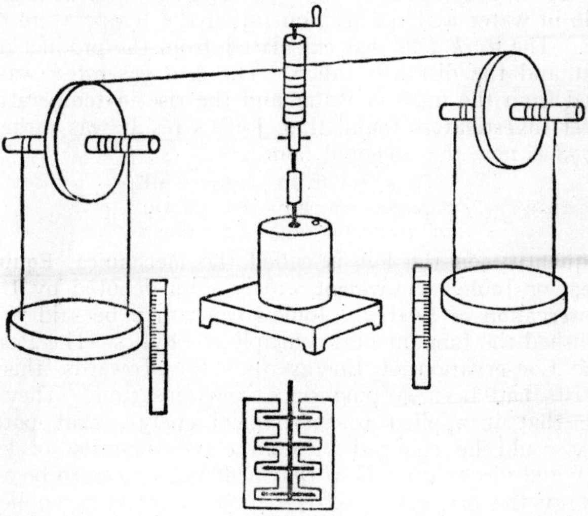

FIG. 91.

question; the heat was not there already, as the calorists thought, but was produced by the conversion of work into heat.

The next blow to the caloric theory was due to Sir Humphry Davy (1778–1829). Davy fastened two blocks of ice by wire to two bars of iron. The ice blocks were then rubbed violently together by a mechanical device. The temperature of the ice at the beginning was 29° F. The friction melted most of the ice and raised the temperature of the water produced to 35° F. The "filings" produced by the rubbing here is water which the calorists knew to have twice the thermal capacity of ice!

As a result of their experiments, Rumford and Davy came to the conclusion that heat is not matter but motion energy. When the temperature of a body is raised, it means that the molecules are moving faster; their kinetic energy is increased. During friction this extra energy comes from the work done.

Between 1842 and 1849 James Prescott Joule showed that there was a definite relation between heat generated and work done. His experiments showed that 772 ft.-lb. of work would produce 1 British Thermal Unit. One piece of apparatus used by Joule is illustrated in fig. 91. Falling weights rotated a paddle in water and the friction raised the temperature of the water. The *work done* was calculated from the product of the weight and the distance fallen. The *heat generated* was calculated from the mass of water and the rise in temperature.

Later investigators found that Joule's result was rather low and 778 is now the accepted figure.

Thus 778 ft.-lb. = 1 B.Th.U.
or 42,700 cm. gm. = 1 calorie
or $4{\cdot}2 \times 10^7$ ergs = 1 calorie.

The quantity on the left is called the **Mechanical Equivalent of Heat** or **Joule's Equivalent** and is often denoted by **J**.

Conservation of Energy. Joule's work may be said to have established the fundamental principle of physics—The Principle of the Conservation of Energy (p. 62). Towards this fact scientists had been groping since Newton's time. They were aware that it applied to mechanical energy, that potential energy could be changed into an equal quantity of kinetic energy and vice versa. Now that heat was shown to be a form of energy the principle was seen to be universally applicable; energy could be transformed from one kind to another but could not be created or destroyed. This law of nature indicates the folly of trying to make a "perpetual motion" machine which would give out more energy than is put in.

As an example of the way in which energy may be transformed we may consider an electric power station worked by a waterfall. The water at the top has potential energy which is changed into kinetic energy during the fall. At the turbine, part of this energy is converted into heat and part into the kinetic energy of the rotating shaft. The latter is converted into electrical energy. Some of this will be stored as chemical energy in accumulators, some carried away by cables. In the cables some of the electrical energy will be converted into heat owing to the resistance of the cables, the rest will pass on to appear as heat and light energy in lamps and heating devices or used to run motors where it becomes mechanical energy. The electrical energy may be converted into chemical energy by the electrolysis of various compounds, *e.g.* sodium and chlorine have more energy than common salt. A fair amount of the original energy will be used in overcoming friction and this will appear as heat and sound energy.

Now a little thought will convince you that whether the energy is used at once or stored in accumulators or otherwise, it always ends its career as heat energy which passes off and warms the surroundings. We sometimes speak of a sportsman as " running to fat." Energy has a similar weakness—it " runs to heat." Moreover, this heat is low-temperature heat. Heat is constantly passing from hot bodies to colder bodies and we know no method of making it go the other way; we cannot take the calories out of a tepid bath and use them to boil a small kettle! Even in refrigeration we only make heat go the reverse way by using up a further supply of energy. Thus although energy cannot be destroyed it is constantly being *dissipated*.

It is interesting to notice that the energy we use on the earth is mainly due to the sun. You will learn in Light (p. 244) that the green colouring matter, chlorophyll, of plants is capable of absorbing part of the radiation of the sun. This energy enables the plant to cause carbon dioxide and water to react to form complex compounds like sugar, starch, and cellulose, oxygen being set free as a waste product. This process is known as *photosynthesis*. The sun's energy is thus transformed into chemical energy and stored as such. When these compounds are oxidized again into carbon dioxide and water, energy is again liberated. This may occur in an animal which has eaten the plant or in a second animal which ate the first animal. The plant may also be burnt as a fuel and the energy liberated as heat energy. The coal of to-day was produced by the absorption of radiation by the chlorophyll of prehistoric plants. The oil used to-day is said to be of animal origin, but whatever the explanation, the oil is certain to be in some way caused by the sun. Again, it is not difficult to see the relation of waterfalls and wind-power to the sun.

Transformation of Heat Energy into Mechanical Energy. There are two well-known methods of converting heat energy into mechanical energy, the steam engine and the internal-combustion engine. One of the most striking features of these heat engines is the amount of heat energy wasted. The *efficiency* of a heat engine is defined as

$$\frac{\text{Work units got out}}{\text{Work units put in as fuel}}.$$

Now 1 lb. of coal would yield, when burnt, say 14,000 B.Th.U., the equivalent of 14,000 × 778 ft.-lb. of mechanical energy. A good steam engine returns about 20% of this as mechanical energy! A locomotive is worse still, its efficiency being less than 10%.

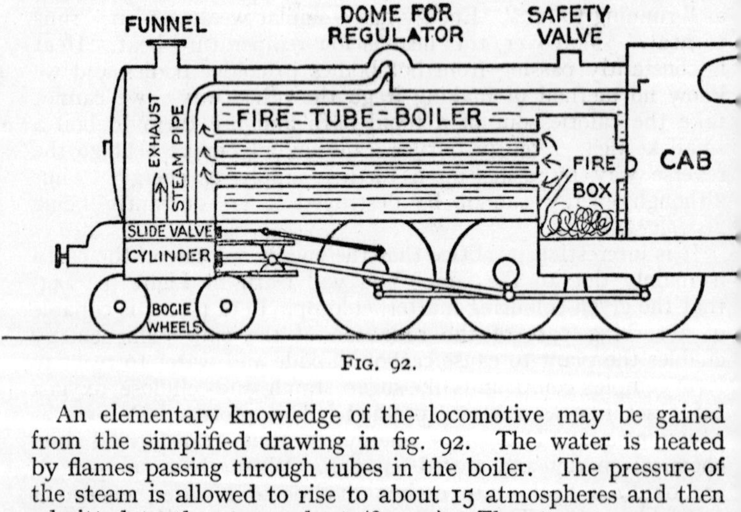

FIG. 92.

An elementary knowledge of the locomotive may be gained from the simplified drawing in fig. 92. The water is heated by flames passing through tubes in the boiler. The pressure of the steam is allowed to rise to about 15 atmospheres and then admitted to the steam chest (fig. 93). The steam now passes into the cylinder by way of the left *port*, say. Here it expands and cools while pushing the piston along. On the back stroke, steam comes in through the right port, the *slide valve* having moved to the left to allow of this. The to-and-fro motion of the piston is communicated to the driving wheels by the connecting rod.

At the end of each stroke, the used steam escapes through the exhaust E, and here we have one of the great sources of loss, for since the steam escapes as steam the latent heat of vaporization is lost. Other losses occur by hot gases passing out of the flue, radiation from the boiler and other parts, hot ashes raked out of the fire-box and friction in all moving parts.

In most locomotives the steam is led back through pipes placed in the fire tubes before it is allowed to enter the steam chest. By this device (not shown in the figure) the steam is *superheated* and the efficiency increased somewhat, but the locomotive even then never reaches an efficiency of 10%.

The engine used on a motor-cycle or car is a good example of the internal-combustion type. Air is drawn through a car-

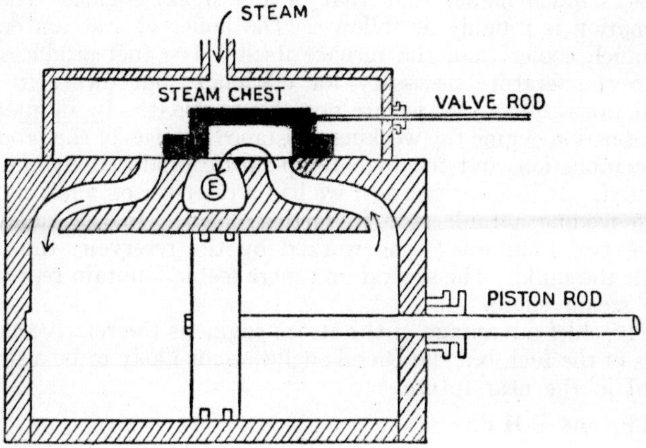

FIG. 93.

burettor where it is charged or "carburetted" with a small quantity of combustible vapour. This intimate mixture is compressed into about a fifth of its volume and exploded by an electric spark. The chemical action which goes on throughout its volume causes intense heat followed by rapid expansion and cooling. This is the *working stroke* of the piston. The piston then sweeps out the products of combustion during the *exhaust stroke.* This is the so-called four-stroke cycle, the successive strokes being *suction, compression, working,* and *exhaust.*

The Diesel engine is another and more efficient example of the internal-combustion type. It also has a four-stroke cycle, but there are some striking differences. While the compression ratio of the petrol engine is about 5 to 1, that of the Diesel is 12 to 1. As a result of the great heat of compression, the temperature is sufficiently high to ignite the mixture without the aid of a sparking plug. Since almost any kind of crude oil can be used, these engines are cheaper to run than those using petrol. The suction stroke draws in air only. At the end of the compression stroke a spray of oil is forced in by means of a pump. The mixture is then ignited and we have the working stroke followed by the exhaust stroke.

The efficiency of an internal-combustion engine is about 30%. This is much higher than that of any steam engine. The explanation is roughly as follows: The boiler of a steam engine is much cooler than the furnace itself. The fuel produces the high temperature necessary for efficiency, but owing to constructional difficulties we are not able to use it. In an internal-combustion engine the working substance consists of the products of combustion, and the high temperature produced by the fuel *is* used. It is somewhat as if we had a reservoir on a hill 2000 ft. high feeding a tank 1500 ft. farther down. In the valley we have two fountains: one worked by the reservoir, the other from the tank. The second and more feeble fountain represents the steam engine.

The chief advantage of the steam engine is the relative cheapness of the fuel, but the Diesel engine seems likely to be a serious rival in the near future.

I.H.P. and B.H.P.

The *I*ndicated *H*orse *P*ower of an engine $= \dfrac{plan}{33,000}$

where p = mean effective pressure in lb. per sq. in. of piston
l = length of stroke in ft.
a = area of piston in sq. in.
n = number of strokes per minute.

If the engine does work on the forward and backward stroke as in a locomotive the formula becomes

$$\frac{2plan}{33,000}$$

The "mean effective pressure" is determined by connecting to the cylinder a device which measures and records the varying pressure on an *indicator diagram*. Hence the term *Indicated Horse Power*. The I.H.P. is the total power put out by the cylinder. Some of this is used in overcoming the friction of the parts and the power actually available for doing external work is called the *B*rake *H*orse *P*ower. Thus

I.H.P. = B.H.P. + Power used to overcome friction.

QUESTIONS

1. Give an account of the experiments performed by Rumford, Davy, and Joule which prove that heat is a form of energy and not a material substance. (O. and C.)

2. A cardboard tube 2 metres long and closed by corks contains 400 gm. of lead shot (S.H. 0·0315). It is inverted 50 times and the temperature of the shot rises by 7·4° C. Calculate J in cm. gm.

3. A tube 6 ft. long containing a little mercury and closed at both ends is rapidly inverted 50 times. What is the maximum rise in temperature of the mercury that can be expected?

[Spec. ht. of mercury = $\frac{1}{30}$. One B.Th.U. is equivalent to 778 ft.-lb.] (L.)

4. Explain the statement "one calorie is equivalent to $4{\cdot}2 \times 10^7$ ergs." The height of a waterfall is 50 metres. What will be the rise in temperature of the water due to falling through this distance?

[Acceleration due to gravity = 981 cm./sec.^{2}] (L.)

5. What is meant by saying that a British Thermal Unit is equivalent to 780 ft.-lb., and how has this statement been established?

If a lump of lead falls from a height of 200 ft. on to a stone pavement, by how much would its temperature rise, supposing that all the heat generated by the blow is retained in the metal? [Spec. ht. of lead is 0·03.] (D.)

6. What is meant by the mechanical equivalent of heat?

Find the rise in temperature, when a lead bullet, travelling at 300 metres per second, strikes a target, assuming that half the energy remains in the bullet as heat. [Spec. ht. of lead = 0·03, $4{\cdot}2 \times 10^7$ ergs = 1 calorie.] (C.W.B.)

7. The boilers and steam turbines of a power-plant have an over-all efficiency of 22% and deliver 5000 H.P. If the plant is operated for 10 hours a day, what is the daily consumption of coal, which yields 14,000 B.Th.U. per pound when burnt?

[1 B.Th.U. = 778 ft.-lb. 1 H.P. = 550 ft.-lb. per second.] (O. and C.)

8. Explain what is meant by the efficiency of an engine.

A Diesel engine consumes 30 gallons per hour of a fuel oil which yields 150,000 B.Th.U. per gallon on combustion. If the efficiency of the engine is 24%, calculate the horse-power which it develops.

[1 B.Th.U. = 778 ft.-lb.; 1 H.P. = 550 ft.-lb. per sec.] (O. and C.)

CHAPTER XIII

TRANSMISSION OF HEAT

HEAT energy may travel from one place to another in three different ways:

(*a*) A source of heat may cause the nearest molecules of a body to vibrate more rapidly; this increased motion is passed on to the next molecules and from these to their neighbours and so on, but all the molecules keep the same relative positions. This method of heat transference is typical of solids and is called *conduction*.

(*b*) When liquids and gases are heated, the molecules nearest the source have their speed increased and move upwards, making room for other molecules. In other words, the liquid or gas expands, becomes less dense and rises. Currents of moving molecules are thus set up, hot molecules constantly departing and cooler molecules arriving. This process is known as *convection*.

(*c*) It is well known that heat travels from the sun to the earth. Since the greater part of the journey is through a vacuum, the heat cannot be travelling by conduction or convection. The modern view is that it arrives by a transverse wave motion somewhat like water waves but of very short and mixed wave lengths. The wave lengths vary from about 0·04 cm. to 0·00003 cm. The medium in which these waves travel is called *ether* and is supposed to be present in all space. The sun's energy is thus transformed into a wave motion for the journey and only transformed back into heat energy when the waves are absorbed by matter. Some of the waves of medium length produce *light* and these will pass through a material like glass without being absorbed, but even these finally strike some material which will absorb them and they too are then converted into heat energy.

The name *radiation* is used for this *process* and for the *form* in which the sun's energy is stored during its journey (see also

Light, Chap. XXII). But this process of radiation is not peculiar to the journey from sun to earth; any body is capable of sending out heat in this way. Thus if we hold the hand *below* an electric-light bulb, it is evident that heat has travelled to the hand mainly by radiation.

Conduction. The fact that some solids conduct heat more readily than others is a matter of common experience. In the summer a galvanized-iron roof *feels* hotter than the adjoining

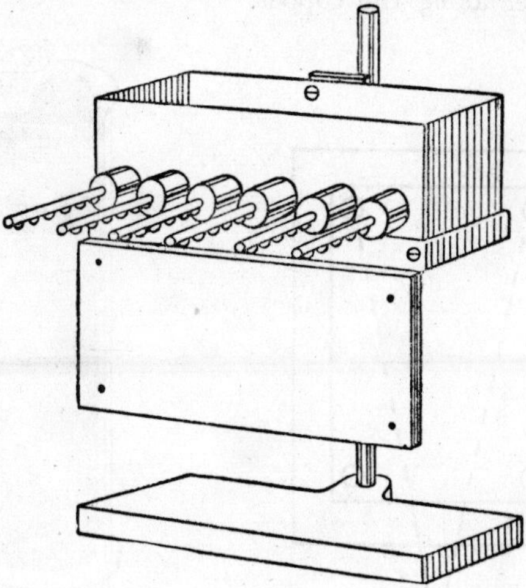

FIG. 94.

woodwork because the former conducts heat more readily to the hand. In the winter the gate latch *feels* colder than the wooden gate for a similar reason.

To show that different solids have different conductivities there is a well-known experiment suggested by Benjamin Franklin to John Ingenhousz (fig. 94).

Six rods of equal length and thickness but different material are coated with wax into which lead shot are stuck. When the ends are heated with hot water, the shot begin to fall off. In the case of two metals like iron and aluminium, when a steady temperature has been reached, more shot will have fallen from the aluminium rod owing to its greater conductivity.

The relative conductivity of, say, copper and iron can be well illustrated by Jamieson's heat-sensitive paper, or failing this a large filter paper or a sheet of drawing paper can be soaked in a solution containing 5% cobalt chloride and 5% calcium chloride. Two rods of copper and iron of equal length and thickness are placed on a piece of wood and a sheet of sensitive paper pinned down over them (fig. 95). On heating the wires with a bunsen at A, a green coloration will be seen which travels farther along the copper.

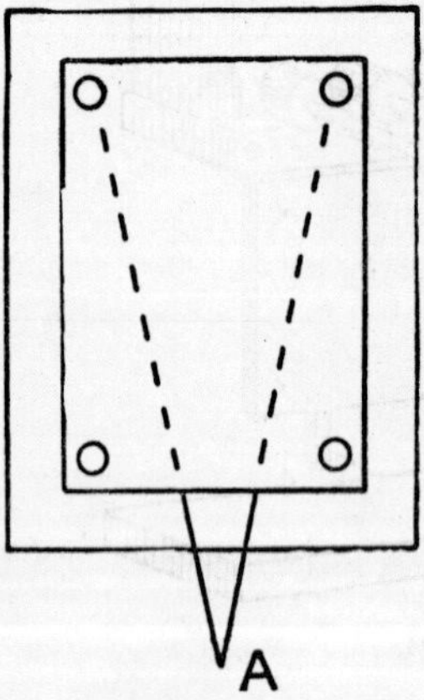

Fig. 95.

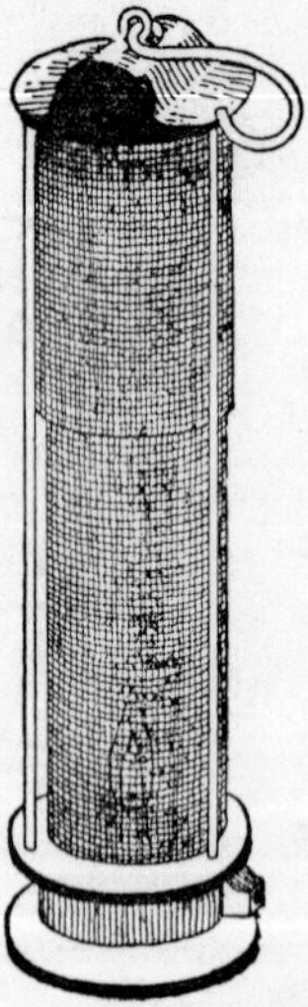

Fig. 96.

Hold a piece of metal gauze above a bunsen, set for a luminous flame. If the gas is now ignited above or below the gauze, the flame will not strike through. This is due to the fact that the gauze is a good conductor of heat and the gas on the other side never gets hot enough to ignite.

This fact was discovered and applied by Sir Humphry Davy in the safety lamp for miners (fig. 96). Oil is burnt in the lamp, and although the methane or fire-damp gets in through the gauze and burns as a "cap" on the flame, the gas outside does not ignite. For general use the lamp has now been superseded by an electric lamp, but the Davy lamp is still used to estimate the amount of methane in the working places, for above a certain percentage it would still be liable to ignition by sparks from the miner's pick.

Tie a piece of lead to a lump of ice and drop it to the bottom of a test-tube nearly full of water. Heat the top of the water with a bunsen. It is possible to boil the water at the top without melting the ice; water is a bad conductor of heat. With the exception of mercury, this is true of liquids and gases in general.

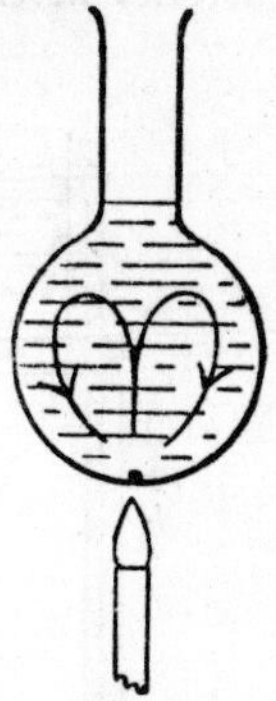

FIG. 97.

Bad conductors have their uses no less than good conductors. The efficiency of clothing depends partly on the bad conductivity of the fabric and partly on that of the air enclosed by the fabric. Flannel and felt are frequently wrapped round water pipes in the winter, while straw is often used to protect a football field from frost. The porous nature of snow makes it a bad conductor and a fall of snow often saves the underlying crop from more severe cold.

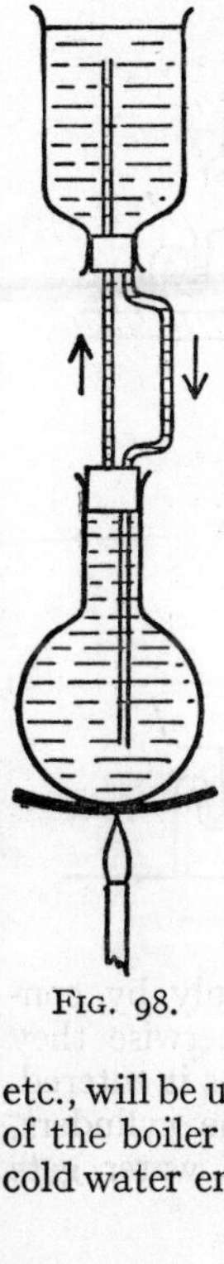

FIG. 98.

Convection. The mode of transport of heat in liquids can be easily shown. Drop a crystal of potassium permanganate down a wide glass tube to the bottom of a round-bottomed flask full of water. Withdraw the tube and heat with a small bunsen flame (fig. 97).

The hot-water system of a house is a well-known application of convection currents. The process can be illustrated in the laboratory by means of the apparatus shown in fig. 98. A crystal of potassium permanganate is dropped into the "tank" represented by an inverted bell-jar. When the boiler is heated, convection currents will be seen travelling in the direction shown.

The actual lay-out of the boiler, tank, pipes, etc., will be understood from a study of fig. 99. Notice the shape of the boiler and its low position in the system. Note also that cold water enters at the bottom and hot water leaves at the top.

If a *radiator* is connected into the system, this, in spite of its name, will warm a room mainly by setting up convection currents in the air.

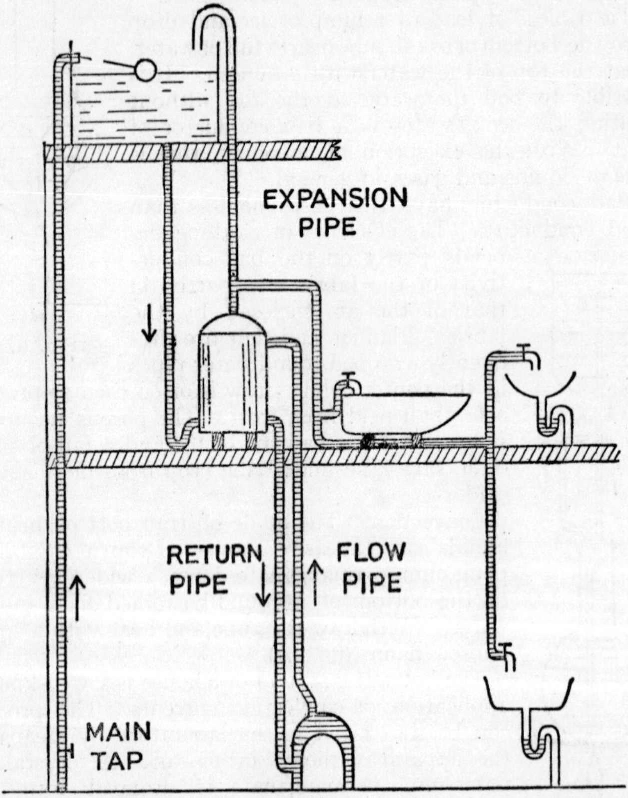

FIG. 99.

The "radiator" of a motor-car also works mainly by convection. It is necessary to cool the cylinders, otherwise they would get hot enough to ignite the mixture as soon as it entered. Cooling water is therefore made to flow round the cylinders, entering the water jacket at the bottom. As the water gets heated it expands and flows to the top of the radiator. Here the water begins to be cooled by air circulation produced by a fan and the motion of the car. As the water passes down through the radiator tubes, this cooling continues until the water again reaches the inlet. A continuous convection current is thus maintained.

To understand the action of convection currents in water during the cooling of a pond you should refer again to Hope's experiment (p. 84).

Convection plays an important part in the ventilation of rooms. Hot air rises to the top of a room owing to its lower density and cooler air flows in to take its place. The ideal in

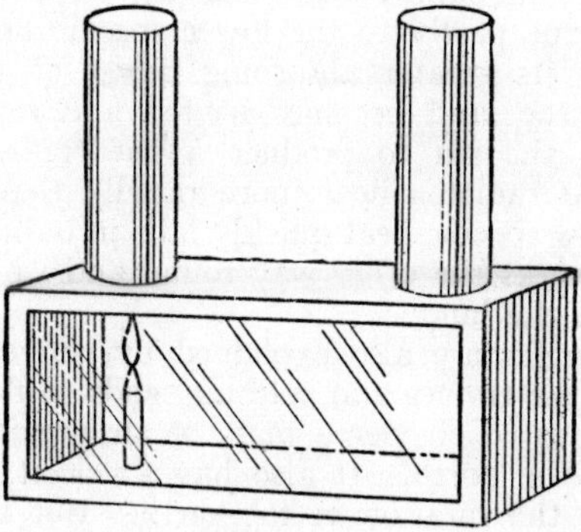

FIG. 100.

ventilation is to renew the air without creating an uncomfortable draught. With this aim in view, ventilators are often sloped upwards so that the air is warmed as it comes in, or the air inlet may be placed behind a radiator. It is often said that most of the heat of a fire goes up the chimney, but it must not be forgotten that a chimney with any kind of fire at the bottom is a valuable aid to ventilation.

The convection currents produced by a fire and a chimney can be illustrated by the apparatus shown in fig. 100. A smouldering piece of brown paper or blotting-paper is pushed down the right-hand chimney. The apparatus also illustrates the old method of ventilating mines, the cold fresh air going down the winding shaft while a fire was kept burning at the base of the other. The draught is due to the difference in weight between the cold column of air and the light expanded column. In a house there is not of course an extra chimney full of cold air, but since the air in the house communicates with that out of doors there is an effective column of cold air just the same. Generally speaking, the taller the chimney the greater the draught, because the column of light gas is longer and this causes the speed of the gas to be greater. This is why factory chimneys are made tall, but there is no advantage unless there is a big enough fire at the bottom to keep the gas hot all the way up.

Convection currents also account for **Land and Sea Breezes.** During the day the land reaches a higher temperature than the sea. This is due partly to the lower specific heat of the land and partly to its greater absorbing power of solar radiation. The air over the land becomes heated and rises. Cooler air flows in from the sea to produce a sea breeze. During the night the land radiates heat more rapidly than the sea, and owing to its low specific heat quickly falls in temperature. Convection now works the other way round and we have by night a breeze from the land.

The **trade winds** are also explained by convection. Heated air rises over the tropics and cold air tends to flow in from the north and south. Consider a mass of air moving towards the equator from the north. It also has a velocity from west to east owing to the rotation of the earth. But it is constantly approaching places having a still greater velocity from west to east. It thus becomes converted into a NE. wind (see *relative velocity*, p. 58). The SE. trade wind is caused in the same way.

Radiation.[1] It has already been mentioned that the sun's energy comes to us in the form of waves of many different wave lengths. All these waves are converted into heat when absorbed by matter, and one small group of them happen to have the additional property that they can be detected by the eye. These we call *light* waves. There is much evidence to support this view of the relation between heat waves and light waves.

(*a*) During an eclipse of the sun, heat and light are cut off simultaneously, showing that both travel at the same speed.

[1] This should be read in conjunction with "Dispersion and Colour," see Light (Chap. XXII.)

(*b*) It can be proved that heat waves travel in straight lines.

(*c*) When light is reflected by mirrors, heat is also reflected.

(*d*) When the image of the sun is produced on a piece of paper by means of a convex lens, the paper burns; light and heat are refracted similarly.

(*e*) As the distance from a source of light is increased, the intensity falls off according to the Law of Inverse Squares (see Light, p. 256). The intensity of heat follows the same law.

To fix our ideas about heat waves and light waves, let us consider a coil of wire being heated in a dark room by means of an electric current. It soon gets warmer than its surroundings and we become conscious of the heat it is sending out. These are long waves. When the current is increased a greater variety of waves will be sent out. In addition to the long waves there will now be shorter ones and the coil will be *seen* to be dull red. The coil next becomes bright red and finally white, as more and more and shorter and shorter waves are added to its output. All the time the heat given out has also increased because light waves are also heat waves.

It is easy to believe that any hot body gives out heat waves, but when you stand near a lorry delivering ice, it seems to be radiating "cold." This is because all bodies above 0° absolute, radiate heat and at the same time absorb heat. The final effect is due to an exchange. In the case considered, the bystander radiates to the ice more heat than he receives from the ice. The cooling is also of course partly caused by the convection currents starting from the bystander.

Radiation and Absorption. There are many ways of showing that the rate at which a body absorbs heat depends very much on the nature of its surface. It is also found that a surface which absorbs heat well when cold, radiates well when it is hot. A surface coated with *lampblack* is the best absorber and radiator. On the other hand, a good reflector is a bad absorber and radiator.

(*a*) Two equal "tin" cans (say cocoa-tins) are taken. A hole is drilled in each lid to take a thermometer. The thermometers should be tested to see if they correspond. One tin is then smoked all over with a candle or camphor flame. Both cans are filled with cold water and placed equidistant from a gas fire or other constant source of heat. The black tin will warm up more rapidly.

(*b*) The same tins are filled with boiling water, screened from one another and allowed to cool. The black tin will cool more rapidly.

(*c*) A sheet of Jamieson's sensitive paper is partly coated on the non-sensitive side with tin foil stuck on with seccotine or paste, partly painted with lampblack and a third strip painted dead white. The varied surface is then held towards a fire or other source of heat and the sensitive surface watched for a colour change.

(*d*) A Leslie's cube (fig. 101) is a "tin" can with one face painted dead black, one face dead white, one left rough and

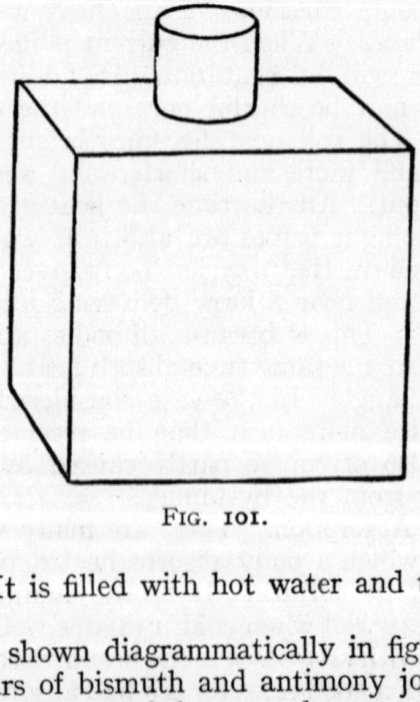

FIG. 101.

one polished. It is filled with hot water and then kept gently boiling.

A thermopile shown diagrammatically in fig. 102 consists of a number of bars of bismuth and antimony joined together in couples. About 16 or 25 of these couples are made into a block. When one set of junctions is heated and the other set kept cool, an electric current flows from bismuth to antimony at the hot junction. When joined to a sensitive galvanometer, it is a good detector of radiation.

The dead-black surface of the Leslie cube is set to face the thermopile and the distance adjusted so as to give a reasonable galvanometer deflection. The cube is then turned so as to bring each surface in turn opposite the thermopile and the same distance away.

It will be found that the dead-black surface is the best radiator and the polished one the worst. The dead-white surface may turn out to be almost as good a radiator as the black one and we might therefore expect its absorbing power to be equal to that of black. This is true if we confine our attention to long waves like those given off by a Leslie cube. But when a black surface and a white surface are exposed to sunlight, the black surface wins easily because black absorbs all wave lengths while white *scatters* the short luminous waves. That is why black *looks* black and white *looks* white.

This has an interesting application in daily life. We wear " whites " in summer to keep cool. The " body " inside is just

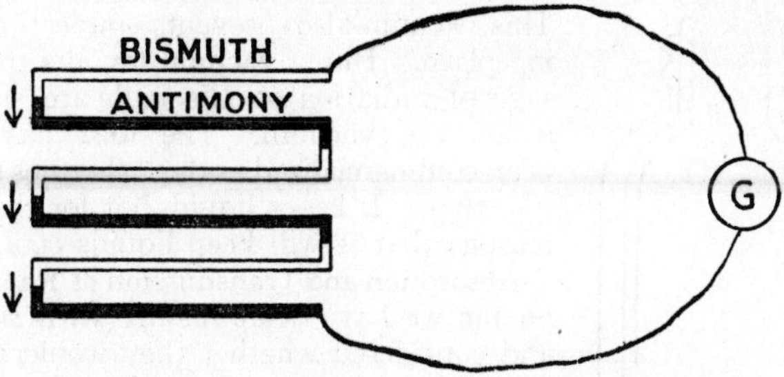

FIG. 102.

warm enough to give off long waves, and white is a good radiator of these and of any long waves absorbed from the sun. The short waves are not absorbed but scattered.

Specific Heat by Cooling. If a calorimeter containing a hot liquid is placed inside a larger vessel and allowed to cool, it is found that it will *lose calories* at the same rate no matter what the liquid is, provided :

(*a*) The same volume of liquid is taken.

(*b*) The liquid is cooled through the same temperature range.

The *drop in temperature* will of course depend on the specific heat of the liquid.

Problem. A copper calorimeter (S.H. 0·1) weighing 20 gm. and containing 50 c.c. (63 gm.) of glycerine cooled from 50° C. to 40° C. in 321 sec. 50 c.c. of water under the same conditions took 420 sec. to cool from 50° C. to 40° C. Calculate the specific heat of glycerine.

Calorimeter lost $20 \times 0{\cdot}1 \times 10 = 20$ cals.
Water lost $50 \times 1 \times 10 = 500$ cals.
Glycerine lost $63 \times s \times 10 = 630s$ cals.
Rate of loss for calorimeter + water $= \frac{520}{420}$ cals./sec.

$$\text{Rate of loss for calorimeter + glycerine} = \frac{630s + 20}{321} \text{ cals./sec.}$$

$$\text{but } \frac{630s + 20}{321} = \frac{520}{420} \quad \therefore s = 0{\cdot}60.$$

The Vacuum Flask. The vacuum flask was invented by James Dewar to store liquid air. Heat cannot get in by conduction because glass is a bad conductor, and the vacuum between the walls is a worse one. This vacuum also prevents convection taking place. But a vacuum favours the passage of radiation so the walls are silvered inside the vacuum. The idea has since been commercialized as the "thermos flask" (fig. 103). It keeps liquids hot for the same reasons that it will keep liquids cool.

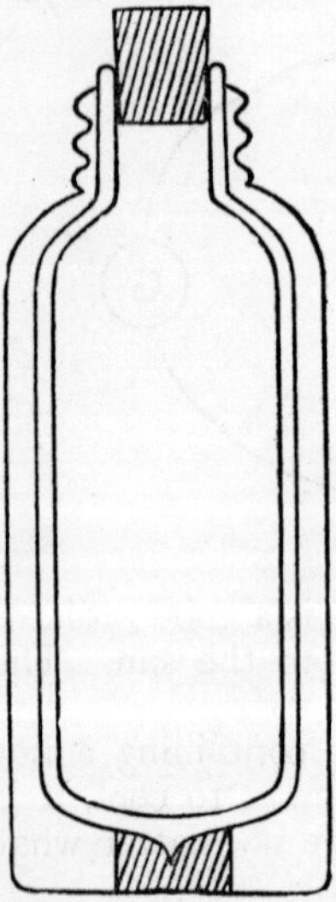

FIG. 103.

Absorption and Transmission of Radiation. So far we have dealt mainly with *surfaces* and considered whether they would absorb or reflect radiation. But there is another possibility—a body may allow the radiation to pass through it, in other words it may be *transmitted.*

Most substances exert a selective action on the waves which strike them, absorbing certain wave lengths and transmitting others. Thus ordinary glass absorbs the short ultra-violet waves, transmits the light waves and absorbs most of the long infra-red waves. This explains why the temperature inside a greenhouse is higher than that of the air outside. The waves which get through the glass when the sun shines are absorbed by the interior. These absorbed waves become heat, but the articles inside never get hot enough to be luminous, *i.e.* they only radiate long waves. These cannot get out but are absorbed by the glass and radiated back into the interior. Moreover, the waves which the glass absorbed from the sunlight also become heat, and some of this is also radiated into the interior.

The waves given off from a fire are mainly long infra-red waves. A **glass fire-screen** will absorb most of these and re-radiate them, but now they will travel in all directions and not straight at the person sitting behind the screen. One therefore gets the advantage of seeing the fire by means of the short waves which pass through while much of the heat is cut off.

Quartz glass and "vitaglass" (2% boric oxide and no iron oxide) will transmit ultra-violet radiation and are often used for window-panes in hospitals and zoological gardens.

A special kind of glass can be made which transmits the infra-red radiation. This is now used for camera lenses, and these, in conjunction with plates sensitive to this wave band, are now used in long-distance photography.

The absorption and transmission of radiation play a very important part in climate. The air transmits most of the sun's radiation. Very little is absorbed, so the air is not warmed directly. The ground absorbs the radiations and gives off long heat waves. The air is thus mainly warmed from below by radiation and convection, and we find that **the temperature falls about 1° F. for every 300 ft. rise.** An airman at an altitude of 3000 ft. would find the temperature about 10° F. lower than at sea-level. Consider a mountain of this altitude. The ground absorbs the sun's radiation, but this heat is very readily radiated back into space on account of the rarity of the atmosphere. If the air gets slightly warmed, it rises and very cold air from around flows in. Therefore the temperature at the top of a mountain is generally lower than at sea-level.

It is common experience that a clear calm night is usually colder than a cloudy night. This is because clouds are practically opaque to the long heat waves radiated from the ground. The fact is sometimes used by fruit-growers who cover their orchards with a thick smoke to protect the trees from night frosts.

QUESTIONS

1. When the surface water of a lake is at 0° C. the bottom is at 4° C. What would happen then if water were a good conductor of heat?

2. What is meant by *convection of heat* ?

Describe examples of its utilization in everyday life. (C.W.B.)

3. Describe experiments you would make to show that (*a*) copper is a better conductor of heat than iron, (*b*) mercury is a better conductor of heat than water, (*c*) a lamp-blacked surface is a better radiator and also a better absorber of radiant heat than a polished surface. (D.)

4. A flask of hot water stands on a table. Give a concise account of the various ways in which it loses heat.

In what way would the rate of loss be affected if a large sheet of copper wire were placed under the flask and a glass beaker inverted over it so as to enclose it completely? (B.)

5. Explain why ice sometimes forms on puddles on a clear night although the temperature of the air is above freezing-point.

6. Write short notes on the methods of transference of heat and point out how they are illustrated in the action of a thermos (vacuum) flask. (L.)

7. A calorimeter of mass 100 gm. and specific heat 0·1 containing 150 gm. of water cools from 60° C. to 55° C. in 4 min. If the same calorimeter containing an equal volume of glycerine of specific heat 0·6 and specific gravity 1·25 is allowed to cool through the same range, how long will it take? (O. and C.)

8. A 50-gm. calorimeter (S.H. 0·1) containing 100 c.c. of water cooled from 50° C. to 40° C. in 210 sec. The same calorimeter containing 100 c.c. (87 gm.) of turpentine cooled through the same range in 83 sec. Find specific heat of turpentine.

SOUND

CHAPTER XIV

PRODUCTION AND TRANSMISSION

The Cause of Sound. Sound is always produced by some movement of matter. We are worried by some sounds, but soothed by others. The worrying sounds are those that occur at irregular intervals. These we call *noises*. When the movement of matter is regular and rapid our nerves are not jarred. You will probably have heard the story of the man who heard a boot falling in the bedroom above. Some hours later he went up to find out when the other boot was going to fall! It was the irregularity which was worrying him.

If the vibrations are between 30 and 30,000 per second the human ear is conscious of a definite *musical note*. These limits of audibility vary with different people. Some people cannot hear the squeak of a mouse or the chirp of a grasshopper because the vibrations causing these sounds are too rapid.

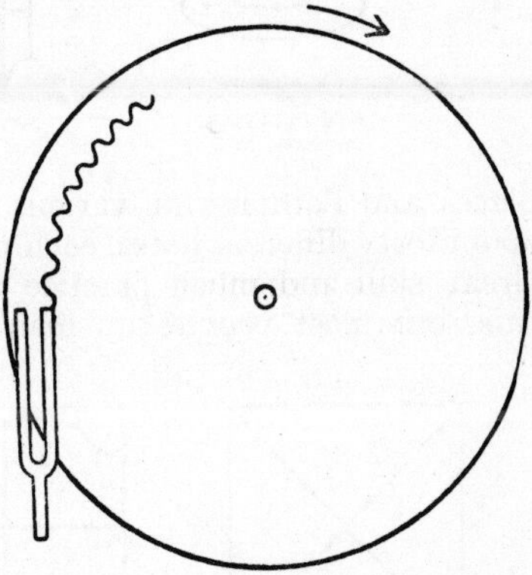

FIG. 104.

There are several interesting ways of proving that a sounding body, say a tuning-fork, is in rapid vibration.

Strike the fork and hold it against the tongue or the teeth, or allow it to touch a suspended pith-ball.

A neater method is the following. Attach a tiny brush to one prong of the fork by means of plasticine. Clamp the fork in a burette stand and ink the brush. On a gramophone turntable place a disc of drawing paper. Set the table rotating, strike the fork and allow the brush to dip lightly on to the paper (fig. 104). The experiment may be varied by attaching a *bristle* to the fork and making it travel along a smoked plate of glass.

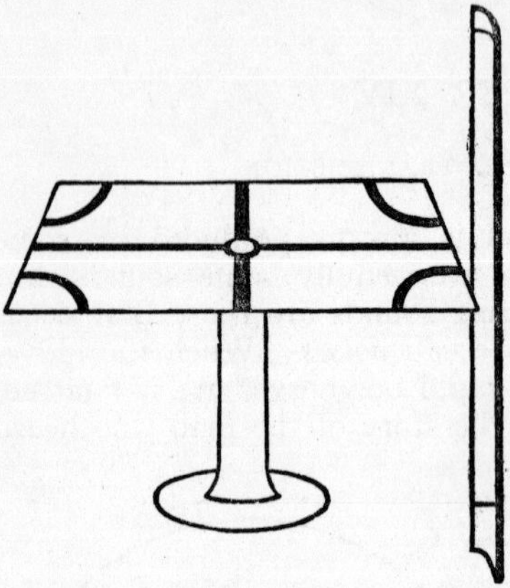

FIG. 105.

The vibration of a sonorous body is beautifully illustrated by what is known as a *Chladni's plate* (fig. 105). The plate is of metal or glass and has a little fine sand scattered over it. When a violin bow is rubbed vertically against the smooth edge, the plate is set in vibration and gives out a definite note. The sand is thrown away from the moving parts of the plate and gathers along lines where the vibration is least—the so-called *nodal lines*. By bowing at different places and damping at various other places, Chladni obtained about forty different notes, each note giving its own sand pattern. Great skill and much practice are necessary to do as well as this, but most people can manage a few notes.

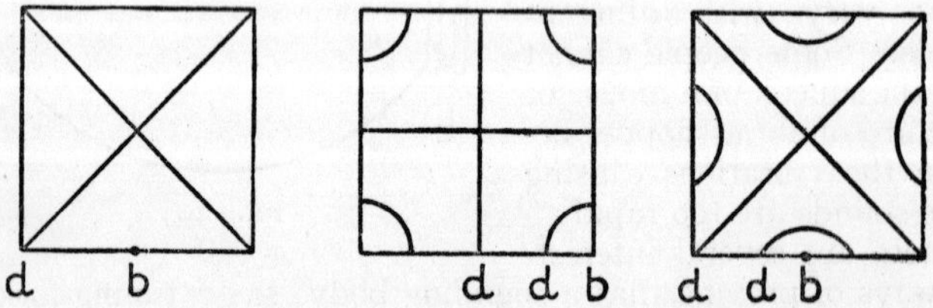

FIG. 106.

In fig. 106, *b* represents the bowed point and *d* the point where the plate is damped by touching gently with a finger. A damped point will of course start a nodal line, while the vibration is a maximum at the bowed point and all other points symmetrical with it.

Sound is not transmitted across a Vacuum. Although sound is always caused by matter in motion, we may have a vibrating body which is not producing a sound. This is the case when the vibrations take place in a vacuum. In order to verify this fact a very efficient air-pump is necessary.

Thread a needle with 36 d.c.c. copper wire and pass it twice through a rubber stopper (fig. 107). These form the electrical leads from a battery and plug key to a buzzer hanging inside a bell-jar on the air-pump plate. On exhausting the bell-jar, the sound of the buzzer gets more and more feeble.

The method can also be adapted to show that the loudness of a sound depends partly on the density of the gas surrounding the source. This is done by connecting the exhausted jar in turn to sources of hydrogen and carbon dioxide. The sound will be louder in the second case because carbon dioxide is 22 times as dense as hydrogen.

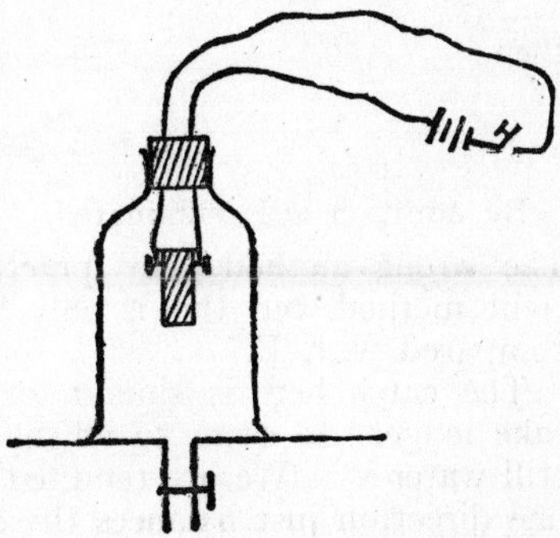

FIG. 107.

The fact that sound does not travel across a vacuum is probably a very good thing for us. On the other side of that huge vacuum which we call *interstellar space*, violent disturbances may be taking place in the sun, moon and other heavenly bodies. From these noises we are effectively cut off.

Velocity of Sound in Air. The fact that sound does not travel instantaneously is well known. If we watch a cricket match from a distance, we see the stroke, then hear the click. We see the lightning before we hear the thunder. You can probably think of other examples to illustrate the same fact.

An interesting experiment on the velocity of sound in air was carried out in 1822 just outside Paris. The observers adopted the method known as *reciprocal firing* of two cannon stationed about 11 miles apart. The cannon at one station was fired and the observer at the distant station noted on a chronometer the interval between the flash and the arrival of the sound. The other cannon was then fired and the time taken for the sound to travel in the opposite direction. In this way the effect of the wind was allowed for. The distance was 18612·5 metres and the times 54·4 and 54·8 sec.

Are you sure that you know the correct way of working out the velocity of sound from these figures? It is worth while looking into this question in detail, for there is an interesting catch lurking in it. You will probably say, "Average the two times and divide into the length."

The correct method is this:

Let V = velocity of sound in metres/sec. in still air
w = velocity of the wind in metres/sec.

then $$V + w = \frac{18612 \cdot 5}{54 \cdot 4}$$

and $$V - w = \frac{18612 \cdot 5}{54 \cdot 8}$$

By addition w is eliminated.

The wrong method gives practically the same answer as the right method, but this is only because w happens to be small compared with V.

The catch here is similar to the old question, "Which will take longer—to swim 50 yd. upstream and back or 100 yd. in still water?" We are tempted to think that the assistance in one direction just balances the opposition in the other, but we must remember that the opposition acts for a longer time than the assistance, and therefore has more effect on the final result. Therefore "upstream and back" takes the longer time.

Whenever *time* comes into problems we always have to be specially careful not to go astray.

It will be noticed that we assume the flash to arrive instantaneously. When we remember the tremendous velocity of light (186,000 miles/sec.), we see that it is quite reasonable to neglect the time taken for the flash to travel 11 miles.

The velocity of sound in air is found to be independent of the atmospheric pressure, but increases with the temperature. At 0° C. the velocity is 332 metres per second and increases by 60 cm. or 2 ft. for every rise in temperature of 1° C. In British units it is roughly 1090 ft. per second at 0° C. and increases by 2 ft. per second for each rise of 1° C.

Transmission of Sound. Let us now consider how sound is transmitted from the sounding body to the ear. The air-pump experiment showed that sound reached the ear when there was air in the jar, but not when the jar was vacuous. It cannot therefore be a case of the projection of air particles from the sounding body to the ear because these would be stopped by the jar.

The only reasonable explanation is that sound is carried by *waves.* These are not waves in the ether like light waves because we could *see* the vibrating body even when we could not *hear* it. The wave motion must be carried by the air.

You will remember that in water waves and light waves

Fig. 108.

something vibrates *across* the direction in which the wave is passing. In water waves we often see a cork or a boat bobbing up and down while the wave itself is travelling in to the shore. Such waves are called *transverse* (*trans*—across).

Suppose we have a tuning-fork which gives the same note as middle C on the piano. It will make 256 vibrations per second. Each time it swings outwards, it hits the air particles so that they crowd together, causing the air to be slightly compressed. When it swings inwards, it causes a partial vacuum. Therefore close to the tuning-fork there is a *compression* followed by a *rarefaction* 256 times per second.

But consider the behaviour of a single air particle. When hit by the tuning-fork, it passes the bump on to its neighbours and then bounces back. It thus helps to form a compression, then a rarefaction, then a second compression. In this way compressions and rarefactions travel outwards until they reach the ear (fig. 108).

Since the air particles move to and fro *along* the direction in which the wave is travelling, such waves are called *longitudinal*.

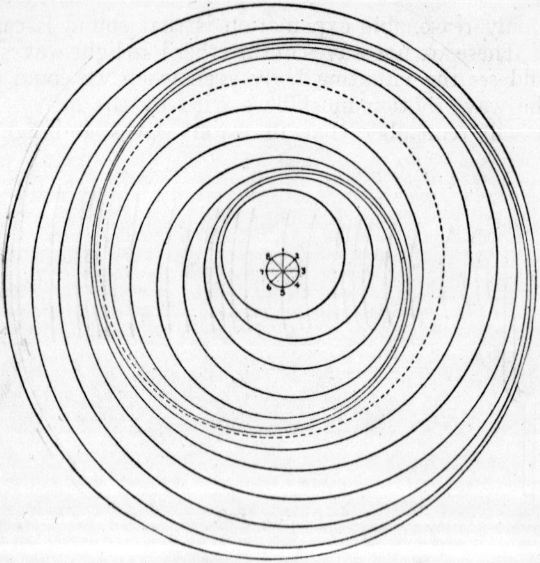

FIG. 109.

Longitudinal waves can be very well illustrated by a device known as *Crova's disc* (fig. 109). Draw a circle of radius $\frac{1}{4}$ in. in the middle of a disc of cardboard as large as your gramophone turntable will take. Divide the circumference of this small circle into eight equal parts and number the points. Starting with the 1st point as centre, draw a circle of radius 1 in. With the 2nd point as centre draw a circle $1\frac{1}{4}$ in. radius. Repeat with the other points in order, increasing the radius each time by $\frac{1}{4}$ in. The circles should be done in ink, making one of them red (dotted in fig. 109). Bore a small hole at the centre so that the disc will fit on to the turntable.

Cut out another large piece of cardboard as shown on a reduced scale in fig. 110. On it draw a tuning-fork. Cut a slot equal in length to the radius of the disc. Bore a hole near the end of the slot. Place this second piece of cardboard on the turn-table on top of the disc.

When the top cardboard is held and the under one rotated, compressions and rarefactions are seen travelling from the tuning-fork along the slot. By concentrating the attention on the red circle, the to-and-fro motion of a single air particle will easily be understood. The maximum distance moved from its position of rest is called the *amplitude.* The larger the amplitude, the louder the sound.

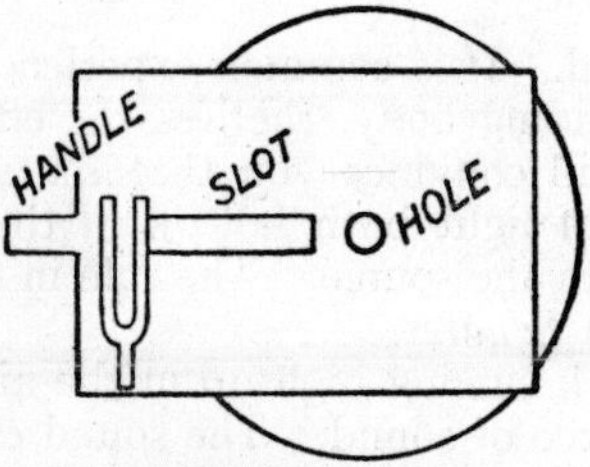

FIG. 110.

Frequency and Wave Length. In transverse wave-motion the distance between consecutive crests or troughs is called the *wave length.* In longitudinal waves the wave length is the distance from the middle of one compression to the middle of the next or the distance between corresponding points of two consecutive rarefactions.

How far will a compression travel in air in 1 sec.? *1,100 ft.* How many waves will the middle C fork put into this length in 1 sec.? *256.* It will therefore be readily seen that the length of each wave must be 1,100 ft. ÷ 256. In other words

Wave Length = Velocity ÷ Frequency
or Velocity = Frequency × Wave Length
or $V = n\lambda$

The Greek letter λ (lambda) is universally used to denote wave length.

The relation between Velocity, Frequency and Wave Length may be shown graphically as in fig. 111 where the wave length λ will obviously be 2 ft.

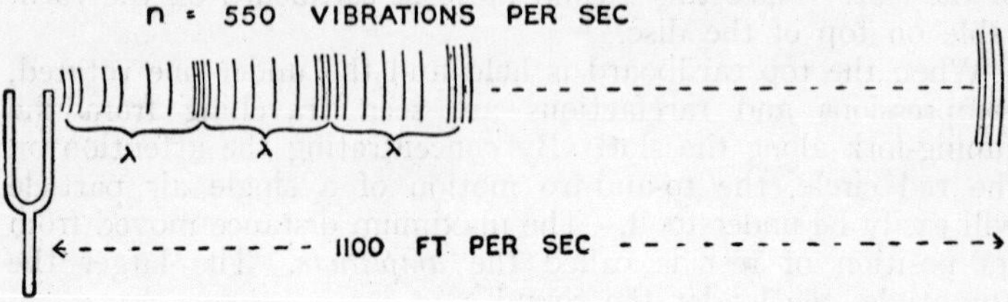

FIG. 111.

Intensity of Sound. It is common experience that the farther we are from a sounding body, the less the effect upon the ear. A little thought will convince you that the intensity of sound and the intensity of light both fall off in the same way when we travel away from the source. The rule in each case is called the *Law of Inverse Squares.*

Imagine a skylark singing high up in the air. We have here almost a point source of sound. The sound energy sent out by the bird spreads over a larger and larger sphere. At a distance of 1 yd. the energy is shared over a sphere of area $4\pi \times 1^2$ or 4π sq. yd. At double the distance the sphere has an area of $4\pi \times 2^2$ or 16π sq. yd. Therefore when we double the distance the sound is four times weaker. Similarly, when the distance is trebled the sound is nine times weaker, and so on. In other words, *the intensity is inversely proportional to the square of the distance.* We may also say that the amplitude of the air particles becomes less according to the same rule.

Reflection of Sound. We often meet examples of the reflection of sound. If you shout at some distance from a cliff there is frequently an echo. The first time you drive a motor-cycle through a tunnel or archway, the repeated echoes or reflections from the walls will probably give you the idea that your machine is falling to bits! A flash of lightning is accompanied by a thunder *clap,* but this becomes a *peal* because the sound is reflected several times from earth to cloud and back. In Switzerland you will see the "Alphornblasser" (fig. 112), a man who blows a tune through a large horn resting on the ground;

the tune returns several times from the sides of the Alpine valley.

In rooms of ordinary size the sound of a speaking voice is reflected back so quickly that it blends with the original sound, but in badly designed public buildings such echoes can be quite a nuisance. This is less marked when the hall is full of people as the sounds are not then reflected from the floors. The walls of broadcasting studios are covered with heavy curtains and the floor fitted with a very thick carpet.

FIG. 112.

You will occasionally meet a musical sort of echo when walking near palings or long flights of steps. The cause of this musical note will be readily understood from a consideration of fig. 113. If a walking-stick is struck on the pavement, the sound will be

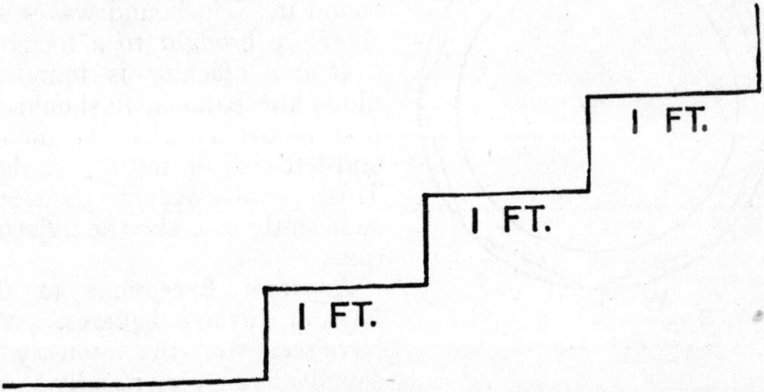

FIG. 113.

reflected from the vertical portion of each step at regular time intervals of $\frac{2}{1100}$ second because successive echoes have a path difference of twice the width of a step. A note of frequency 550 will then be produced.

Refraction of Sound. The refraction of sound may be illustrated by means of the apparatus shown in fig. 114. Two filter

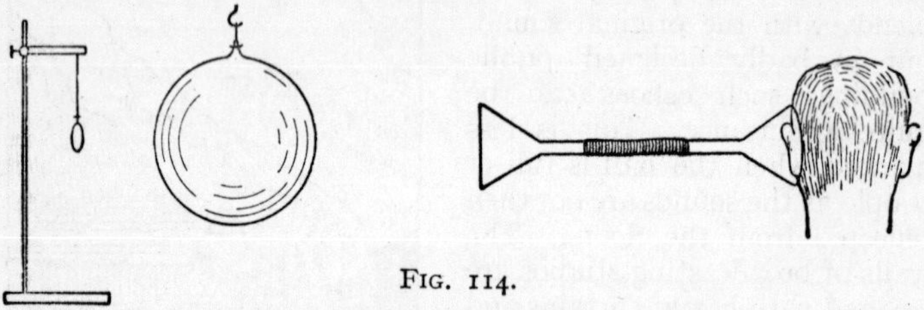

Fig. 114.

funnels are joined by a few inches of rubber tubing and held in such a position that the ticking of the suspended watch just cannot be heard. A toy balloon filled with carbon dioxide from a Kipp's apparatus is then hung up between, and its position varied until the sound from the watch is a maximum. The balloon of gas thus acts as a lens, the gas being heavier than air just as the glass of an optical lens is denser than the air round it. The sound waves are therefore brought to a focus.

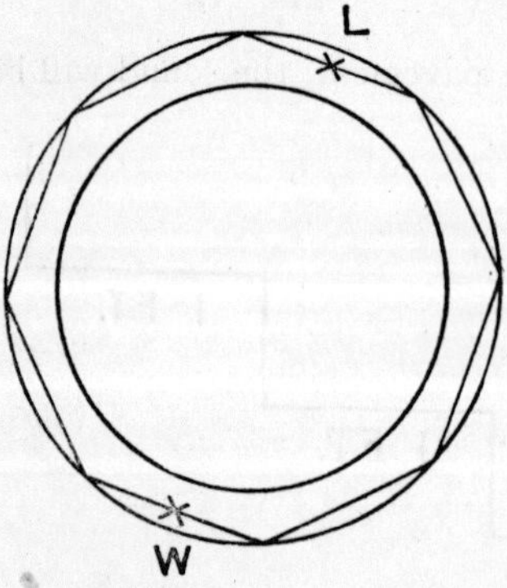

Fig. 115.

If any difficulty is found in filling the balloon, it should be first blown up with the mouth and left tied up until next day. This generally weakens the fabric sufficiently to make the inflation easy.

Apparent Exceptions to the Law of Inverse Squares. We have seen that the intensity of sound falls off very rapidly as we recede from the source, *e.g.* if we *double* the distance, the sound is *four* times as weak. Yet it is quite easy, by means of a speaking tube, to carry on a conversation with a person in a distant room.

We apparently have here an exception to the Law of Inverse Squares. But this law is only true when the waves are able to spread out in all directions. Anything which confines the sound to a definite path will tend to diminish the rate at which the intensity falls off. In the *speaking-tube* and the *megaphone* the energy is sent in one direction. In 1816 the French physician Laennec, listening to the beating of a patient's heart through a roll of paper, also made use of this fact. To-day doctors regularly use the *stethoscope* for listening to the sounds of heart and lungs. We meet the same fact in the whispering gallery of St. Paul's Cathedral.

A whisperer at W is plainly heard by a listener at L (fig. 115). If the whisper came across directly, its intensity would be lost, but it goes round as in a speaking-tube. In the diagram the reflections are represented as taking place along eight chords, but this number is only chosen for convenience.

QUESTIONS

1. Say what you know of the resemblances and differences between the physical effects known as "sound" and "light."

2. What will be the wave length when a 256 fork vibrates in air at 15° C.?

3. Compare the intensity of the sound of an explosion at two places 2 miles and 8 miles away.

4. What evidence can you produce to show that sounds of different pitch travel at the same speed?

5. A clap of thunder occurs 5 sec. after the lightning flash. If the temperature of the air is 25° C., how far away was the lightning?

6. An echo from a cliff is heard 10 sec. after the sound is made. If the temperature of the air is 10° C., how far away is the cliff?

7. (*a*) Give a drawing of a transverse wave-train of wave-length 3 cm., and amplitude 1 cm.

(*b*) If these waves are propagated at a speed of 300 metres per second, find their frequency.

(*c*) In what way or ways do the waves which you have drawn differ from sound-waves? (O. part question.)

CHAPTER XV

MORE ABOUT MUSICAL SOUNDS

WE have already learnt that musical sounds are produced by regular vibrations, while noises are produced by isolated or irregular vibrations. In describing the top note of a soprano and the bottom note of a bass, we say that the *pitch* of the first is higher than that of the second. It is easy to show that pitch depends on the frequency of vibration of the source.

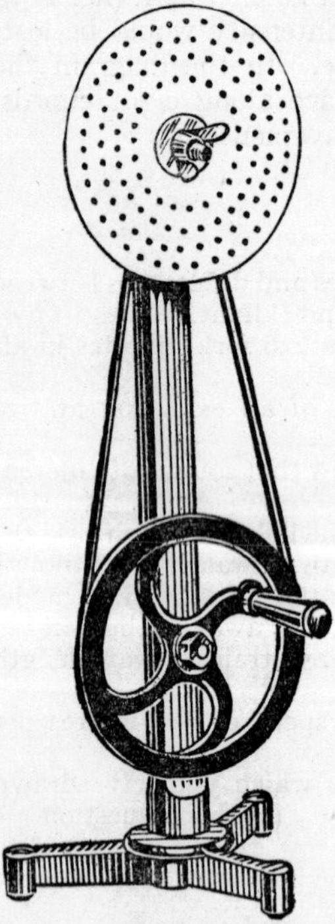

FIG. 116.

A Simple Siren. Take a disc of cardboard about 10 in. diameter. From its centre draw circles whose radii are in the ratio 4 : 5 : 6 : 8. On these circles drill 24, 30, 36, and 48 holes respectively. This can be done with the smallest tube of a set of cork borers. The holes should be evenly spaced. To do this the circles should be divided into arcs subtending angles of 15°, 12°, 10° and $7\frac{1}{2}$° respectively and holes drilled at the ends of the radii.

Now push through the centre a piece of threaded brass rod and secure it with two nuts. Insert the other end of the rod in a hand drill.

Steady the drill on a table and revolve rapidly while an assistant blows against the holes with a piece of glass tubing. The sounds emitted should be d m s d', the note of highest pitch being given by the largest circle. If the disc does 10 revolutions per second the pitch of this note will be $24 \times 10 = 240$, because there will be 240 puffs per second.

The above arrangement is designed for use at home. At school you will probably see the same thing done rather more effectively on a whirling table (fig. 116). But a gramophone turntable does not revolve fast enough.

The Pitch of a Fork. It will now be readily understood that, if we had a device for counting the revolutions, we could tune the siren in unison with any given tuning-fork and thus find the absolute pitch of the fork. This is done on the more elaborate sirens.

The frequency or pitch of a fork can also be found by using a gramophone in the manner illustrated in fig. 104, p. 143. On the disc of drawing paper mark a radius. Place the disc on the turntable and find the number of revolutions in half a minute. Calculate the time taken for 1 revolution. As on p. 144 allow the inked brush to make a wavy line on the disc. Count the waves in, say, 60°. The frequency of the fork can then be calculated.

EXAMPLE. A gramophone turntable makes 110 revolutions in 1 min. A fork makes 23 waves in 60°. What is the frequency of the fork? *Ans.* 253.

Musical Intervals. In our experiment with the siren we saw that when the vibration frequencies were in the ratio

24 : 30 : 36 : 48, we obtained
the notes d m s d'

When these notes are sounded either together or in succession, they give pleasure to the ear. The pleasurable effect seems to be intimately connected with the simple ratios between the numbers. Thus the most pleasing effect is given by the two dohs, and the ratio is here $\frac{48}{24}$ or $\frac{2}{1}$. The next most pleasurable interval is s : d and the ratio is $\frac{36}{24}$ or $\frac{3}{2}$. Our musical scale is made up of eight notes whose frequencies are in the ratio of the numbers

	24,	27,	30,	32,	36,	40,	45,	48	and these we call
	d	r	m	f	s	l	t	d'	
or	C	D	E	F	G	A	B	C'	

This scale has gradually grown up with us through the centuries, and it now seems quite reasonable to call it the *natural scale*. The intervals are as follows:

	C		D		E		F		G		A		B		C
		$\frac{27}{24}$		$\frac{30}{27}$		$\frac{32}{30}$		$\frac{36}{32}$		$\frac{40}{36}$		$\frac{45}{40}$		$\frac{48}{45}$	
or		$\frac{9}{8}$		$\frac{10}{9}$		$\frac{16}{15}$		$\frac{9}{8}$		$\frac{10}{9}$		$\frac{9}{8}$		$\frac{16}{15}$	

We thus have five intervals of about the same magnitude and two smaller intervals.

If now we wanted to start with D or E as the key note, the smaller intervals would come in the wrong places, and for each new key we should require some new notes. There is, of course, no difficulty in the case of the violin or the human voice. Why?

But on a piano something must be done to get over the trouble. The difficulty is overcome by introducing five extra black notes, so that the octave is divided up into 12 small intervals each equal to $2^{\frac{1}{12}}$. From C to C♯ is one of these intervals, from C♯ to D is another. The interval between C and D is therefore equal to two of these intervals or $2^{\frac{1}{12}} \times 2^{\frac{1}{12}}$, which equals $2^{\frac{1}{6}}$. The ordinary eight notes will now have the following intervals:

C		D		E		F		G		A		B		C
	$2^{\frac{1}{6}}$		$2^{\frac{1}{6}}$		$2^{\frac{1}{12}}$		$2^{\frac{1}{6}}$		$2^{\frac{1}{6}}$		$2^{\frac{1}{6}}$		$2^{\frac{1}{12}}$	

This scale is called the *equally tempered scale.*

Vibrating Strings. The facts relating to vibrating strings were first investigated by the Greek philosopher Pythagoras who lived about 500 B.C. You have probably met his well-known theorem in geometry.

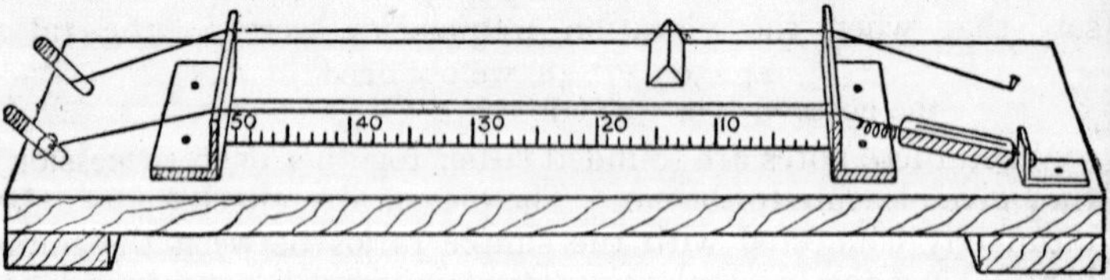

FIG. 117

To-day the properties of vibrating strings are illustrated by an instrument called the Sonometer (fig. 117).

The laws are as indicated below:

(*a*) n *the frequency is inversely proportional to the length.*

This can be shown on the sonometer by shifting the movable bridge along the wire. As the vibrating portion of the wire is shortened, the pitch of the note rises.

The top notes on a piano are given by short wires. The middle and lower strings are often set slantwise so as to allow the use of longer wires. Since some wires then pass *over* others, such a piano is described as *overstrung*. The violin player raises the pitch of a string when he shortens it by finger pressure.

(*b*) n *the frequency is proportional to the square root of the stretching force.*

To double the pitch, the stretching force has to be increased four times. This can be done on the sonometer by tightening the keys. The stretching force is measured either by a spring balance or by hanging weights.

On the piano and violin the pitch is also raised by the tightening of keys. The same fact is often illustrated on the gear wire of a bicycle.

(*c*) n *the frequency is inversely proportional to the square root of the mass per unit length.*

This can be illustrated on the sonometer by using wires of various thicknesses.

The bass notes on a piano are produced by thick wires and the top notes by thin ones. The thick wires are generally made by coiling one wire spirally round another.

This arrangement would cause the top notes to be thin compared with the lower notes. To guard against this, each of the middle and upper notes is often produced by *three* identical wires. The hammer strikes all three simultaneously and a good volume of sound is thus ensured. Such a piano is described as *trichord.*

The above three laws are conveniently summed up in the formula

$$n = \frac{1}{2l \text{ cm.}} \sqrt{\frac{T \text{ dynes}}{m \text{ gm. per cm.}}}$$

Note: 980 dynes = 1 gram weight.

How a String Vibrates.

(*a*) Draw a violin bow across the middle of the sonometer wire. The note given out is called the *fundamental*. The string is vibrating in one segment. The ends are called *nodes* while the point of maximum movement is called the *antinode* or *loop* (fig. 118 (*a*)).

(*b*) Touch the centre of the wire with the edge of a tail feather of a chicken. Bow at the middle of one of the segments. The note given out is the *octave* of the first note. The string is vibrating in two segments. There are nodes at the centre and at the ends (fig. 118 (*b*)). If paper riders are placed at the nodes and antinodes, they will be jerked off at the antinodes.

(*c*) Damp the motion with the feather at a point one-third of the length from one end. Bow the shorter segment. The note given out will be the *twelfth* of the original note. There will now be four nodes and three antinodes, easily discovered again by paper riders (fig. 118 (*c*)).

(*d*) With careful practice the wire can be made to vibrate in four segments and the note will be the double octave (fig. 118 (*d*)).

A long wire can be divided into still more segments and further notes obtained. The fundamental, the octave, the twelfth, the

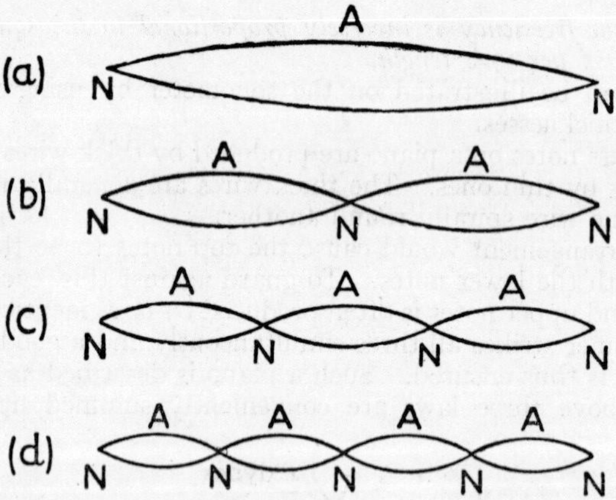

FIG. 118.

double octave, etc., are called *harmonics*, the fundamental itself being generally called the first harmonic, the octave the second, and so on.

The experiment is more striking when carried out close to a piano. The notes corresponding to the harmonics of the string can then be found on the keyboard, and it is easy to find out their relative pitch.

Quality of a Musical Note. We have seen that the pitch of a note depends on the frequency of vibration, and the loudness upon the amplitude. But if a blindfolded person listened to a note of the same pitch and loudness rendered by a piano, a violin, and the human voice, he would easily distinguish between them.

Scientists and musicians say there is a difference in *quality*. But what is quality?

Our last experiment gives us the clue to the explanation. We saw that the same wire by damping could be made to yield several notes. You will be surprised to hear that the natural thing is for the wire to give most of those notes *at the same time*. Our damping was simply a device for "filtering" one note from the rest. Let us repeat our experiment in a slightly different way.

(1) This time *pluck* the sonometer wire with the finger about a quarter of the way along, and immediately touch the wire at the middle with the feather. The fundamental will be first heard, then the octave or second harmonic. Both were there at first, but the octave was faint and could only be heard when the fundamental was quenched by forcing a node to form at the centre.

(2) Again pluck at the same place and immediately damp at one-third. The fundamental is heard, but this and the octave are quenched by the damping and the twelfth or third harmonic is heard.

(3) Pluck a little nearer to the end and damp at one-quarter. This gives the fourth harmonic.

Note here that to get this fourth harmonic, we had to change the plucking point because we want a node at the quarter length. If you pluck at the quarter length the fourth harmonic cannot be present.

There is an application of this fact in the piano; the seventh harmonic does not blend well with the others, therefore the hammers are made to strike the wires at about one-seventh of the length. A node cannot then form at this point and the seventh harmonic will be missing.

We are now better able to understand what is meant by the Quality of a musical note. *The quality of a note depends on the number of harmonics present and also on their strength.*

Resonance. If a vibrating tuning-fork is held over a column of air in a burette (fig. 119), it is found that when the column has a certain length, the air resounds loudly.

The explanation of this is quite simple. Consider the lower prong. If it is a 256 fork, it travels from A to B and back to A 256 times per second. In travelling downwards from A it sends a compression down the tube. When the resonance is a maximum, it means that this compression has travelled down the tube and back and is ready to assist the prong in its upward motion from B to A. The fork is then able to give bigger sound waves to the surrounding air. (*Note:* "bigger" refers to the amplitude.)

In these circumstances, if l is the length of the resonance column, the compression has travelled

$$2l \text{ in } \tfrac{1}{2} \text{ of } \tfrac{1}{256} \text{ sec.}$$
$$\text{or } 4l \text{ in } \tfrac{1}{256} \text{ sec.}$$

In 1 sec. it travels $4l \times 256$, but in 1 sec. sound travels 1100 ft.

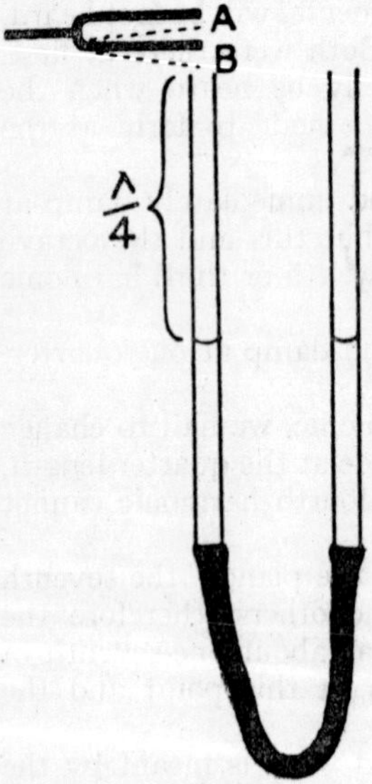

FIG. 119.

$$\therefore 1100 = 4l \times 256$$
or $$V = 4nl$$
but $$V = n\lambda$$
$$\therefore \lambda = 4l.$$

This resonance experiment gives us a means of finding the pitch of a fork if we are given the velocity of sound in air, or the velocity of sound if we are given the pitch of a fork.

Lord Rayleigh has shown that the true value of $\frac{\lambda}{4}$ depends slightly on the diameter of the tube. The observed length should be increased by 0·3 of the diameter.

Organ Pipes. The above experiment on resonance shows that air columns have their own natural frequency, and that this frequency depends upon their lengths. We may illustrate the same point in a very amusing way as follows:

Take seven test-tubes and add water to varying depths from a pipette (fig. 120), so that on blowing across the tubes or striking them with a lead pencil, the following succession of notes is produced—B C D E F G A.

Very little musical skill will then enable you to play the National Anthem.

Doppler's Principle. The pitch of a locomotive whistle is noticed to drop sharply as the engine passes the observer. The explanation is simple. Suppose the engine, stationary at E (fig. 121 not to scale), emits a note of frequency 550 and let O

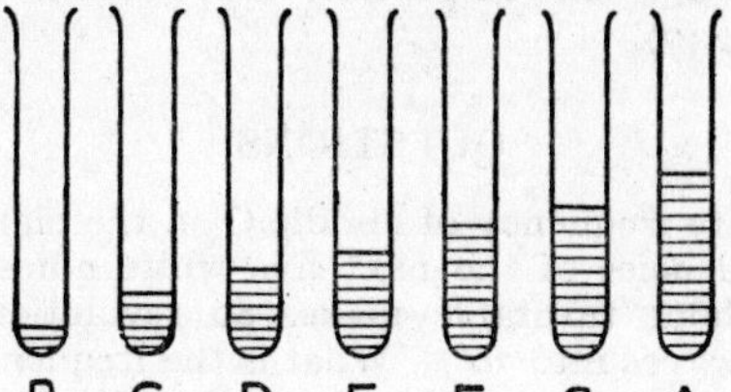

FIG. 120.

be the observer 1100 ft. away. The engine puts 550 waves per second into EO and the wave length is 2 ft. If now the engine

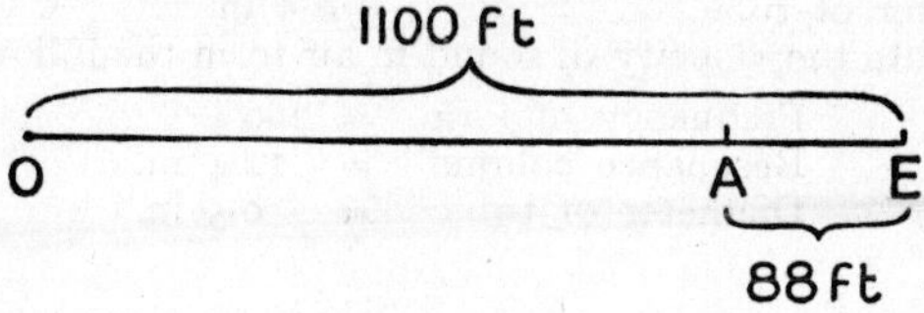

FIG. 121.

approaches at 88 ft./sec. (60 m.p.h.), the 550 waves will be put into AO a distance of 1100 − 88 ft. and the wave length will be

$$\frac{1100 - 88}{550} = 1{\cdot}84 \text{ ft.}$$

When the engine passes the observer and recedes, the same 550 waves will be put into 1100 + 88 ft. and the wave length will be

$$\frac{1100 + 88}{550} = 2{\cdot}16 \text{ ft.}$$

The pitch on *approach* is got from

$$\frac{V}{\lambda} = \frac{1100}{1{\cdot}84} = 598.$$

The pitch on *receding* is got from

$$\frac{V}{\lambda} = \frac{1100}{2{\cdot}16} = 509.$$

This change of pitch caused by the motion of the source was first explained by an Austrian physicist, Johann Christian Doppler (1803–53). It has an important application in astronomy (see Light, p. 247).

QUESTIONS

1. The absolute frequency of middle C on the piano is 256. Calculate the frequencies of the next five white notes.

2. A gramophone turntable makes 80 revolutions per minute. A fork puts 24 waves into 30°. What is the frequency of the fork ?

3. String A is twice as long as string B and is stretched by four times the force acting on B. Compare the pitch of the two strings given that the material and thickness are the same.

4. Calculate the frequency of a fork from the following data:

Velocity of sound in air (9° C.) = 1,118 ft. per second.
Resonance column = 6·4 in.
Diameter of tube = 0·5 in.

5. Calculate the velocity of sound in air from the following data:

Frequency of fork = 269
Resonance column = 12·4 in.
Diameter of tube = 0·5 in.

LIGHT

CHAPTER XVI

RECTILINEAR PROPAGATION, SHADOWS, VELOCITY OF LIGHT

WE describe bodies like the sun, an electric bulb, or a candle as giving out *light* and we know that this light affects the eye. Such bodies are called *luminous*. But the eye is also affected by things which are not luminous. Why can we see a book? It is certainly not luminous. The answer is that there is some luminous body throwing light on the book. Some of this light, after striking the book, is reflected, and it is by means of this light that we are able to see the book.

It has been realized, ever since man began to think about the matter at all, that light travels in straight lines; we do not

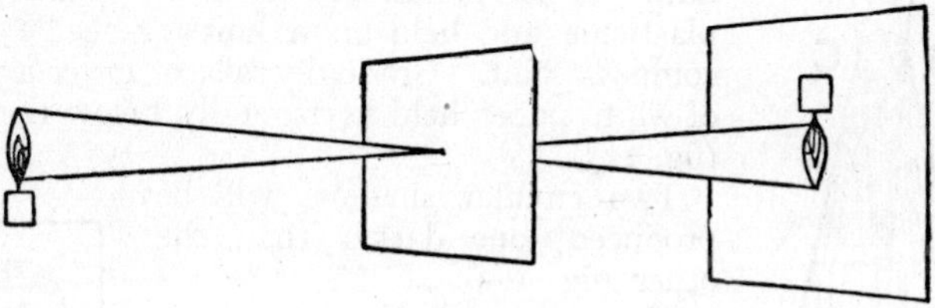

FIG. 122.

expect to see round a corner. The scientific fact may be stated thus, **light travels in straight lines in a transparent homogeneous medium.**

A homogeneous medium is one which has the same density all through. Any straight line along which light is travelling is called a *ray*. The path of a ray is reversible, *i.e.* if the eye and the object change places, the path will be the same.

There are many other illustrations of the fact that light travels in straight lines in a transparent homogeneous medium.

When light comes through a small opening into a room, the straightness of the path is made obvious by the dust particles.

Experiment. Set up two pieces of cardboard and a candle as shown in fig. 122. Make a small hole in the middle of the first sheet of cardboard. The image on the second card will be inverted because the extreme rays go straight through the aperture and cross one another. This is the principle of the pinhole camera.

It may be remarked here that many simple and interesting experiments in light can be carried out in a sitting-room or bedroom with apparatus readily available in every house, while the use of a "chemistry set," if tolerated at all, involves deserved exile in the scullery or a shed in the garden.

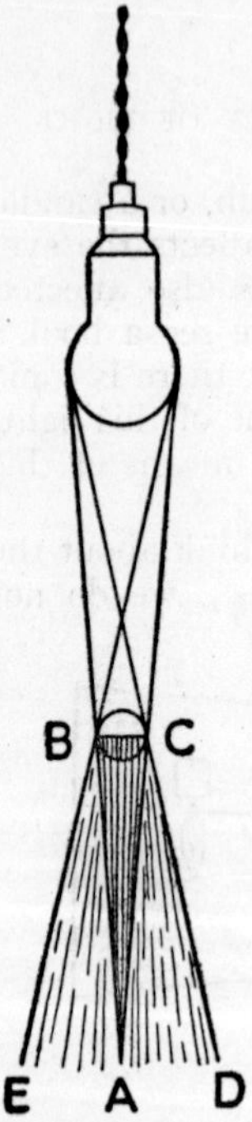

FIG. 123.

Shadows. The rectilinear propagation of light is well illustrated in the formation of shadows.

Experiment. Below an electric-light bulb having "milky" or frosted glass or a covering of tissue paper, hold a ball smaller than the bulb. A ball of suitable size may be made from plasticine and held on a knitting-needle or a compass point. Gradually raise or lower a piece of white paper held horizontally below the ball (fig. 123).

Two circular shadows will be produced, one darker than the other (fig. 123).

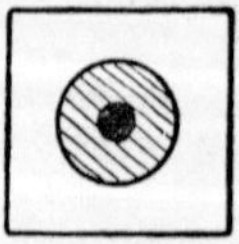
FIG. 124.

The name *umbra* is given to the darker circle and also to the shadow cone ABC (fig. 124). The lighter circle and the shadow region ACD and ABE are called the *penumbra.* Note that the prefix *pen* means *almost* (*pen*-insula).

Eclipses. The above experiment also illustrates the production of eclipses.

(*a*) *Eclipse of the Moon.* In this case the dark ball of our experiment is the earth (fig. 125). When the moon is totally immersed in the umbra we have a total eclipse. Since the moon goes round the earth every month, it might be thought that the moon would suffer eclipse every month. But we must remember that the moon's orbit round the earth is inclined to the earth's orbit round the sun. In order, therefore, that an eclipse should take place, the moon (*a*) must be on the far side of the earth from

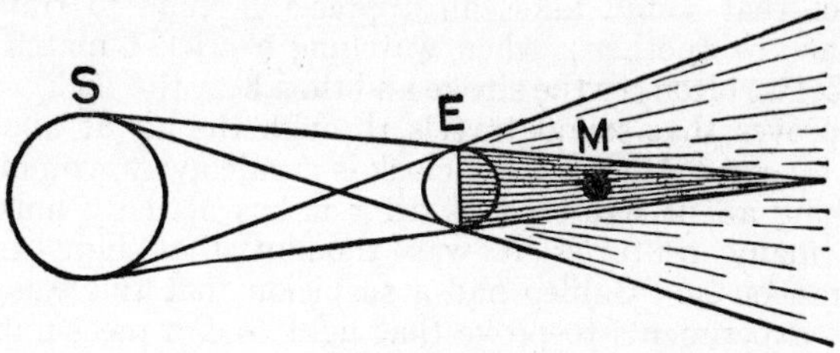

FIG. 125.

the sun, (*b*) must be in or near the earth's orbit. In other words, even when condition (*a*) is satisfied three things may happen:

(1) The moon may pass entirely above or below the umbra.

(2) It may pass partly through the umbra, producing a partial eclipse.

(3) It may pass quite through the umbra, causing a total eclipse.

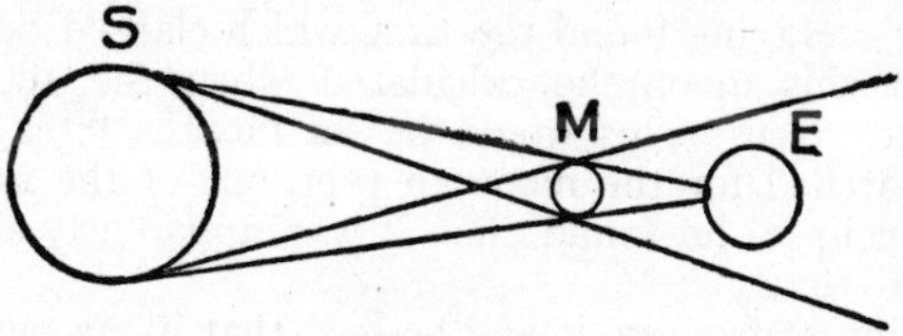

FIG. 126.

(*b*) *Eclipse of the Sun.* The dark ball forming an umbra is in this case the moon (fig. 126). Since the moon is smaller than the earth it is impossible for the latter to be completely immersed in the umbra. It will therefore be readily understood that whereas a total eclipse of the moon may be visible simultaneously all over a hemisphere of the earth, a total eclipse of the sun is only seen at one time by the inhabitants of a small part of the earth.

As in the case of the moon, it might be thought that the sun would suffer eclipse once a month, but this is not so for the reason mentioned above.

The Velocity of Light. We are quite well acquainted with the fact that sound takes an appreciable time to travel from one place to another; when watching a cricket match from a distance, we often see the stroke and then hear the click. Experiment proves that sound travels through the air at about 1100 ft. per second. If your town clock is a mile away, you may hear it striking about five seconds after it has actually finished.

For many centuries it was thought that light travelled instantaneously. Galileo had a suspicion that this was not so, but his experiments to prove that light took a measurable time to travel were not very decisive.

It is interesting to notice, however, that it was Galileo's work in another direction which finally helped to solve the problem. In 1610, with his newly invented telescope, Galileo discovered the four [1] moons of Jupiter. Sixty-five years later a young Danish astronomer, Olav Roemer, was studying the eclipses of these moons at the royal observatory of Paris.

We have already seen how our own moon is eclipsed when it enters the umbra cast by the earth. In just the same way, Jupiter eclipses its moons, but much more frequently.

Roemer concentrated his attention on the moon nearest to the planet. Having found the time which elapsed between two eclipses of this moon, he calculated when the 100th eclipse would take place. This would be six months later, but when Roemer watched for the moon to peep out of the umbra after its 100th eclipse, he found that it was apparently about 1,000 sec. behind time.

On looking at fig. 127, it will be seen that in six months' time the earth will have travelled round to the opposite side of its orbit. But since Jupiter takes nearly twelve years to go round the sun, it will only have travelled about 15°.

Roemer came to the conclusion that it was not the eclipse which was late but the light travelling from Jupiter to the earth. In other words, at the first eclipse the light had only to

[1] In 1892 another small moon was discovered, and since then the number has been increased to nine.

travel from J_1 to E_1, but at the 100th eclipse it had to travel from J_2 to E_2, which meant an extra distance equal to the diameter of the earth's orbit. This extra distance is equal to 93,000,000 miles × 2, and to travel this distance the light took 1,000 sec. Therefore light travels roughly 186,000 miles per second, or in metric units 300,000 kilometres per second.

This means that light travels in one second a distance of more than seven times the earth's circumference. We now readily understand why it was only when Roemer used these vast astronomical distances that it was possible to prove that light had a definite speed. Any distance on the earth itself

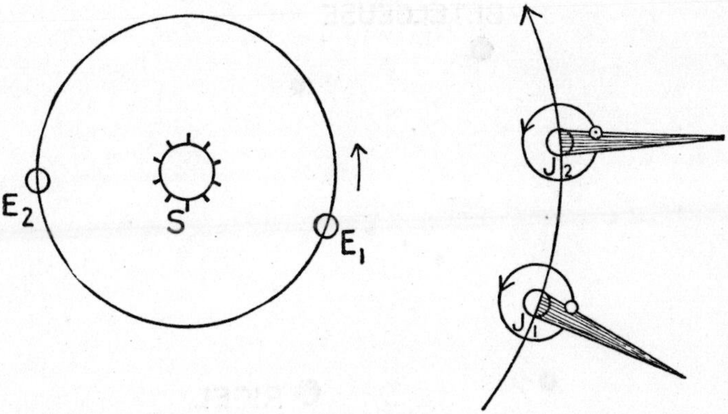

FIG. 127.

would be covered in such a small fraction of a second that these philosophers of 300 years ago could not measure it. They had thus come to the conclusion that light travelled instantaneously.

We have referred to a distance of 186 million miles as being "vast," but though this is large compared with terrestrial distances, it is quite small in astronomy. Light from the sun reaches the earth in about 8 min., but light from the Pole Star takes forty-seven years! When we see the Pole Star shining, we do not know whether it is still in existence or not; we only know that it was giving out light forty-seven years ago.

It will be convenient here to introduce the astronomical unit of length. If the light from a star takes a year to reach the earth its distance is 186,000 × 365 × 24 × 60 × 60 miles. This gives such a very large number that it is found more convenient to say that the *distance* of the star is one *light-year*. Similarly, the distance of the Pole Star is given as forty-seven light-years. The use of time to express distance is really quite common in ordinary life; we speak of a house as being "5 minutes" from the station.

The distance of the Pole Star is truly immense, but the two brightest stars in Orion, Betelgeuse and Rigel (fig. 128), are between 300 and 500 light-years away. Other stars are farther still, their distances being estimated in *millions* of light-years.

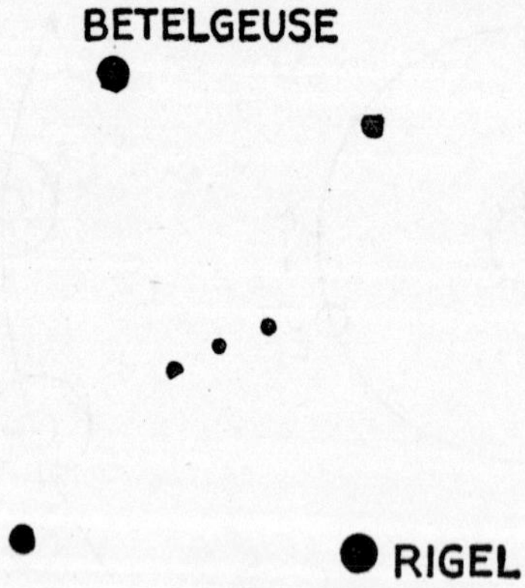

Fig. 128.

The fact that light has a definite velocity and does not travel instantaneously has often provided imaginative writers with useful material. Thus if we imagine an observer on some star which is about 900 light-years away, and that the observer has either superhuman sight or a wonderful telescope, then we can also picture him still watching William the Conqueror landing in England, since light from the earth will also take 900 years to reach the star.

A variation of this idea is to imagine an observer shot off from the earth at an enormous speed. With wonderful sight he looks back at his home. If his speed is just equal to that of light he will see everything as a still picture. But if his speed could be greater than that of light, he would be able to catch up with rays of light which had gone before. In this way his past life would be unfolded before his eyes.

QUESTIONS

1. Which of the following are homogeneous: A table jelly, a blanc-mange, a Christmas pudding, the air above the tram lines on a hot day? Is there amongst them a *transparent* homogeneous medium?

2. If there were people on the moon, what would they see during (*a*) a solar eclipse, (*b*) a lunar eclipse?

3. The nearest star to the earth is Alpha Centauri, visible only in the southern hemisphere. Its distance is 4·4 light-years. Express this in miles.

4. Draw diagrams to show the shadows cast on a screen by an object when (*a*) the source of light is a point, (*b*) the source of light is larger than the object. In each case let the object be midway between the source of light and the screen. (L.)

Explain how a total eclipse of (*a*) the sun, (*b*) the moon is formed.

5. Describe, giving diagrams, the formation of the umbra and penumbra in shadows.

A source of light has an area of 3 cm. square. A screen (A) 2 cm. square is placed 10 cm. from the source of light and a second screen (B) is placed farther from the source than (A). Where must (B) be placed so that there will just be no *umbra*? Determine (by using a diagram) the areas of the umbra and penumbra if (B) is 4 cm. from (A). (D.)

CHAPTER XVII

REFLECTION: PLANE SURFACES

In the foregoing chapter, the rays of light were considered to be travelling in a homogeneous medium. When the rays strike the surface of a new medium, several things may happen.

Let us consider the case where the new medium is a plane mirror. We shall call a collection of rays—a *beam of light*. If the rays are parallel we have a *parallel beam*; rays spreading out from a point produce a *divergent beam*, while if the rays travel towards a point we have a *convergent beam*.

Experiment. The apparatus shown (fig. 129) consists of two pieces of cardboard 7 in. × 9 in. and a plane mirror 6 in. × 1 in. carrying a tiny blob of plasticine in which a pin is stuck by the head. In the vertical sheet a slit is cut $\frac{1}{12}$ in. wide and 6 in. long.

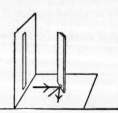

FIG. 129.

Place the apparatus on a table about 6 ft. away from an electric lamp hanging 3 ft. above the table. The room need not be darkened provided the sunlight is not too powerful. Hold the vertical cardboard in one hand and the mirror in the other. An almost parallel beam will be produced. When this strikes the mirror, we call it the *incident ray*. The pin serves as the *normal* to the mirror. On rotating the mirror, a *reflected ray* will be produced.

Observe the angle between the incident ray and the normal and that between the reflected ray and the normal. These are called, respectively, the *angle of incidence* and the *angle of reflection.*

With this simple apparatus, you should be able to verify three important facts.

1. The incident ray, the normal, and the reflected ray are in the same plane.

2. The angle of incidence is equal to the angle of reflection.

These two facts are called the Laws of Reflection.

3. If the direction of the incident ray is kept unchanged and the mirror is rotated through any angle, the reflected ray moves through twice that angle.

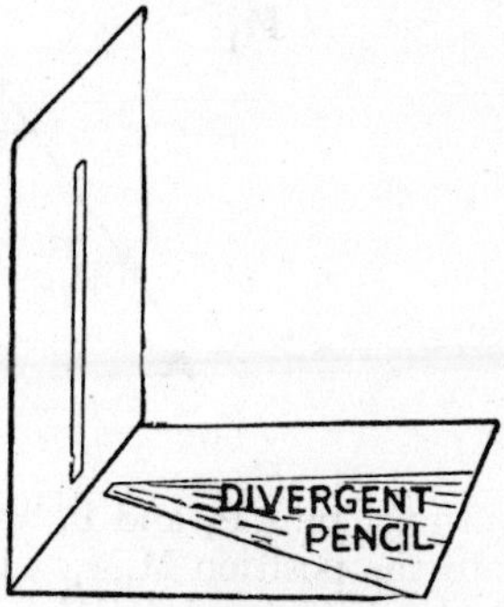

FIG. 130.

This third fact is the cause of the amusement you obtain in throwing the sun's image on the ceiling, but it has more important uses; the sextant used by sailors is based on this fact, likewise certain electrical galvanometers.

If instead of an electric bulb, we use daylight with our pieces of cardboard (fig. 130), we shall obtain a very good illustration of a *divergent* beam.

Note that when a beam is divergent or convergent, it is often referred to as a *pencil* on account of the shape. Thus we meet the expressions "divergent pencil" and "convergent pencil."

The Laws of Reflection can also be verified by means of a mirror and a few pins.

Experiment. Fasten a piece of white paper on a drawing board. Somewhere near the middle, set a plane mirror on edge, and support it by means of a block of wood or a cork in which a slit has been cut.

Draw a straight line at the back of the mirror (fig. 131). Fix a pin P_1 vertically in the paper. From the point where this pin enters the paper an infinite number of rays will pass. Fix a second pin P_2. The two points will indicate the path of a *single* ray or at any rate the path of a very narrow beam. Looking in the mirror, place another pair of pins P_3P_4 in line with the images of the first pair.

Remove the pins and the mirror, then draw lines P_1P_2 and P_3P_4. They should meet at a point B at the back of the mirror. At B draw a line perpendicular to the mirror. This is the *normal*. It will be seen that $\underline{|ABN} = \underline{|CBN}$. Thus the second law is verified.

Replace the mirror and notice that the lines P_1P_2, P_3P_4 and the normal are continuous with their respective images. Thus the first law is verified.

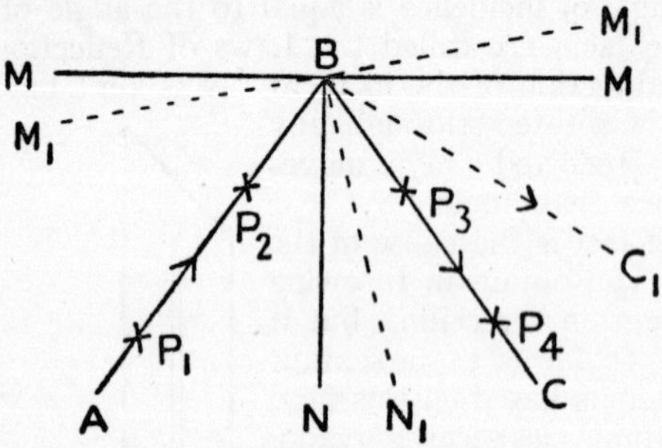

FIG. 131.

Insert pins P_1 and P_2 and rotate the mirror through, say, 10° into the position M_1M_1. Find the new reflected ray. Compare angles CBC_1 and MBM_1.

The Image of a Point.

Experiment. Fix up a mirror on paper as before. Stick a pin O in the paper to serve as object (fig. 132). Insert pins A and B in line with the image of O. Remove them and draw a straight line through the points A and B. On the other side of O insert pins C and D in line with the image. Remove the pins and draw a straight line through the points C and D.

Produce the lines AB and CD until they meet behind the mirror at a point I. This is the *image* of the point O. Measure the distances of O and I from the mirror.

If the experiment is done carefully, it will be found (1) that the line joining object and image is perpendicular to the mirror and (2) that the image is as far behind the mirror as the object is in front.

But what is an *image* and how is it caused? You will not need to be told that there is really nothing behind the mirror. You probably satisfied yourself on that point some years ago when you looked into a mirror and tried to touch the "other baby." Kittens are often seen to be similarly mystified.

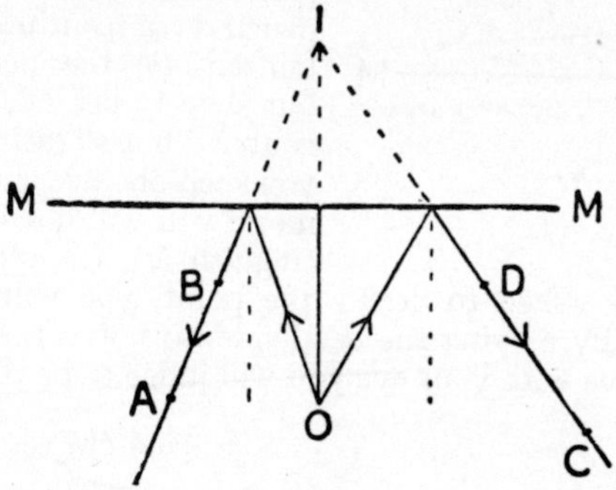

FIG. 132.

The explanation is quite simple when we realize that the point O (fig. 133) throws out rays in all directions, and that those rays which strike the mirror are reflected in such a way that they all

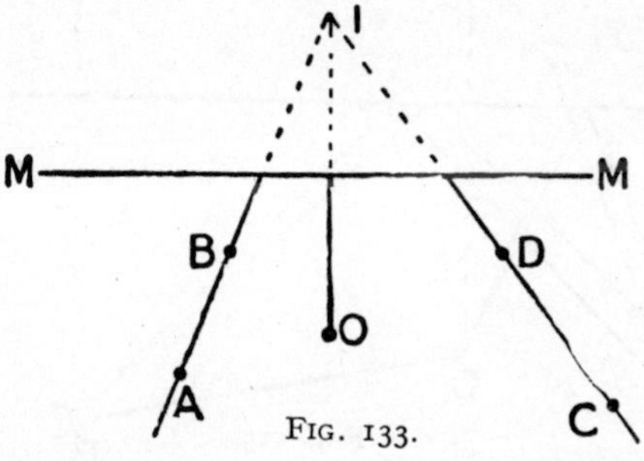

FIG. 133.

seem to be starting from the point I behind the mirror. The eye takes no account of the fact that the rays have been bent back by the mirror.

There is another instructive method of finding the image of a point. It is based on what is called the **Principle of Parallax.**

Consider for a moment a clock at 12.30. If you view it from the right, it will possibly say 12.31, while from the left it seems to be 12.29. There is *parallax* between the minute hand and the painted figures on the dial.

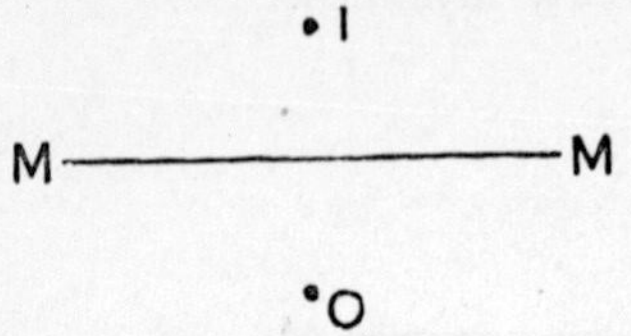

FIG. 134.

Next get someone to hold a pencil over a bunsen so that (*a*) the pencil is a continuation of the bunsen, (*b*) the pencil is above but slightly behind, (*c*) the pencil is above but slightly in front. If you keep one eye shut and do not move, you will not be able to distinguish (*a*), (*b*) and (*c*).

If you are asked to decide the point, you will find yourself quite naturally moving the head sideways, and the object which seems to move with your eye you will judge to be the farther one.

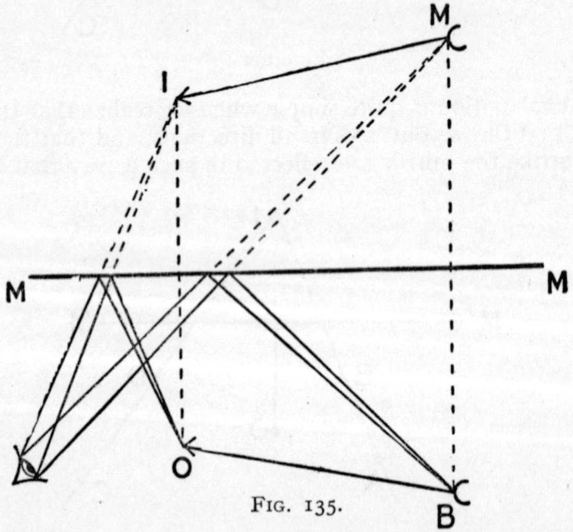

FIG. 135.

We may sum up this question of parallax by saying—**Parallax is an apparent change in the relative position of two objects due to a change in the position of the observer's eye; of two objects, the farther one seems to move *with* the observer's eye.**

Experiment. To find the image of a pin by parallax.

Insert a short pin O in the paper in front of a mirror (fig. 134). Place the eye at such a height that you can only see the lower part of the image. Hold a longer pin behind the mirror, and move it about until the upper portion of it seems to be a continuation of the lower part of the image, no matter how you move the eye sideways. In other words, *adjust for no parallax.*

The Image of an Extended Body. Since any body may be regarded as made up of a number of points, it is quite easy to construct the image of some simple object. Thus to construct the image IM of the object OB (fig. 135), we need only take points in OB and mark corresponding points at the same perpendicular distance behind the mirror.

The construction of the rays by which the eye sees the image will also be readily understood.

Properties of the Image formed by a Plane Mirror.

(*a*) The image is as far behind the mirror as the object is in front.

(*b*) The image is the same size as the object.

(*c*) There is " lateral inversion."

Lateral Inversion is an interchange of sides. A right hand becomes a left hand (fig. 136). A man with his right arm in a sling gazes at another whose left arm is in a sling. Most faces are slightly unsymmetrical, in other words, the two sides do not balance. So when we look into a mirror, we do not " see ourselves as others see us." We can, however, by using two mirrors, produce two lateral inversions and thus get the ordinary view of ourselves.

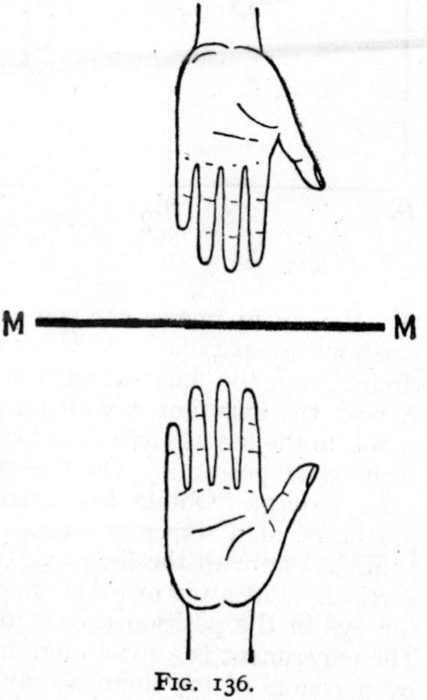

FIG. 136.

A clock which seems to show nine o'clock in a mirror

is really registering three o'clock, and again we can get it right by looking into a second mirror.

Lateral inversion by a plane mirror is a fact well known to writers of detective stories. The detective holds a blotting-pad before a mirror, and there behold the criminal has written his name and address! The pad has laterally inverted the writing, the mirror does the same, so the writing can be read.

Experiment. Hold a piece of cardboard horizontally in front of a vertical mirror. Looking into the mirror, try to draw a square quickly on the cardboard.

Images formed by Two Inclined Mirrors.

Experiment. Set up two strips of mirror so that they make an angle of 90° (fig. 137). Place a pin at any convenient point

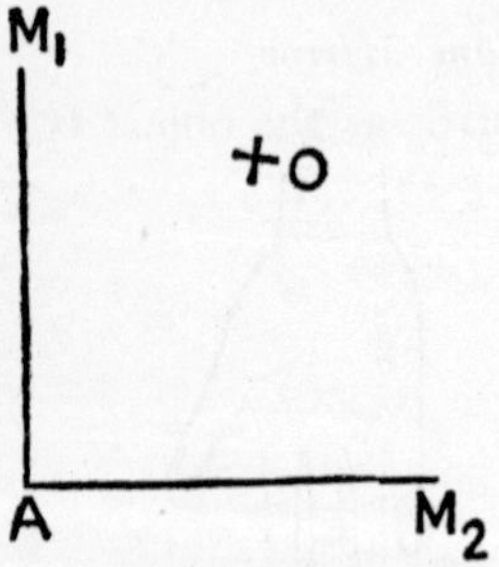

FIG. 137.

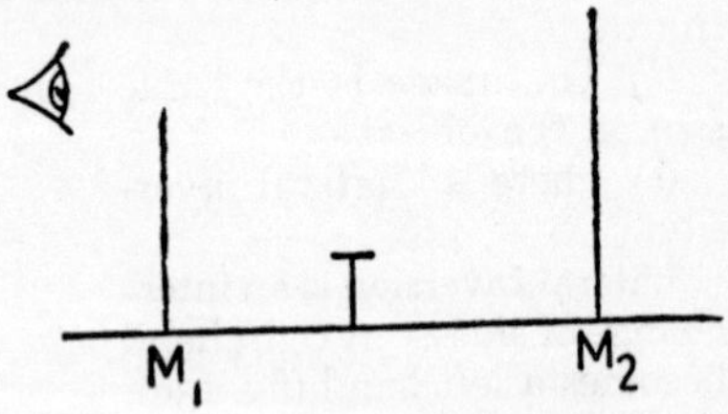

FIG. 138.

O. How many images can you see? Using a long pin, find their positions by parallax. With centre A and radius AO draw a circle. Are the images on the circumference of this circle? Repeat the experiment with an angle of 60°.

Set up the mirrors at 45° and count the images without finding their exact positions. Do the same for 30°.

Experiment. Obtain two small wall mirrors such as can be purchased at a sixpenny bazaar. Set them up parallel to one another, one with the *length* vertical, the other with the *breadth* vertical. Put a pin or other small object between them. Place the eye in the position shown (fig. 138) and count the images. The experiment is a little more interesting if the pin is replaced by a couple of toy animals, say cows.

The results of this and the preceding experiment should agree with the following table:

Angle		*Images + Object*
90°	. . .	$\frac{360}{90} = 4$
60°	. . .	$\frac{360}{60} = 6$
45°	. . .	$\frac{360}{45} = 8$
30°	. . .	$\frac{360}{30} = 12$
0°	. . .	$\frac{360}{0} = \infty$

Exercise. To find geometrically the positions of the images formed by two inclined mirrors, and to draw the rays by which an eye sees an image after two reflections.

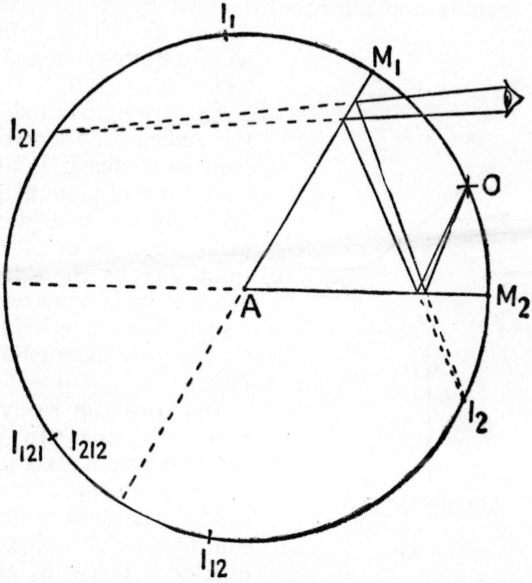

FIG. 139.

Let M_1 and M_2 be two mirrors inclined at 60° with an object at O (fig. 139). With centre A and radius AO describe a circle. Remembering that the perpendicular distance from the object to the mirror is equal to the perpendicular distance from the image to the mirror, it is easy to mark the images I_1, I_{12}, I_{121}. Then mark the images I_2, I_{21}, I_{212}.

You will notice that we continue until the image is behind both mirrors. What do you observe about the images I_{121} and I_{212}?

The second part of the exercise will be easily understood from the figure.

Exercise. Work out the images formed by two parallel mirrors, and draw the rays by which the eye sees an image after two or three reflections.

Some Simple Optical Illusions.

"*Burnt at the Stake.*" This is an interesting stage trick in which a man is apparently surrounded by flames and yet is uninjured. The explanation will be quite obvious from fig. 140.

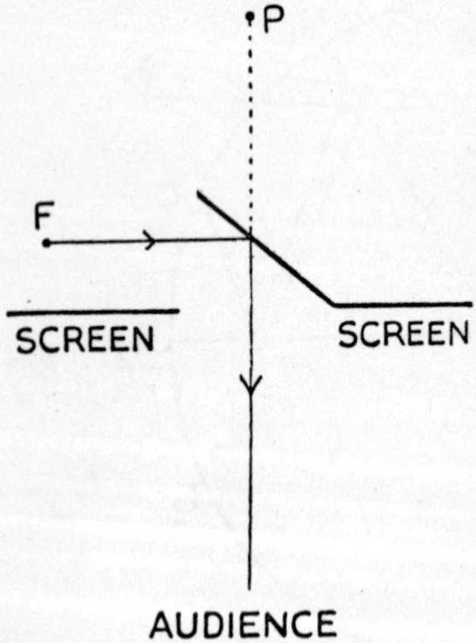

Fig. 140.

The fire is at F, hidden from the audience by a screen; the man to be burnt is at P. A large sheet of plate glass is set vertically on its edge so as to make an angle of 45° with the front edge of the stage. The effect is made more realistic by keeping the stage lighting dim in the neighbourhood of the victim.

The trick can easily be imitated at home. In place of the man put a glass of water, instead of the fire about 2 in. of candle; the sheet of plate glass can be an old photographic quarter-plate with the film washed off, and a couple of pieces of cardboard will serve as screens. It will then be quite easy to convey the impression that a *candle is burning in a glass of water*.

Pepper's Ghost. This is an illusion which was very popular in the latter half of the nineteenth century. It was exhibited by John Henry Pepper (1821–1900). A "ghost" appeared on the stage and mixed freely with the actors.

There are at least two ways of producing the effect. Thus in fig. 140 an actor can be placed at F and strongly illuminated, while the actors at P are in dim light.

Another good method is that illustrated in fig. 141. G is a large sheet of plate glass placed at an angle of 45° with the main stage S_1. M is a plane mirror placed at 45° with the sub-stage

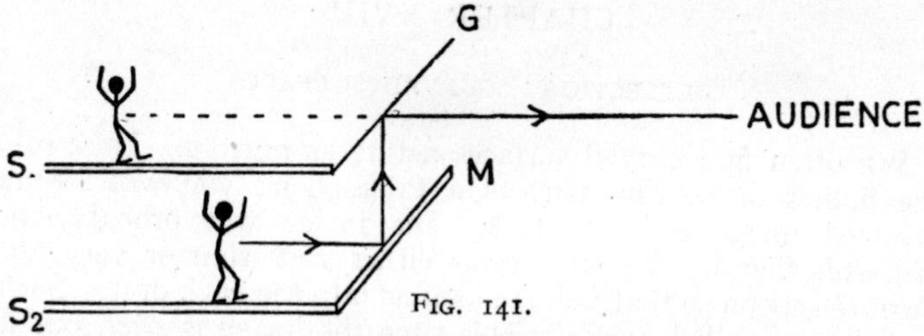

FIG. 141.

S_2. The actor on the sub-stage is strongly illuminated from the side. His "ghost" appears on the main stage. It will be readily understood that the actors can walk through the "ghost" and vice versa.

Why is the "ghost" farther away from the audience than the actor on the sub-stage?

QUESTIONS

1. Assuming that the angle of incidence is equal to the angle of reflection, prove by geometry that in fig. 131, p. 174, $\angle CBC_1$ is twice $\angle MBM_1$.

2. Explain how two parallel mirrors fixed in a long tube would enable a small boy to see a football match over the heads of the people in front of him. (*Hint:* Study fig. 141, above.)

3. Draw the rays by which an eye sees an image of the fourth order (*e.g.* I_{1212}) in parallel mirrors.

4. State the laws of reflection of light.

A man stands in front of a looking-glass of the same height as himself. Show that he only requires one-half of the mirror in order to see a full-length image of himself; illustrate your answer by a diagram. (O. and C.)

5. How would you arrange two plane mirrors so that you could see the back of your head? Show on a diagram the path of the light to the eye. (C.W.B. part question.)

CHAPTER XVIII

REFLECTION: CURVED SURFACES

WE often find curved surfaces acting as mirrors. Look into the hollow or con*cave* part of a tablespoon; you will see an inverted image of your face. The image will probably be *distorted*, that is, the face seems either very thin or very fat. Turn the spoon so that you are looking into the back of it. Such a surface is called *convex*. This time the image is *erect*, but it is probably again distorted.

In order that there shall be no distortion, the curved surface must be part of a sphere. In other words, it must be a spherical mirror. A good example of a spherical convex mirror is that seen on motor vehicles. Such a mirror gives an image of quite a large area behind the vehicle. Occasionally the mirror in a lady's vanity bag is of the convex variety for a similar reason.

You will undoubtedly have in your laboratory spherical mirrors of the concave and convex kinds. Hold a convex mirror at arm's length and gradually bring it closer to you. The image is always erect and always diminished.

Repeat with a concave mirror having a pronounced curvature. The image is at first magnified and inverted, then there is a blur and finally you get a magnified erect image of your face.

Let us see if we can use the two laws of reflection and arrive at a satisfactory explanation of the peculiarities of these mirrors.

The Concave Mirror. With centre C and radius CP draw an arc to represent the section of a concave mirror (fig. 142). CP is called the *radius of curvature,* and if P is at the middle of the arc, then CP may also be called the *principal axis* of the mirror while P is the *pole.*

Consider any ray OA travelling close to, and parallel to, the principal axis, and striking the mirror at A. Now a spherical mirror may be regarded as made up of a large number of tiny plane mirrors. A small length of the tangent at A will represent the section of one of these tiny mirrors. But we know from geometry that the radius of a circle is perpendicular to the tangent. Therefore CA is the normal and the reflected ray will be AF.

Now $\angle OAC = \angle FAC$ . . Laws of Reflection

but $\angle OAC = \angle FCA$ . . Alternate angles

$\therefore \angle FAC = \angle FCA$

$\therefore FA = FC$

but OA is *close* to CP

$\therefore FA = FP$

$\therefore FC = FP.$

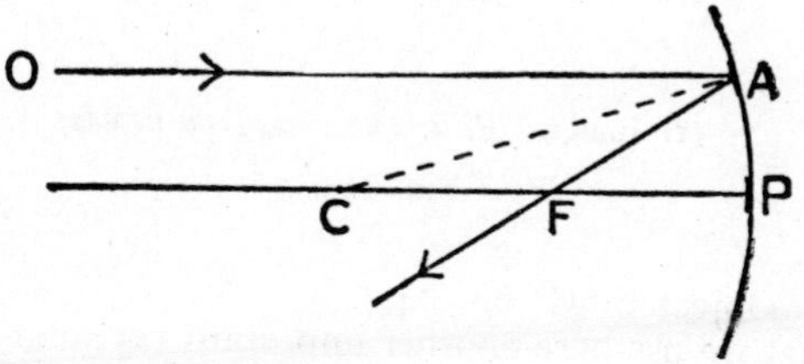

FIG. 142.

All rays travelling close to and parallel to CP will after reflection pass through this point F, which is therefore called the *principal focus* of the mirror. Thus **the principal focus of a concave mirror is that point on the principal axis to which a ray is reflected after travelling close to and parallel to the principal axis.**

The distance PF is called the focal length of the mirror and, as shown above, it is equal to half the radius of curvature or $2f = r$.

We are now able to show that there are five distinct effects obtainable with a concave mirror depending on where the object is placed with reference to the points C and F.

Case (1). Object beyond C.

Notice that rays from the object OB, which pass through C, return along the same path. Why?

From our diagram (fig. 143) it appears that the image IM is formed in mid-air. This is really so, and the image may be put on to a screen of thick white paper or cardboard. Try this, using as object, a candle, an electric lamp or a chimney on the skyline. Such an image is described as *real*, while that formed by a plane mirror is called *virtual*. Rays of light actually pass through a real image while they only *appear* to come from a virtual image. A real image is in front of the mirror and can be obtained on a screen. A virtual image is behind the mirror and cannot be put on a screen.

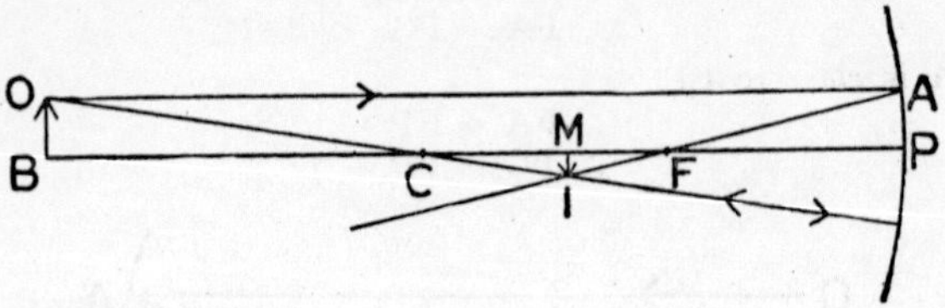

(1) Image: *Real, Inverted, Diminished.*

FIG. 143.

Case (2). Object at C (fig. 144).

Note that we use here another important ray, namely, the one which travels from the top of the object to the pole of the mirror. The principal axis is then the normal and the angle of incidence FPO is equal to the angle of reflection FPI. We may also use the ray which travels from the top of the object through F. How would it travel after reflection?

Case (3). Object between C and F (fig. 145).

Case (4). Object at F (fig. 146).

Case (5). Object between F and P (fig. 147).

Here the rays do not meet in front of the mirror but, as in the case of the plane mirror, *appear* to come from behind the mirror. The image is therefore *virtual*.

Note that in Cases (1) and (3) image and object have changed places. In such cases the points B and M are called *conjugate foci*. **Conjugate foci are two points such that an object placed at either of them forms an image at the other.**

It is worth noticing that we can illustrate all five cases by using the basic or fundamental diagram of fig. 142, p. 183, and rotating a ruler or a piece of string round the point C. Try this. One fact of great importance will be discovered in this way—as

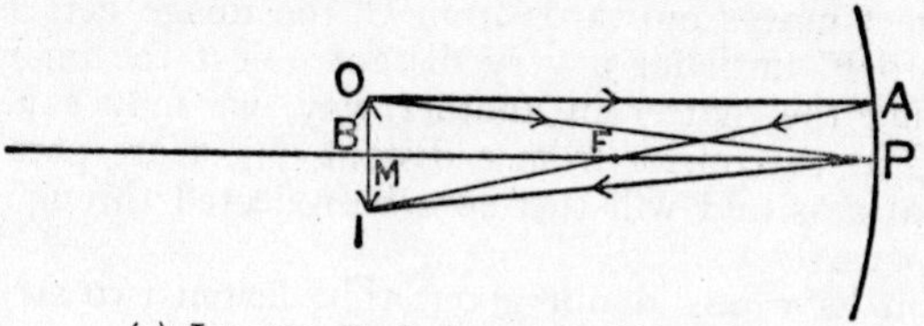

(2) Image : *Real, Inverted, Same size.*

FIG. 144.

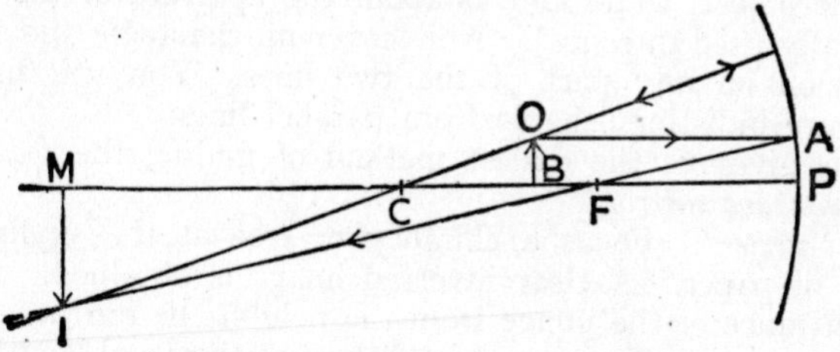

(3) Image : *Real, Inverted, Magnified.*

FIG. 145.

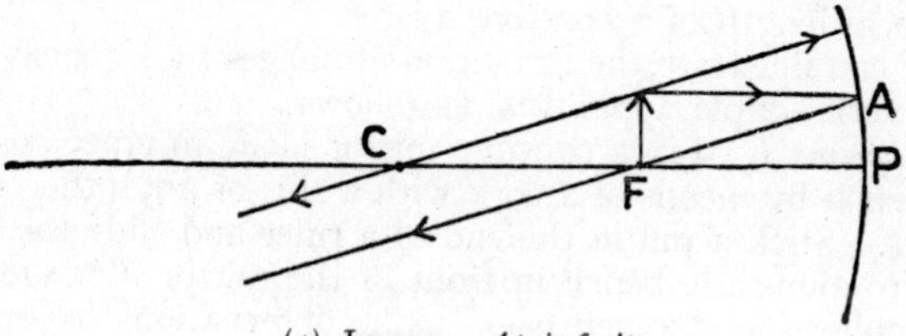

(4) Image : *At infinity.*

FIG. 146.

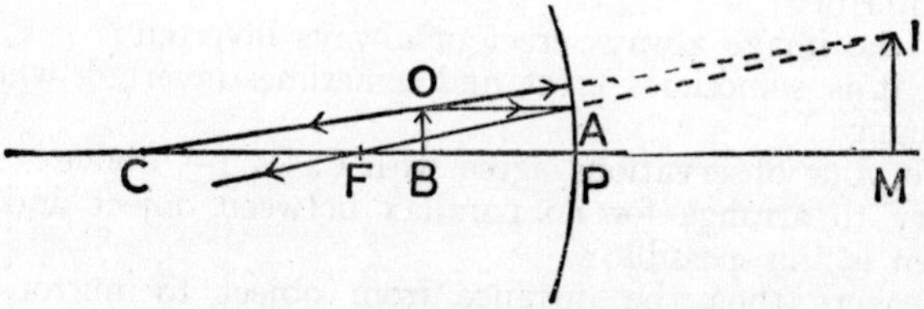

(5) Image : *Virtual, Erect, Magnified.*

FIG. 147.

the object moves outwards from C, the image gets nearer and nearer to F, until for a very distant object the image is *at F*.

Putting the matter in another way, we may say that rays arriving at the mirror from a distant object are parallel to the principal axis and will therefore be reflected through the principal focus.

If you have any doubt about this, fasten two strings about 30 ft. long to a nail in the wall, and get an assistant to hold the free ends about 2 in. apart. The nail represents a point on the distant object, while 2 in. is about the aperture of the mirrors generally used in school. Now cover up the angle and fix your attention on any part of the two lines. You will find that they are indistinguishable from parallel lines.

This gives us the easiest method of finding the *focal length of a concave mirror*.

Experiment. Focus a chimney or tree at the skyline on a sheet of paper. A clear inverted image is obtained. Measure the distance of the image from the pole of the mirror. Repeat several times. The average result gives the focal length of the mirror.

This is often described as the *distant object method* of finding the focal length of a concave mirror.

We can illustrate the formation of images by a concave mirror with very simple apparatus, as follows:

Experiment. Fix a concave mirror M in an erect position on the bench by means of a cork with a slit, or any other available holder. Stick a pin in the end of a ruler and slide the latter to and fro along the bench in front of the mirror (fig. 148).

Keeping the eye well back, make observations to answer the following questions:

How does the size of the image alter as the pin recedes from the mirror?

Is the image always erect or always inverted?

If it is sometimes erect and sometimes inverted, when does it change?

Do your observations agree with Cases 1–5 above?

Try to arrange for no parallax between object and image. When is this possible?

Measure then the distance from object to mirror. What name do you give to this distance?

You will find that in certain positions of the object pin, it is an advantage to bring up a piece of cardboard C to a point just below the eye. This makes the image pin clearly visible against a white background.

Our investigations have shown that in certain cases the image is formed somewhere in the air in front of the mirror. It will

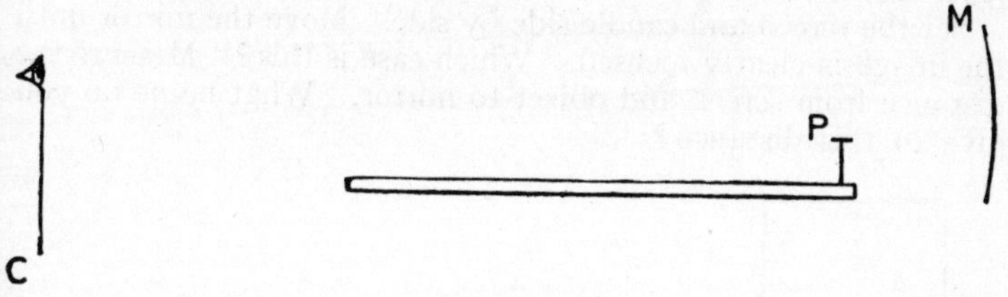

FIG. 148.

be more convincing if we can focus the image on a screen. For this purpose we must use a well-lighted object. A short candle-end is generally available and this will serve quite well.

Experiment. Find the focal length of a concave mirror by the distant object method, and then set it up on the bench so that it faces the window. Put a lighted candle-end on the bench

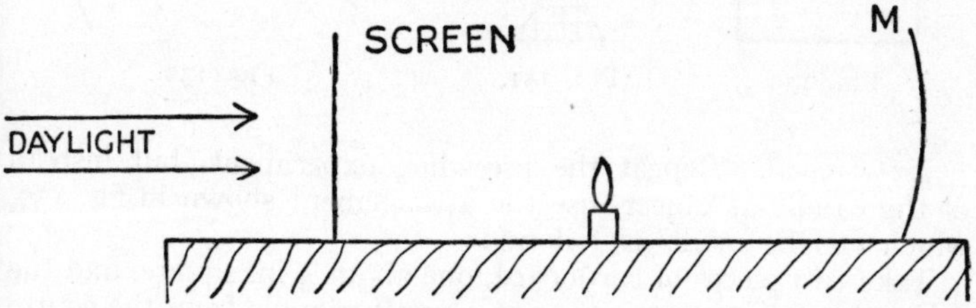

FIG. 149.

in front of it and a cardboard screen with its back to the window (fig. 149). In this way the confusing effect of the sunlight will be reduced to a minimum.

If the focal length is, say, 4 in., set the candle at a distance of 6 in. from the mirror. Which case is this? Where will you search for the image? To get the image on the screen you will probably have to tilt the mirror gently forwards, backwards or sideways. When the image is clearly focused on the screen, measure its distance from the mirror.

Place the candle 10 in. from the mirror. Which case is this? Where will you search for the image? When found, measure the distance as before. Keep the numerical observations recorded in this experiment. They will be useful later, p. 192.

Set the screen and candle side by side. Move the mirror until the image is clearly focused. Which case is this? Measure the distance from screen and object to mirror. What name do you give to this distance?

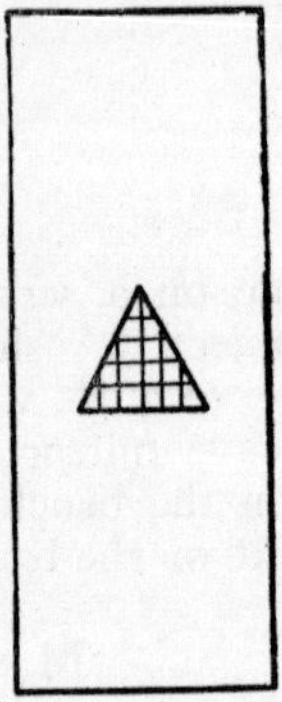

FIG. 150.

FIG. 151.

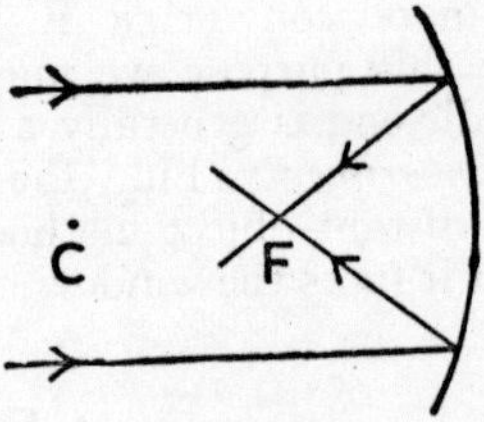

FIG. 152.

Experiment. Repeat the preceding experiment, but instead of the candle as object, use the arrangement shown in fig. 150, which can be made as follows:

Take two pieces of cardboard, one about 4 in. square, and the other about 4 in. × 10 in. Cut a small triangle from the centre of each. Stick them together with a piece of gauze between to cover the hole. Illuminate the hole with an electric lamp.

Case (2) will be specially striking, for the image and object can be made to touch at their vertices (fig. 151).

In Case (1) very accurate adjustment is possible.

Case (3) can also be illustrated if the lamp is shaded on one side or if a cardboard box is made in which the hole and gauze form a window.

Experiment. Set up the apparatus shown on page 172, but

have *two* slits in the cardboard about an inch apart. Hold a concave mirror vertically across the beams. It will be readily seen that rays, close to and parallel to the principal axis, cross at the focus after reflection (fig. 152).

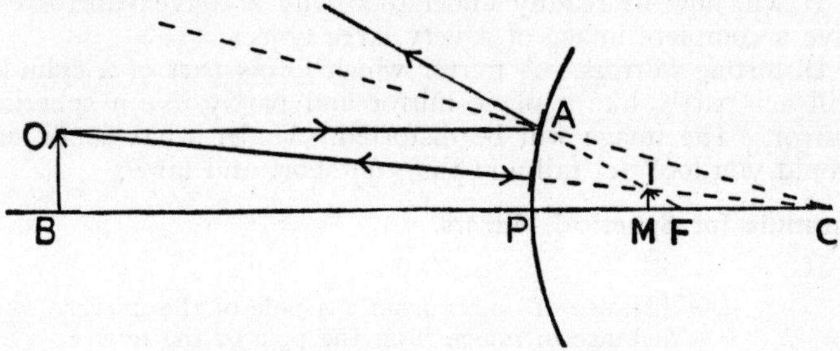

Image: *Virtual, Erect, Diminished.*
FIG. 153.

The Convex Mirror. Let us now use the laws of reflection in an attempt to explain why the convex mirrors used on motor-cars and cycles always give an erect diminished image.

As before, draw an arc to represent the section of the mirror (fig. 153). Consider a small object situated at OB. The ray

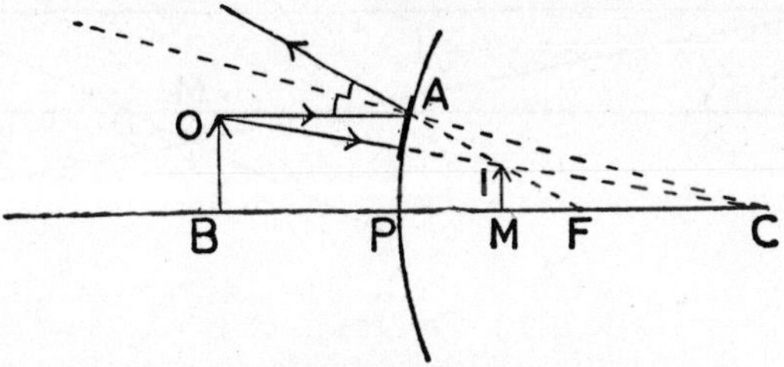

Image: *Virtual, Erect, Diminished.*
FIG. 154.

OA travelling close to and parallel to the principal axis will be reflected in such a way that it appears to be coming from F. CA will be the normal.

A ray travelling from O towards C, the centre of curvature, will be reflected back along its own path and will appear to be coming from C.

Thus rays from OB will, after reflection, *seem* to be coming from an image IM. This image is *virtual*, erect and diminished. Fig. 154 shows that the image becomes larger as the object approaches the mirror.

It will now be readily understood why a convex mirror can give a complete image of a very large object.

Distorting Mirrors. A mirror which forms part of a cylinder will act partly like a plane mirror and partly like a spherical mirror. The image will be distorted. Under what conditions would you look (*a*) tall and thin, (*b*) short and fat ?

Formula for Spherical Mirrors.

If

u = distance of object from the pole of the mirror
v = distance of image from the pole of the mirror
f = focal length of the mirror

then
$$\frac{1}{v} + \frac{1}{u} = \frac{1}{f}.$$

Proof for Concave Mirror.

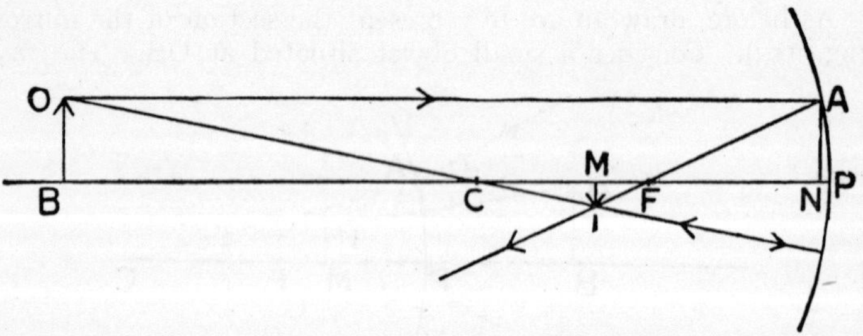

FIG. 155.

In fig. 155 OB represents the object and IM the image.
$\triangle$s OBC and IMC are *similar*

$$\therefore \frac{OB}{IM} = \frac{BC}{MC}$$

$\triangle$s ANF and IMF are similar

$$\therefore \frac{AN}{IM} = \frac{NF}{MF}$$

but OB = AN, $\therefore \frac{BC}{MC} = \frac{NF}{MF}$

but for mirrors of small aperture NF = PF*

$$\therefore \frac{BC}{MC} = \frac{PF}{MF}$$

$$\therefore \frac{u - 2f}{2f - v} = \frac{f}{v - f}$$

Cross multiply and divide by *uvf*

then $$\frac{1}{v} + \frac{1}{u} = \frac{1}{f}$$

The formula $\frac{1}{v} + \frac{1}{u} = \frac{1}{f}$ can also be proved to hold good for convex mirrors. When using this formula you must remember that

(*a*) distances are always measured from the mirror;
(*b*) distances measured *with* the incident light are positive;
(*c*) distances measured *against* the incident light are negative.

Thus the focal length of a concave mirror is negative, while the focal length of a convex mirror is positive.

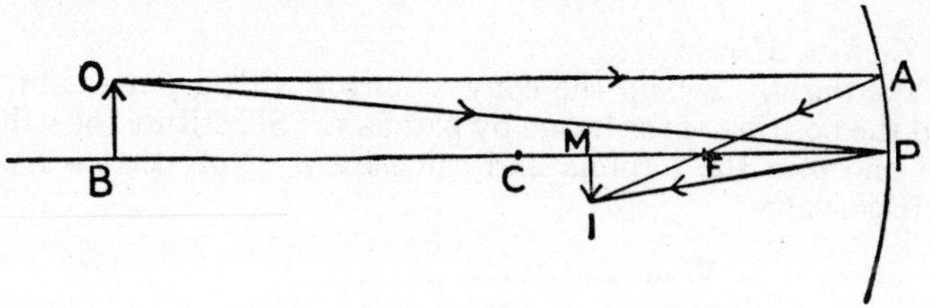

FIG. 156.

Size of image. Use fig. 156 to prove that

$$\frac{\text{Size of image}}{\text{Size of object}} = \frac{v}{u}$$

This result also applies to convex mirrors.

* Beginners are inclined to treat this step with suspicion, but if you draw one of the school mirrors with the aperture and radius "life size," you will find that the suspicion is quite unfounded; our mirror always has a small aperture, in other words, the mirror is never more than a very small fraction of its sphere, but our diagrams are generally exaggerated

To find the Focal Length of a Spherical Mirror.

A. *Concave Mirror.*

1. The Distant Object Method. See p. 186.

2. Coincident Object and Image Method.

When object and image are at the same distance from the mirror, both are situated at the centre of curvature. This method therefore gives r the radius of curvature which of course equals $2f$. We met this method in the experiments on pages 187 and 188.

3. The Formula Method.

Experiment. Use the numerical observations obtained in the experiment with the candle and concave mirror, p. 188. Substitute these values of u and v in the formula for spherical mirrors and calculate f. Note that u has a negative value.

Fix up a concave mirror in a holder on the bench. Stick a pin in a cork or ruler and place it in front of the mirror in such a position that an erect image is seen. Where will you search for this image? Find its position by parallax, using a long glass-headed pin. What is the sign of v in this case? Substitute the values of u and v in the formula. Repeat for different positions of the object pin and obtain an average value for f.

B. *Convex Mirror.*

Experiment. Set up the convex mirror with a pin as object. Find the position of the image by parallax. Substitute the values of u and v in the formula and calculate f. Note that u has a negative value.

The Effect of a Wide Aperture.

Experiment. On a sheet of graph paper draw a large semicircle to represent a concave mirror of wide aperture (fig. 157). From a point X on the axis distant about two and a half radii, draw a number of straight lines to represent incident rays travelling to the mirror from a point source of light. From C draw the normals (in dotted lines to prevent confusion). Find the reflected rays by applying the second law of reflection. It is very important to use the extreme ray XA.

You will find that the reflected rays do not come to a focus but that neighbouring rays intersect at points situated on a well-defined curve. This curve repeats itself on the other side of the axis. It is called a *caustic curve.* You will immediately recognize here an old acquaintance, for caustic curves are frequently seen on cups of tea and glasses of milk.

If now we confine our attention to the rays striking the small portion of mirror just round the pole, we see that the reflected rays all pass through Y, the point where the two branches of the caustic curve meet. Y is thus the image of X. In fact, X and Y are conjugate foci, p. 184.

It will now be readily seen that the wide aperture causes a *straying away* of some of the reflected rays from the true focus.

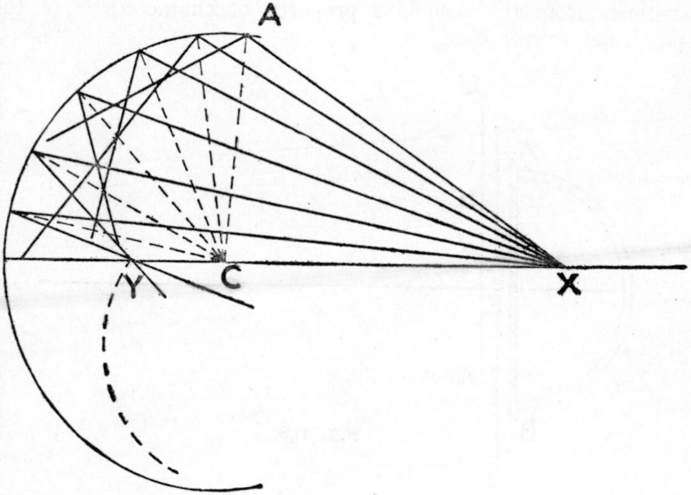

FIG. 157.

They form a number of foci on the caustic curve. We always try to invent a new word to take the place of two or more. So here scientists call this straying away—" aberration," and since we are dealing with a spherical mirror, it is referred to as " spherical aberration." Compare " mental aberration " which means a straying away of *thoughts* from the usual paths.

Experiment. Apply the directions of the last exercise to the case where the incident rays are parallel to the principal axis of the mirror.

A caustic curve will again be formed, the branches intersecting at the principal focus of the mirror, *i.e.* the point midway between pole and centre of curvature.

But why do we always refer to this point as the *principal* focus? The answer is that this is the focus when the object is at infinity. In the last exercise the point Y was a focus when the object was at X and the point X would be a focus if the object were at Y. If the point X were moved farther away from the mirror, its conjugate focus Y would move towards the mirror. When X reaches infinity where will Y be? At the principal focus. The principal focus is a fixed point, and its distance from the pole is a property or characteristic of the particular mirror used.

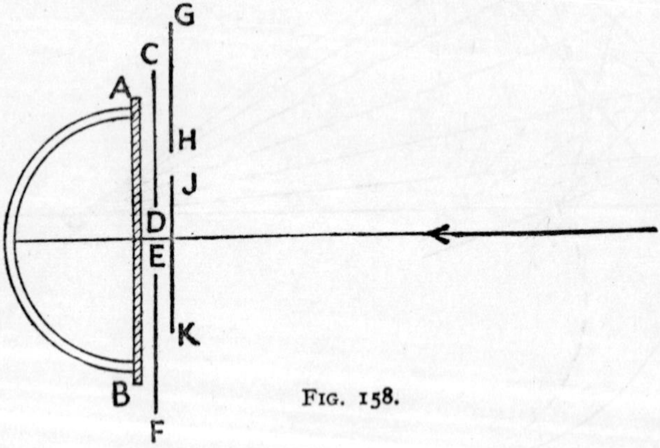

FIG. 158.

If you found the two previous exercises tedious, you will the more readily appreciate the experimental illustrations of them to which we shall now proceed.

Experiment. Take a concave cylindrical mirror strip of about 3 in. radius and set it up on a piece of drawing paper. Mark the outline of the mirror and draw its principal axis. Fix up a gas-filled lamp in a burette stand with its horse-shoe filament *in line* with the principal axis, a few inches above the paper and about 18 in. away from the mirror. A well-defined caustic curve will be obtained.

Let us now follow a suggestion due to Mr. F. A. Meier of Rugby (*School Science Review*, Sept., 1926, p. 58) and set up a comb, teeth downwards in the position AB (fig. 158). The comb should have *wide* and *uniform* spacing. The incident light is thus divided into "rays" and the construction of a caustic curve will be made apparent.

Place two pieces of cardboard in positions CD and EF, and move them outwards and inwards so as to make a mirror of varying aperture. Next place the pieces of cardboard in positions GH and JK so that the intersection of two neighbouring "rays" can be observed.

On moving the lamp some distance away, the "rays" become nearly parallel, and the second exercise can be illustrated.

The experiment is best done in a darkened room, but this is not absolutely essential provided the mirror is set up with its back to the daylight and screened by means of a large book or otherwise.

The Paraboloidal Mirror. We have seen that a spherical mirror of wide aperture will not reflect, to a single-point focus, all rays parallel to its principal axis.

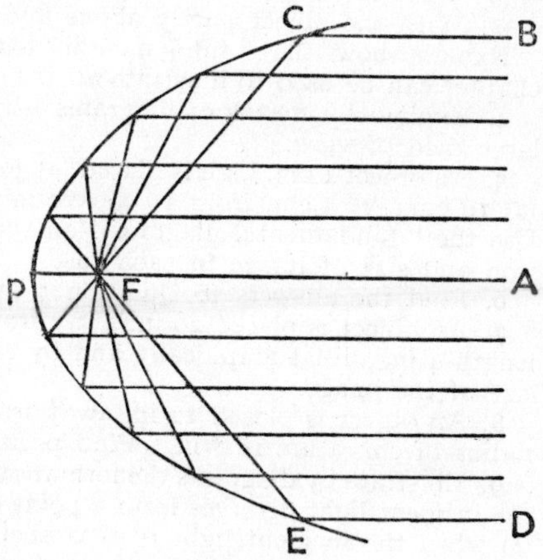

FIG. 159.

There is, however, a mirror capable of doing this. Its surface is not part of a sphere, nor is its section a circular arc. It is called the *paraboloidal* mirror, and its section is a *parabola* (fig. 159).

All rays parallel to AFP, even extreme ones like BC, DE, will, after reflection, pass through the focus F.

Now suppose that instead of sending light on to the mirror from a distance, we put a small source of light at F. What will be the result? The mirror will send out a parallel beam of light. Such paraboloidal mirrors are used as reflectors in searchlights and lamps for cycles and motors.

QUESTIONS

N.B.—In graphical work on spherical mirrors, a more accurate result is obtained if the mirror is represented by a straight line instead of a curve.

1. Explain *real image, virtual image, principal focus, conjugate foci, centre of curvature, pole.*

2. What are the four most important rays to consider when dealing with concave mirrors?

3. Draw five diagrams illustrating the properties of a concave mirror.

(*a*) With the object standing on the principal axis.

(*b*) With the object below but touching the principal axis.

(*c*) With the object partly above and partly below.

Explain how the "fundamental diagram" mentioned in the chapter can be used to illustrate all the cases.

4. Explain by means of diagrams why a convex mirror gives a large field of view.

5. An object 1 cm. high is placed (*a*) 30 cm., (*b*) 20 cm., (*c*) 15 cm., (*d*) 10 cm., (*e*) 5 cm. from a concave mirror of focal length 10 cm. Use the "fundamental diagram" on squared paper and find position and size of image in each case.

6. Find the answers to Question 5 by calculation.

7. An object is placed 20 in. away from a convex mirror of focal length 4 in. Find graphically and by calculation the position and size of the image.

8. An object is placed 12 in. away from a concave mirror whose radius of curvature is 8 in. Find position and size of the image.

9. Illustrate by diagrams the formation of a caustic curve (*a*) when the incident light diverges from a point on the axis of the reflector, (*b*) when the incident light is a parallel beam.

10. An object 1 cm. high is placed in front of a concave mirror whose focal length is 6 cm. The image is real and twice as large as the object. Find graphically and by calculation the position of the object.

11. A concave mirror has a focal length of 18 in. Where would you place an object so as to obtain a magnification of 3 when the image is (*a*) real, (*b*) virtual?

12. How would you arrange a concave mirror and a candle or other source of light in order to look into a person's throat?

13. A convex mirror of focal length 8 in. forms an image 6 in. away from the mirror. Where is the object?

14. An object of height 2 cm. is placed at a distance of 15 cm. from a concave mirror, and the image is found to be inverted and 8 cm. in height. What is the radius of curvature of the mirror?

(O. and C.)

CHAPTER XIX

REFRACTION

In the last two chapters we studied cases where rays of light meet a new medium and are reflected or "bent back."

In the present chapter we shall consider what happens when the light strikes a new medium and passes into that medium.

Experiment. Set up the apparatus described on page 172 and illustrated again here (fig. 160).

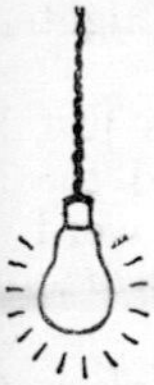

This time it is more essential to have a darkened room for a reason which will appear very soon.

Lay a slab of glass on the cardboard so that the beam of light is perpendicular to one of the faces. Slowly rotate the slab. Note the reflected beam and the emergent beam. Both are naturally weaker than

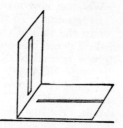

Fig. 160.

the incident beam. This is the reason for darkening the room. Observe, too, that as the angle of incidence increases so the reflected beam increases in strength.

Compare the direction of the incident and emergent beams. Turn the slab into all possible positions so that the various thicknesses may be tried.

It will be found that the beam which gets through the glass is parallel to the incident beam. It is *displaced but not deviated.* The longer the path through glass, the greater is the displacement.

If one of the faces is rubbed on emery cloth until the polish is removed and this ground face is laid on the cardboard, the path of the beam through the glass will easily be seen. The same result is obtained by smearing one of the faces with seccotine or other adhesive and covering that face completely with a sheet of white paper. The layer of adhesive should cover every portion of the glass face. This method has the advantage over grinding, that washing with water will restore the slab to its former condition.

It is also interesting to repeat the above experiment with a rectangular glass cell containing water instead of the glass slab. You may find in your chemical laboratory a red powder called fluorescein. If a little of this is dissolved in dilute caustic soda and added to the water in the glass cell, a peculiar yellowish-green solution will be obtained. The path of the beam of light will then be plainly visible.

This peculiar *bending* of a ray of light which we have just met is called **refraction** and the ray in the glass is called the **refracted ray** (Lat. *frangere,* to break). We use a similar word when we talk of a "fractured limb."

We shall now investigate this bending in another way.

Experiment. To study refraction with pins and a slab of glass.

Lay the slab of glass in the middle of a sheet of paper and make a pencil line round it. Remove the glass and at a point O draw a normal NON_1 to the face of the slab (fig. 161). Make the angle NOA 30°. Replace the glass and fix pins vertically at O and A. Looking through the opposite face of the glass, stick pins B and C apparently in line with the first pair. Produce the line BC to meet the slab at P. Join OP and draw the other normal MPM_1.

You will notice that the ray which leaves the glass is parallel to the ray which entered the glass. In other words, **the emergent ray is parallel to the incident ray.** Notice that each of these two rays makes the same angle with its own normal. This angle is called the angle of incidence $\underline{|i}$. Simple geometry shows that $\underline{|M_1PO} = \underline{|N_1OP}$. Each of these is called the angle of refraction $\underline{|r}$. We have here a good example of the fact that **a ray of light is reversible.**

Repeat the experiment using 45° and 60° for the angle of

incidence. In all three cases measure the displacement. How does it vary?

Make a table of $\angle i$ and $\angle r$. Can you see any relation between $\angle i$ and $\angle r$? It will not be surprising if you do not, for there is no *simple* relation and for many centuries scientists failed to find any relation at all.

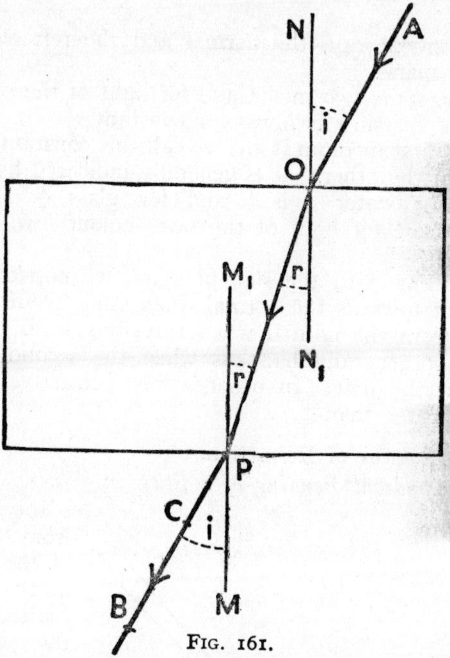

FIG. 161.

Snell's Law. The problem was finally solved by Willebrordus Snellius van Royen (1591–1626). Snell, as he is generally called in England, was Professor of Physics and Mathematics at Leyden University.

Take your table of $\angle i$ and $\angle r$ and find from mathematical tables the *sine* of each angle. Divide sin i by sin r.

$$\frac{\sin i}{\sin r} \textit{ should be a constant.}$$

This was Snell's discovery and is now known all over the world as Snell's Law.

Others had merely sought for a relation between the angles when expressed in *degrees*; only Snell thought of using the *sines* of the angles.

We may now state the **Laws of Refraction.** The first is similar to the first law of reflection and the second is simply Snell's Law.

1. The incident ray, the normal and the refracted ray are in the same plane.

2. For the same two media and for light of the same colour, sin i divided by sin r is always a constant.

When the first medium is air, we call this constant the refractive index of the other. It is generally indicated by the Greek letter μ. For water μ is $\frac{4}{3}$ and for glass $\frac{3}{2}$. The reason for the phrase "for light of the same colour" will be understood later.

When dealing with the slab of glass, we noticed that rays of light bent towards the normal when going from air to glass and away from the normal when travelling from glass to air. This is what generally happens when the second medium is denser than the first. In other words, refractive indices are generally greater than 1.

Some Consequences of Refraction.

(*a*) *The Apparent Bending of a Stick in Water.*

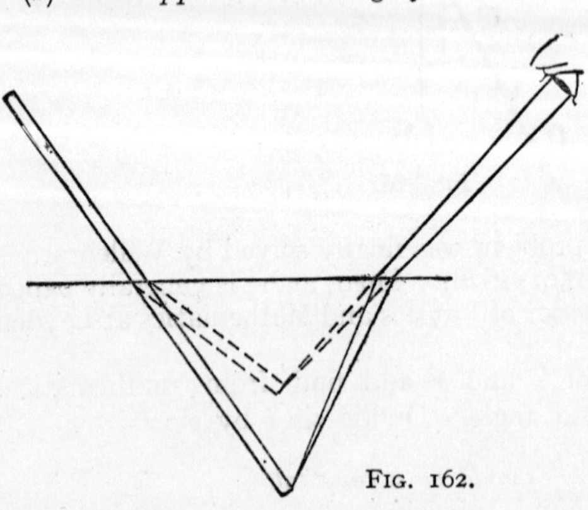

FIG. 162.

Rays of light from the bottom of the stick bend away from the normal on leaving the water. The eye takes no account of this bending. The *stick* therefore appears to be bent at the water surface (fig. 162).

For the same reason it is necessary, when trying to spear fish, to aim below the place where the fish appears to be.

(*b*) *The Coin Experiment.*

In this well-known trick a coin is placed in a cup or basin so that it is just out of sight (fig. 163). When water is poured in, the coin appears to rise into view. This again is caused by the bending of rays of light on leaving the water.

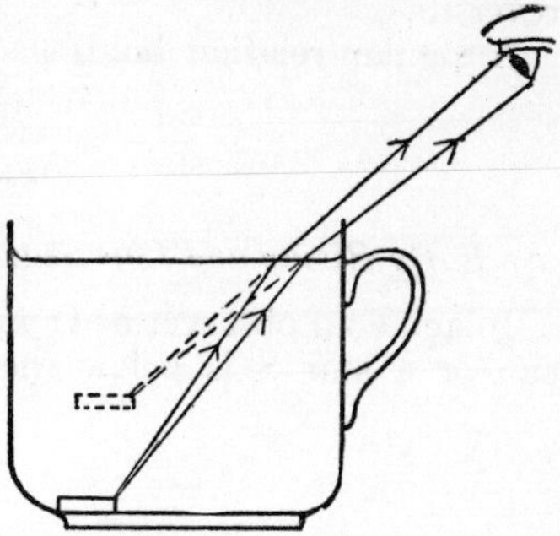

FIG. 163.

(*c*) *Water 4 ft. deep looks 3 ft. deep!*

This is just another way of saying that μ or

$$\frac{\sin i}{\sin r} = \frac{\text{Real depth}}{\text{Apparent depth}}.$$

This fact may easily be proved. *Hint:* First prove that in fig. 164

$$\frac{\sin i}{\sin r} = \frac{AC}{AD}.$$

But an eye looking vertically down on the water could not take in such an oblique ray. In other words, A must be close to B. That is AC = BC (approx.) the real depth, and AD = BD the apparent depth.

Note that the diagram is only drawn with a very oblique ray to make the angles clear. Observe also that although the light is travelling from water to air, it is the angle in the air which is called the angle of "incidence." This is

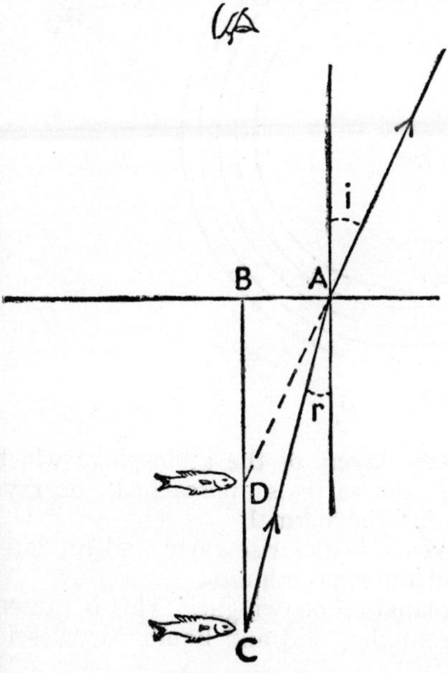

FIG. 164.

quite reasonable when we remember that a ray of light is reversible.

A similar relation holds good for glass and we say μ or

$$\frac{\sin i}{\sin r} = \frac{\text{Real } \textit{thickness}}{\text{Apparent } \textit{thickness}}.$$

(*d*) *Early Rising and Late Setting of the Heavenly Bodies* (fig. 165).

Imagine an observer at O with HH as his horizon. When the sun or a star S is below the horizon, it appears to be at S′

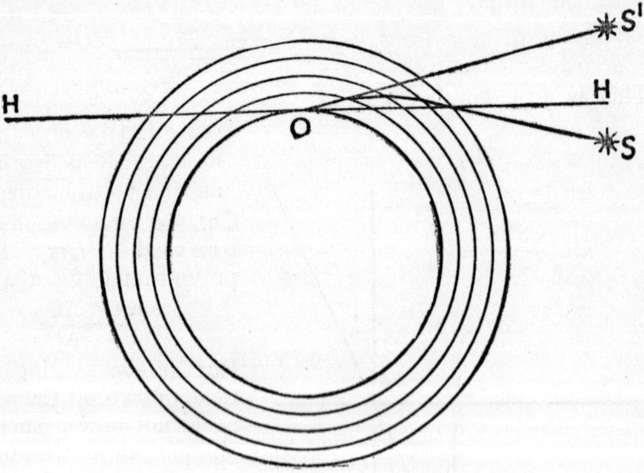

FIG. 165.

because rays from it traverse layers of the atmosphere which gradually become denser as the earth is approached, the rays each time being bent *towards* the normal.

For this reason the heavenly bodies rise early and set late. The day is thus lengthened by some minutes.

The above is not the explanation of twilight. This is caused by reflection of sunlight from the solid and liquid particles in the atmosphere.

Problem. Given the angle of incidence and the refractive index, to find the angle of refraction geometrically.

The problem is a little easier on squared paper. Let the angle of incidence be 60° and the medium water ($\mu = \frac{4}{3}$) Mark off OA = 3 units of length and OB = 4 units (fig. 166). Draw the normal NON_1. Make NOC = 60°. At B erect a perpendicular BI to meet OC produced. With centre O and radius OI draw a circle. From A draw a perpendicular to meet the circle in R.

Then OR is the refracted ray and N_1OR is the angle of refraction.

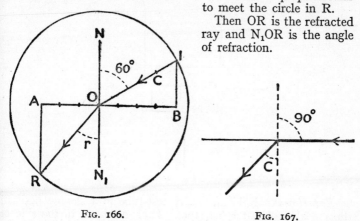

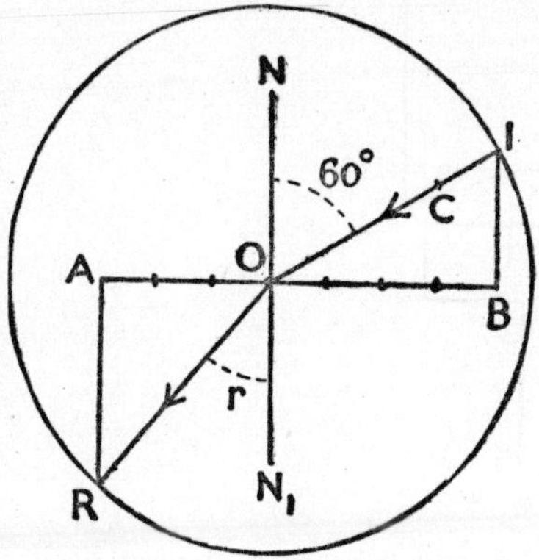

FIG. 166.

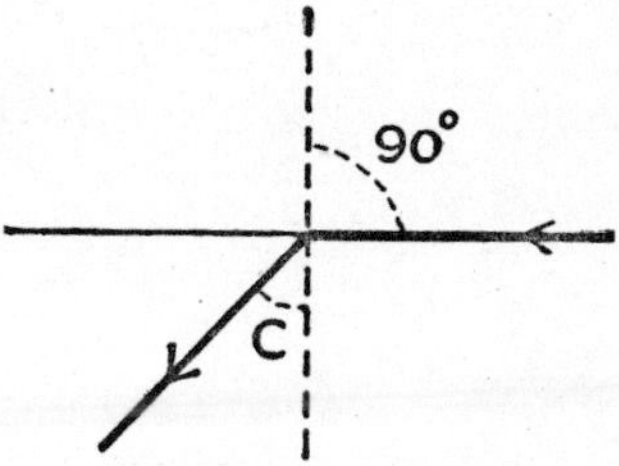

FIG. 167.

The Critical Angle. Repeat the above exercise, using angle of incidence 90° (called "grazing incidence"). The angle of refraction has now its maximum value. Measure it. This maximum angle of refraction is called the critical angle for water (fig. 167).

Repeat the exercise, using $\mu = \frac{3}{2}$ and thus find the critical angle for glass.

Remembering the reversibility of rays of light, let us consider what will happen if the light travels from water to air. If the light strikes the water surface at the critical angle, it will just manage to get out. When the angle increases ever so slightly beyond this there will be no emergent ray—the light is **totally reflected** from the water surface.

To sum up we may say that **when the angle of incidence from air on to a denser medium is nearly 90°, the angle of refraction is called the critical angle for that medium.** The critical angle for water is 49°, for glass 42°.

Illustrations of Total Internal Reflection.

Experiment. Into a beaker put a coin and about half an inch of water. Place the beaker on the edge of a table. When an eye looks in the direction shown in fig. 168, the water surface looks like a plane mirror and the coin is seen by *total reflection.*

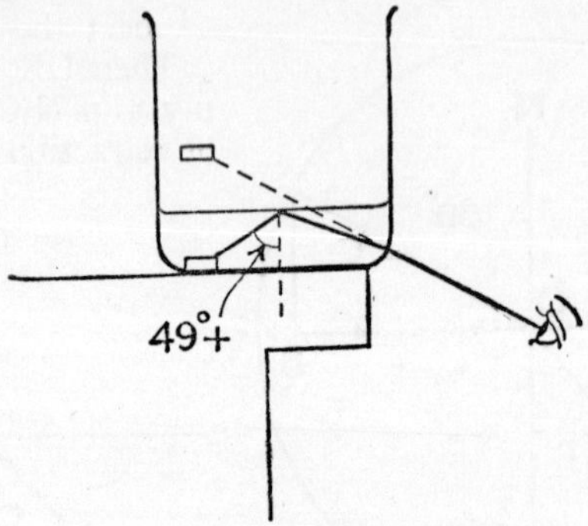

FIG. 168.

Experiment. Hold an empty test-tube in a sloping position in a beaker of water (fig. 169). Look down on to the side of the tube. It looks like a tube of mercury. Write your name on paper with a pen flowing freely. Quickly blot the signature and hold the blotting-paper against the beaker at B. You should be able to read your name by looking down at the sloping tube. Next fill the tube with water and notice the difference.

An interesting variation is as follows: Take two rectangular slips of glass. These may easily be made from an old glass negative with a glass-cutter. On the face of one lay a thin roll of plasticine near the edges. Squeeze the other slip on it so as to enclose a layer of air. Use this in place of the test-tube.

Experiment. Lay an **isosceles right-angled prism** on paper on its triangular base. Fix pins at PP (fig. 170) in front of one of the equal sides. There will be total reflection from the hypotenuse face since the angle of incidence on to it is greater than 42°. The actual path of the light can be shown by sticking a piece of paper on the base and using a "beam" as in previous experiments. Such prisms have many uses in science and at least one in ordinary life; the "skylight" in underground lavatories is frequently made from these prisms and slabs of glass set alternately.

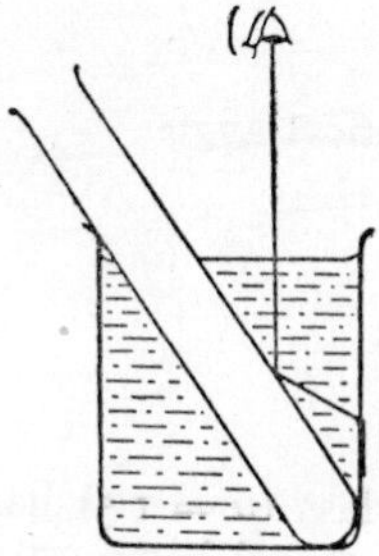

FIG. 169.

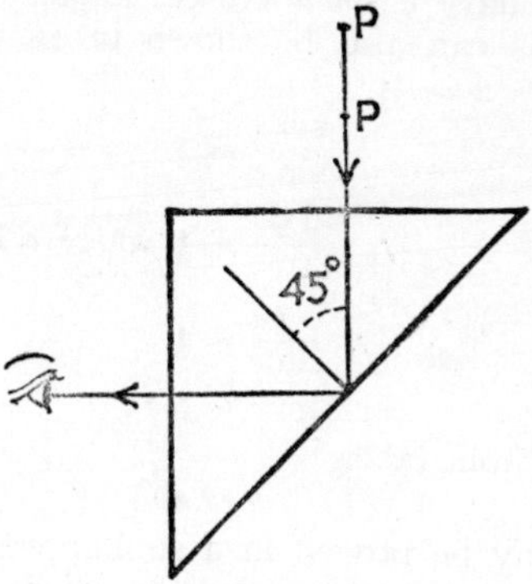

FIG. 170.

When light from an extended object falls on the hypotenuse face, there is total internal reflection at the equal faces and

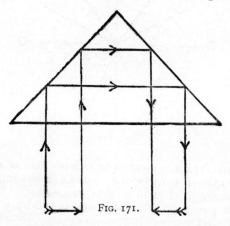

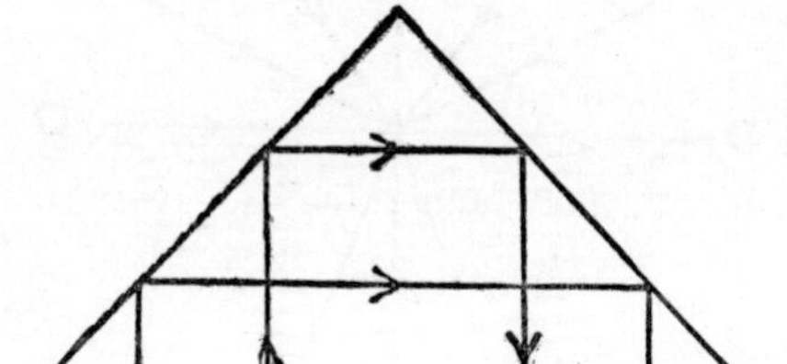

FIG. 171.

the image is "laterally inverted" (fig. 171). This fact is applied in prism binoculars, see p. 236.

The Sparkling of Diamonds.

If you examine figs. 166 and 167 carefully, you will quite easily realize that a substance with a *large* refractive index must have a *small* critical angle.

This can also be shown in another way. Consider air and water ($\mu = \frac{4}{3}$).

$$\frac{\sin i}{\sin r} = \frac{4}{3}$$

$$\therefore \frac{\sin 90}{\sin c} = \frac{4}{3} \text{ where } c \text{ is the critical angle}$$

$$\therefore \frac{1}{\sin c} = \frac{4}{3}$$

$$\therefore \sin c = 0{\cdot}75$$

∴ from tables

$$c = 49°.$$

It may be proved in a similar way that glass ($\mu = 1{\cdot}5$) has a critical angle of 42° and that diamond ($\mu = 2{\cdot}417$) has a critical angle of $24\frac{1}{2}°$.

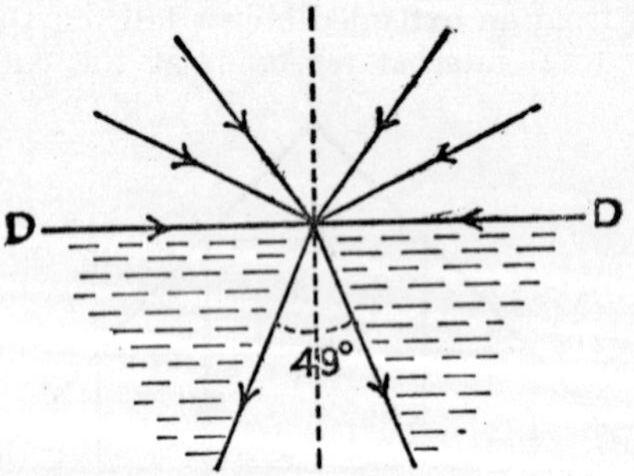

FIG. 172.

Let DD (fig. 172) represent in section one face of a diamond. Rays from 180° on entering the diamond crowd into an angle of 49°. Moreover, when these rays strike another face of the diamond, they only get out if the angle of incidence is between 0° and $24\frac{1}{2}°$; for angles of incidence between $24\frac{1}{2}°$ and 90° they are totally reflected. There is thus only about a one-in-four chance of getting out. At each face where they fail to emerge they are reinforced by another bundle of rays just entering. The result is a powerful beam of light from a few faces while the others look comparatively dark.

The Hot Weather Mirage.

Sometimes the thirsty traveller in the desert is the victim of a cruel delusion; in the distance he sees a palm tree and its reflection in a *pool,* but on approaching nearer, the "pool" disappears!

The explanation will be easily understood from fig. 173. The

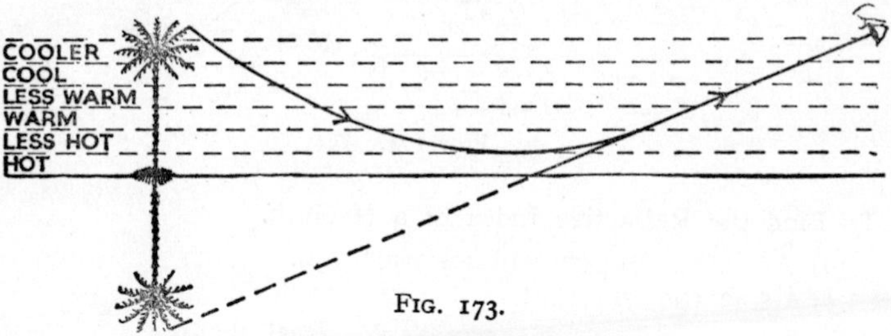

FIG. 173.

air is divided into layers whose density increases upwards. A ray of light from the top of the palm, travelling through the different layers is constantly bent away from the normal until it strikes a layer at an angle greater than the critical angle when it is totally reflected. The eye, as usual, does not allow for this bending and so the illusion is complete.

We often meet the same illusion in our own country on asphalted roads during a hot summer day.

The Cold Weather Mirage.

In polar regions and occasionally in warmer climates, the air above the sea decreases in density *upwards.* The result is that an image of a ship appears in the sky!

The World as seen by a Fish.

From fig. 174 it will be evident that a fish sees objects on the surface of the water apparently crowded into a cone whose slant sides meet at an angle of about 98°. By casting his eye a little beyond this cone, he is able to see objects in the water itself by total internal reflection, even when those objects are hidden by intervening rocks.

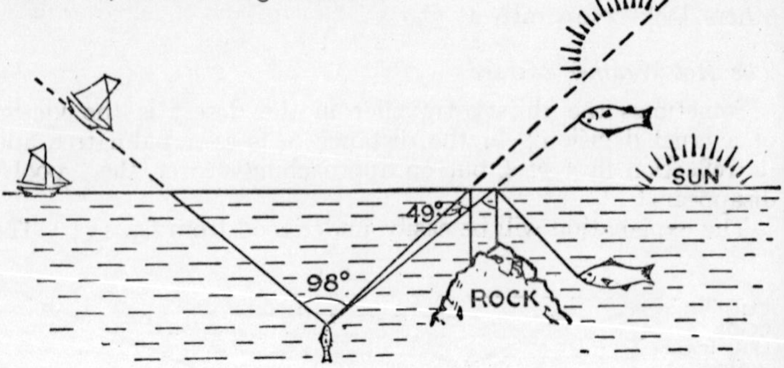

FIG. 174.

To Find the Refractive Index of a Medium.

(*a*) As in the experiment on page 199.

(*b*) Using the fact that

$$\mu = \frac{\text{Real thickness}}{\text{Apparent thickness}} \text{ or } \frac{\text{Real depth}}{\text{Apparent depth}}.$$

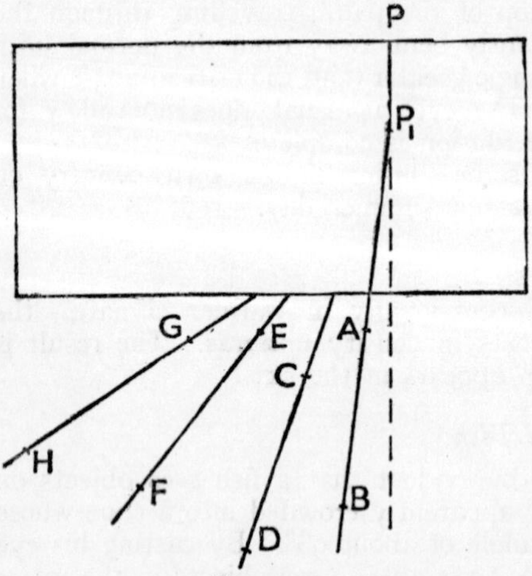

FIG. 175.

Experiment. To find μ for glass.

Place a slab of glass on paper and make a pencil mark round it (fig. 175). Draw a normal to one face. Stick a pin on this normal, behind and touching the glass. *Keeping the eye very close to the normal* put two pins A and B in line with the image P_1. Produce the line through A and B to cut the normal and thus locate P_1.

Measure real thickness and apparent thickness and calculate μ.

It will now be instructive to find the reason for keeping the eye close to the normal. Therefore use a series of more distant rays like CD, EF, GH, etc., until the image disappears.

The image P_1 will now be found to travel along a *caustic curve*. Compare the use of extreme rays in the case of the concave mirror. What is the meaning of the disappearance of the image?

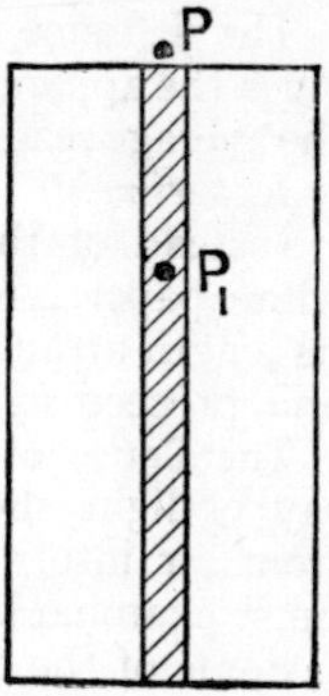

FIG. 176.

Experiment. To find μ for glass by parallax.

Place a pin at the back of the slab as before (fig. 176). Hold another pin on the top of the slab and adjust for no parallax between this pin and the image of the first pin, again keeping the eye close to the normal. The adjustment is made a little more easily if a narrow piece of paper is stuck on the slab. The pin does not then slip on the glass surface. It will readily be understood that the best result will be obtained when the slab is used *lengthwise*. Measure real thickness and apparent thickness as before.

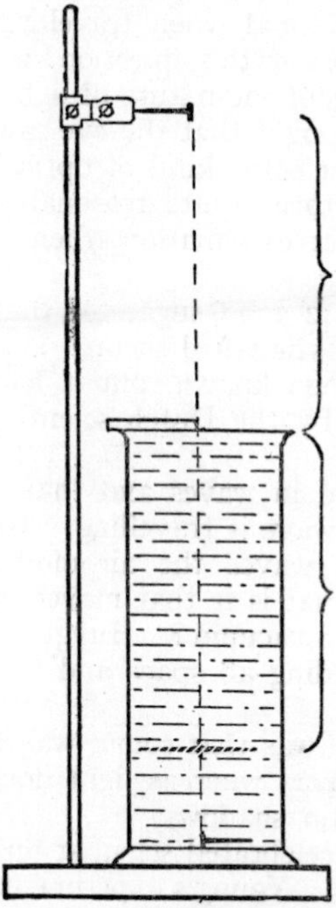
FIG. 177.

Experiment. To find μ for water.

Place a cylinder of water on a piece of white paper. Drop a nib in. Then using a pen against the side of the jar find by the method of parallax the apparent position of the nib. Take several rapid readings of the apparent depth and find the average. Work out μ as before.

Experiment. To find μ for water: the last method improved.

Measure the *real* depth of the gas jar (fig. 177). Place the jar on the base board of a burette stand. Drop a bright pin in and fill to the rim with water. Across the top lay a plane mirror face upwards. Fix a pin in the clamp and arrange for no parallax between the image of this pin and that of the immersed pin.

The distance from the top pin to the back of the mirror then gives the apparent depth. Why? Adjust several times and take the average reading of the apparent depth. Calculate μ as before.

Experiment. To find μ for glass by the preceding method.

Instead of the immersed pin use an ink line on a piece of white paper. Replace the jar of water by a slab of glass with its length arranged vertically. Place the mirror strip in position and proceed as before.

The Cause of Refraction. We have not yet inquired *why* a ray of light should bend towards the normal when travelling from air into a denser medium. To answer this question, we must examine briefly the various theories of the nature of light.

Some of the old Greek philosophers thought that the eye saw objects by sending out either particles or some kind of optical feelers. But one of their number, Aristotle, quite reasonably pointed out that if that were the correct explanation, then it should be possible to see in the dark.

The great scientist Sir Isaac Newton (1642–1727) suggested that the eye *received* particles or "corpuscles" as he called them. This idea agreed fairly well with the facts then known, but it had a rival in a theory first stated in 1678 by the Dutch scientist Huyghens.

Huyghens believed that light travelled in waves and that a ray is simply the direction in which the wave is travelling. He was met with this objection—In sound waves the air moves and in water waves the water moves, what is it that moves in light waves since light will travel through a vacuum? Huyghens suggested that there is a medium pervading all space and this medium he called the "ether."

Newton's objection to this *wave theory* was that sound waves and water waves easily bend round corners whereas light does not; the wave theory could not explain shadows.

This difficulty was cleared up by the celebrated scientist and Egyptologist Thomas Young (1773–1829). Young's experiments indicated that light *did* bend round corners a little but not as readily as sound waves because light waves have a much shorter wave length.

But it was only after 1850 that the wave theory really ousted the corpuscular theory. In that year a French scientist, Foucault, showed that light travelled more quickly in air than in water, and in 1880 an American scientist, Michelson, showed that

$$\frac{\text{Velocity of Light in Air}}{\text{Velocity of Light in Water}} = \tfrac{4}{3}.$$

Where have we met that fraction before? Why should this fact kill the corpuscular theory?

To explain the bending of a ray of light when it enters water, Newton had assumed that water exerted a pull on the corpuscles. In consequence of this pull, the corpuscles would travel faster in water than in air! But the fact discovered by Foucault and Michelson definitely contradicted this, and **when a fact meets a theory the victory is always with the fact.**

Let us now return to the mysterious fraction $\frac{4}{3}$. It is of course the same as the refractive index of water so we have

$$\frac{\text{Velocity of Light in Air}}{\text{Velocity of Light in Water}} = \tfrac{4}{3}$$

and

$$\frac{\sin i}{\sin r} = \tfrac{4}{3}.$$

Is this a coincidence or not? We shall find that it is not, and that the second fact is a *direct consequence* of the first; in other words, that the bending is directly caused by the change in velocity.

Given the Speed Ratio to prove the Refraction Ratio.

Let fig. 178 represent a parallel beam of light or a train of light waves moving through air to a water surface AB. As soon as the point D touches the water, its speed is reduced. Divide CE into 4 units of length. While the point C covers these 4 units, the point D will only do 3 units, and the beam is slewed round into a new direction. Very simple geometry will suffice to prove the equality of the angles similarly marked,

then $$\sin i = \frac{EC}{ED}$$

and $$\sin r = \frac{FD}{ED}$$

$$\therefore \frac{\sin i}{\sin r} = \frac{EC}{FD} = \tfrac{4}{3}.$$

That is, the refraction ratio is the same as the speed ratio.

This slewing round action is perfectly natural. It is what we should expect if light consists of waves. A similar thing is frequently seen on the coast. Water waves travel faster in deep water than in shallow water, so when a wave approaches a sloping shore obliquely it can often be seen to swing round.

Moreover, the action is not peculiar to waves. You can illustrate it at home. Fit up an axle and a pair of wheels so that

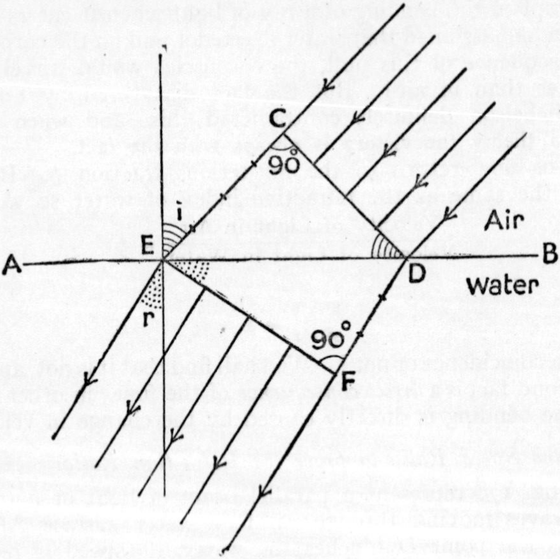

FIG. 178.

they revolve independently of the axle and of one another. Run this down a pastry board or drawing board slightly sloping and with the lower half covered by a towel. The bare surface represents the path of light in air while the covered surface produces the retardation experienced by light travelling in water.

The effect is more marked if the top half of the board is covered with a sheet of glass.

A Graphical Exercise (Problem). A ray of light strikes a slab of glass 8 cm. thick at an angle of 60° ($\mu = 1{\cdot}5$). Draw the path of the emergent ray. Show that it is parallel to the incident ray and measure the lateral displacement.

This is a double application of the problem on p. 203. Make the angle AON = 60° (fig. 179). Mark off OP and OQ 3 units and 2 units long respectively. Why ? Erect the perpendicular PT. With radius OT draw a circle. Draw the perpendicular QV to cut this circle at V. *Then OV is the refracted ray.*

Produce OV to meet the edge of the slab at B. Here the reverse procedure is adopted and BR and BS are made 2 units

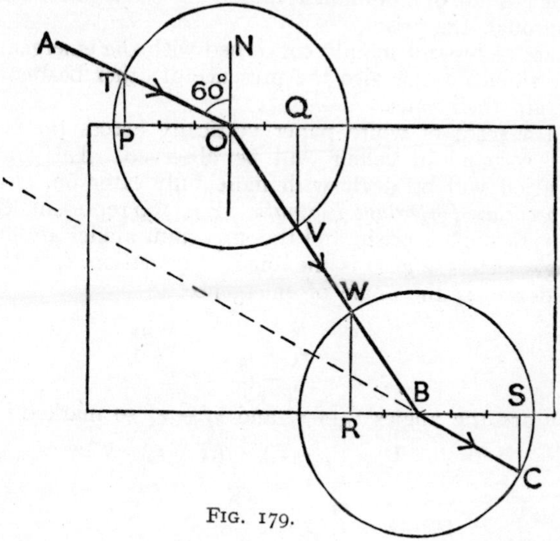

FIG. 179.

and 3 units long respectively. Erect the perpendicular RW. With radius BW (which will be the same length as OT) describe a circle. Draw the perpendicular SC to cut this circle in C. *Then BC is the emergent ray.* Produce it backwards and measure the displacement.

Refraction through a Prism.

Experiment. Stick a piece of white paper on the triangular base of an equilateral or isosceles prism. Place the prism across a " beam of light " (see p. 197). Let the beam make with the face an acute angle on that side of the normal remote from the apex.

You will observe a strong emergent beam making an angle with the incident beam. The incident beam is not displaced as in the case of the slab but is *deviated* towards the base.

Slowly rotate the prism round a vertical axis through its centre. The deviation varies, but there is a certain position where the deviation is a minimum and the emergent beam will be seen to travel up to this position then back.

In the position of minimum deviation, the beam passes symmetrically through the prism.

We are at present mainly concerned with the emergent beam, but we should notice also the presence of other beams and try to explain their causes.

Hold a piece of white paper vertically across the emergent beam. A band of colour will be observed. This important observation will be dealt with more fully later on.

To prove an Important Formula. Fig. 180 represents the path of a ray through a prism and the important angles are indicated by single letters, *e.g.* D is the angle of deviation, i_1 is the angle of incidence, i_2 the angle of emergence.

$$a = A \qquad \text{Why ?}$$

and $$a = r_1 + r_2 \qquad \text{Why ?}$$

$$\therefore A = r_1 + r_2 \quad . \quad . \quad . \quad . \quad . \quad . \quad . \quad (1)$$

Why are the angles $i_1 - r_1$ and $i_2 - r_2$ so marked ?

$$\begin{aligned} D &= (i_1 - r_1) + (i_2 - r_2) \quad \text{Why ?} \\ &= i_1 + i_2 - r_1 - r_2 \\ &= i_1 + i_2 - A \end{aligned}$$

$$\therefore D + A = i_1 + i_2 \quad . \quad . \quad . \quad . \quad . \quad . \quad . \quad (2)$$

But if the prism is set for minimum deviation, the ray passes symmetrically through the prism. Therefore ***the ray forms the base of an isosceles triangle of which A is the vertex.***

In this case $i_1 = i_2$ and $r_1 = r_2$. Why ? We may now rewrite equations (1) and (2) thus:

$$A = 2r$$

$$D + A = 2i$$

$$\therefore \mu = \frac{\sin i}{\sin r} = \frac{\sin \frac{1}{2}(D + A)}{\sin \frac{1}{2}A}$$

We here have an important relation between the angle of the

prism, the angle of minimum deviation and the refractive index of the glass. We can therefore find quite easily the refractive

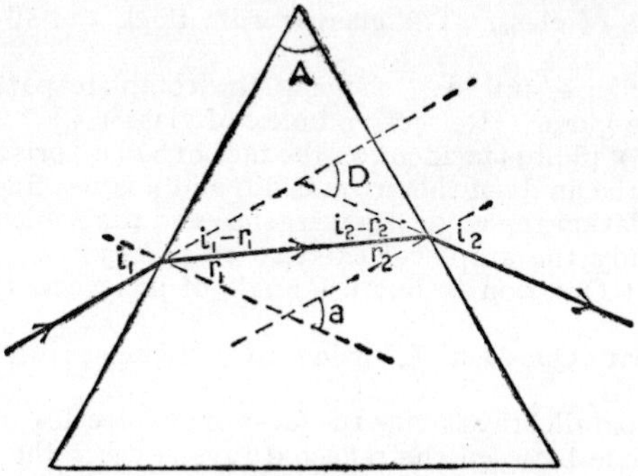

FIG. 180.

index of the glass. Moreover, if we have a hollow prism with thin glass walls, we can fill it with a liquid and determine the refractive index of that liquid.

QUESTIONS

1. A ray of light strikes a cube of glass, and $\angle i = 60°$. If each side is 6 cm. long and μ is 1·5, draw the emergent ray and find the lateral displacement by means of squared paper.

2. A hollow cube having thin glass walls each 6 cm. square contains carbon disulphide ($\mu = 1{\cdot}68$, but use 1·7). A ray of light strikes one face, and $\angle i = 40°$. By construction find the emergent ray and the lateral displacement.

3. Given the sine law and the fact that a ray of light is reversible, prove that the ray emerging from a slab of glass must be parallel to the incident ray.

4. A ray of light is incident normally on one of the equal faces of an isosceles right-angled prism. Prove that it must emerge normally.

5. By means of squared paper find the critical angle of diamond. [$\mu = 2{\cdot}417$, use 2·4.]

Using the more exact value of μ, *calculate* the critical angle for diamond.

6. Draw a cold weather mirage.

7. Define, with reference to a diagram, the meaning of *refractive index*.

A ray of light is incident at 45° on the upper surface of a rectangular slab of glass. The glass is 2 in. thick and silvered on the under side.

Draw a figure, full size, showing the complete path of the ray through the glass. [Refractive index of glass 1·5.] (L)

8. A ray of light is incident on the face of a glass prism at an angle of 50°. If the angle of the prism is 60° and μ is 1·5, find graphically or by calculation the angle of emergence and the angle of deviation. (*Hint :* Study the graphical exercise on p. 213.)

9. Repeat Question 8, but use angle of incidence 20°. Explain your result.

10. Repeat Question 8, using an aniline prism. [μ = 1·59, use 1·6.]

11. Two parallel rays strike the faces of an isosceles prism. Prove that the angle between the reflected rays is twice the angle of the prism. (*Hint :* Produce one side through the apex.]

12. The critical angle for turpentine is approximately 43°. Find its refractive index.

13. The shore of a lake gradually shelves from a depth of 2 ft. to a depth of 16 ft. Calculate the apparent shelving. [μ for water = $\frac{4}{3}$.]

14. A hollow prism of refracting angle 60° contains glycerine. The angle of minimum deviation is $34\frac{1}{2}$°. Calculate μ for glycerine.

15. A ray of light strikes a slab of glass at 45° with the normal. The emergent ray shows a lateral displacement of 2 cm. If the refractive index of the glass is 1·5, find the thickness of the slab.

16. A ray of light strikes a rectangular vessel having thin glass walls and containing a liquid. The angle of incidence is 60°, the lateral displacement 2 cm. and the breadth of the vessel 3·7 cm. Find by means of a diagram on squared paper the refractive index of the liquid.

CHAPTER XX

LENSES

It is almost certain that at some time or other you have used a piece of glass with spherical surfaces to magnify something or to burn a hole in a piece of paper. You will have seen similar pieces of glass in cameras, optical lanterns and in spectacle frames for people who can see far objects but not near objects.

You will probably know that such a piece of glass is called a *lens*. The lenses just mentioned all have one thing in common—they are thicker at the centre than at the rim. They

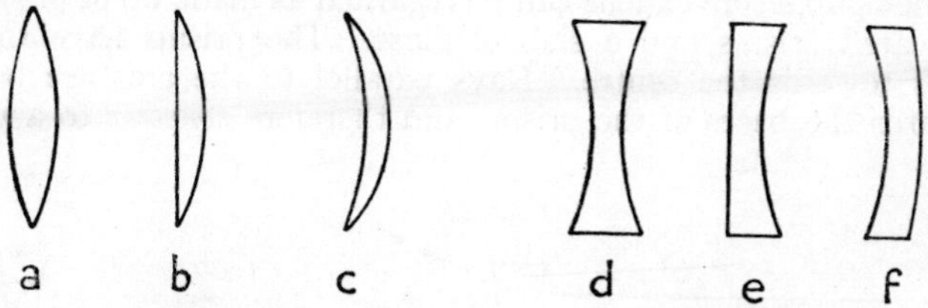

Convex.
Converging.
Thick Centres.

Concave.
Diverging.
Thin Centres.

FIG. 181.

are called convex or converging lenses. Rays of light originally parallel to the axis converge to a real focus after passing through the lens (Lat. *con*, together).

Very short-sighted people have spectacle lenses which are thin at the centre. These are called concave or divergent lenses. Rays of light travelling parallel to the axis diverge from a virtual focus after passing through the lens (Lat. *dis*, apart).

Convex or converging lenses can be divided into three classes: (*a*) *Double* convex, (*b*) *Plano* convex, (*c*) *Concavo* convex (fig. 181).

Concave or diverging lenses can likewise be divided into three classes: (*d*) *Double* concave, (*e*) *Plano* concave, (*f*) *Convexo* concave (fig. 181).

In the present chapter we shall confine our attention to the (*a*) and (*d*) classes and try to account for their most important properties.

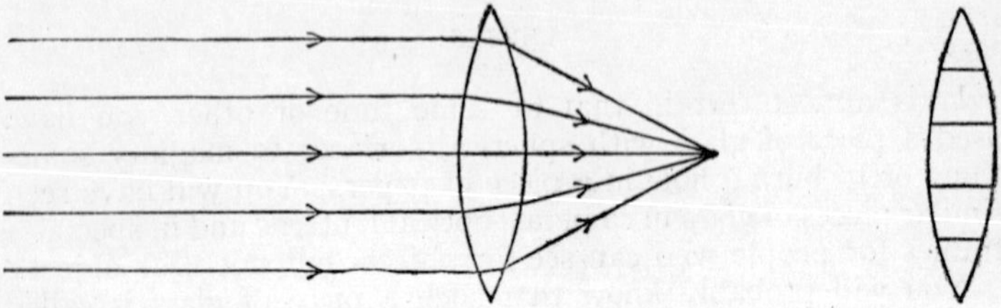

FIG. 182.

The double convex lens can be regarded as made up of prisms, truncated prisms and a slab of glass. The prisms have their bases towards the centre. Rays parallel to the axis are bent towards the bases of the prisms and therefore *converge* to a *real* focus (fig. 182).

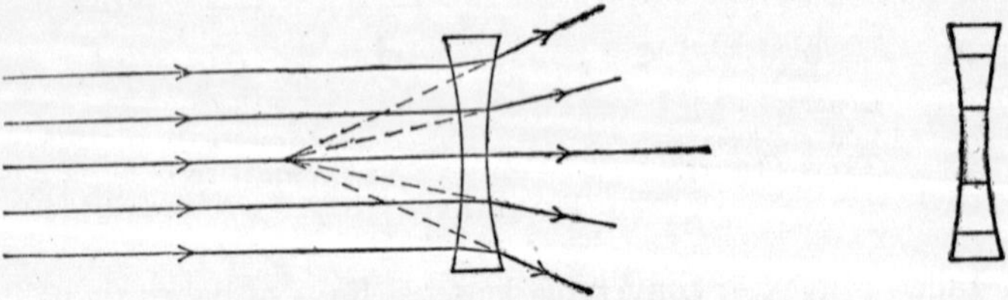

FIG. 183.

The same construction is evident in the double concave lens (fig. 183), but the prisms have their bases facing away from the centre. Rays parallel to the axis are bent away from the axis and therefore *diverge* from a *virtual* focus.

Images formed by a Double Convex Lens. Since most people possess a magnifying or reading glass of some kind, it is quite easy to study this lens at home.

Experiment. Hold up the lens so as to receive parallel rays from a distant chimney-pot on the skyline. On the other side of the lens hold a piece of white paper and vary its position until a clear image is formed. The clearest image is obtained when the skyline is well illuminated and the lens and paper held in a shaded position. Describe the image and measure the distance from image to lens. This is the *focal length.*

If the experiment is done after dark, a candle, gas jet, an electric lamp or the illuminated gauze described on p. 188 will be sufficiently distant to give a reasonable result.

Experiment. Approach from a distance a candle or the illuminated gauze, holding lens and screen as before. Describe the image and note how it changes in size. Observe very carefully the size of the image when the lens is at a distance of about $2f$ from the object.

Bring the lens closer still, noting the changes in size, until the lens is at a distance of about f from the object. What is the effect now?

For distances less than this, there is no image on the screen. Put the screen down and look through the lens. A magnified erect image of the candle will now be seen.

Graphical Work. Let us now try to account for our results by means of carefully drawn diagrams. You will readily understand that a double convex lens has two foci, one on each side equidistant from the lens. There are three important rays which we may use.

1. The ray from the top of the object travelling parallel to the axis. After refraction, this ray passes through the focus on the other side of the lens. This focus is generally called the *second* principal focus.

2. The ray from the top of the object to the *optical* centre of the lens. This ray strikes the "slab of glass" and is therefore not deviated but displaced. But since in an ordinary lens the "slab" is very thin, the displacement is so slight that it could not be shown. Therefore we may assume that this ray goes straight through.

3. The ray from the top of the object to the *first* principal focus. This ray travels parallel to the axis after passing through the lens.

At present we shall only make use of rays 1 and 2, but later you will occasionally find ray 3 very useful.

In fig. 184 we have what may be called a basic diagram which will enable us to solve most of our problems on the convex lens. (Compare the basic diagram for concave mirrors on p. 183.) Consider the following five cases and describe the image formed in each case, real or virtual, inverted or erect, magnified, diminished, or same size.

Case (1). Distance of object greater than $2f$ where f is the focal length. (Stretch a piece of cotton from the top of the object through C the optical centre.)

Case (2). Distance of object equal to $2f$.

Case (3). Distance of object greater than f but less than $2f$.

Case (4). Distance of object equal to f.

Case (5). Distance of object less than f.

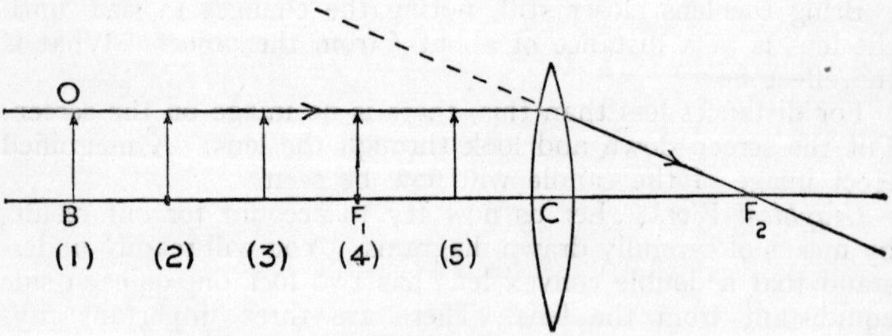

FIG. 184.

Draw separate diagrams to illustrate all five cases and try to answer the following questions. Where is the image when the object is moved to an infinite distance? Of what use is this fact? Describe the beam of light which emerges from the lens when a small electric bulb is placed at one of the foci. When are image and object the same size? Where is the image in *Case* (4)? Where must the object be placed in order to get a real magnified image? Under what circumstances do we get a virtual magnified image? Where must the eye be placed to receive it?

Note that in those cases where the image is real, the image and object can change places and the two points are conjugate foci (cf. concave mirror).

To find the Focal Length of a Convex Lens.

1. *Distant Object Method.* From Case (1) we learnt that when the object is moved to an infinite distance, the rays arriving at the lens are parallel to the principal axis and are therefore refracted through the principal focus. (Compare concave mirror.) We have already used this method of measuring the focal length, our distant object being a chimney-pot on the skyline.

This is the quickest method and should always be used first.

2. *Coincident Object and Image Method.* Since rays parallel to the axis converge to a focus after passing through the lens, rays which *start* from the focus will be parallel to the axis after refraction by the lens. What will happen if we put a plane mirror at right angles to their path?

Experiment. Set up a lens and plane mirror as in fig. 185.

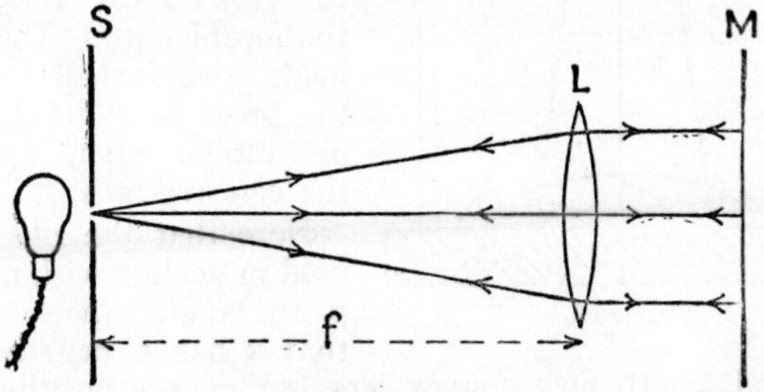

FIG. 185.

Place the screen carrying the illuminated gauze roughly at the focus. Carefully adjust the position of the screen so that a clear image is formed. Measure the distance from the screen to the lens. This will be the focal length.

Compare and contrast this experiment with the corresponding one on the concave mirror. In that case the experiment gave the radius of curvature of the mirror which was twice the focal length.

But lenses have two radii of curvature, one for each surface, and we cannot say that either of them is equal to twice the focal length; it is only by chance that this would happen. In fact, there is no *very simple* relation between these three lengths. We can only say here that the thicker the lens, that is the smaller the radii of curvature, the shorter is the focal length.

Experiment. Lay the convex lens on a plane mirror. Place a pin roughly at the focus (fig. 186). Adjust the height of the pin until there is no parallax between it and its image. Measure the distance from the pin to the lens. This is the focal length.

3. *The Formula Method.* As in the case of spherical mirrors there is a standard formula for lenses. It is $\frac{1}{v} - \frac{1}{u} = \frac{1}{f}$ where v is the distance from the lens to the image, u the distance from the lens to the object and f the focal length. The formula holds good for all lenses, but the proof is a little easier to understand when applied to the concave lens.

Note that the *rule of signs* used in dealing with mirrors on p. 191 applies here also and that u has a negative value. The focal length of a convex lens is therefore positive.

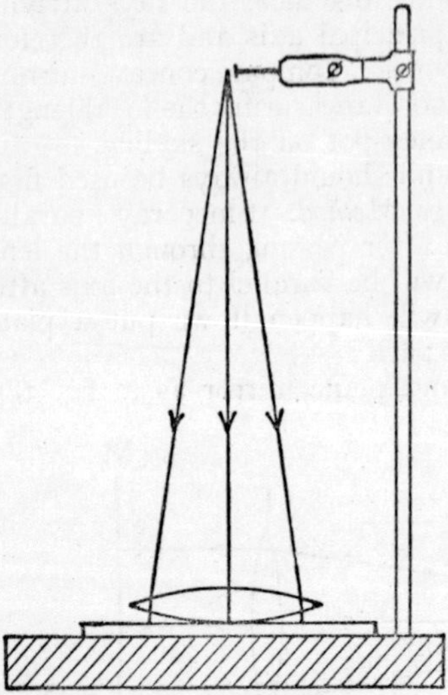

FIG. 186.

Experiment. The formula method or the method of conjugate foci can be applied in two ways, both illustrated in fig. 187.

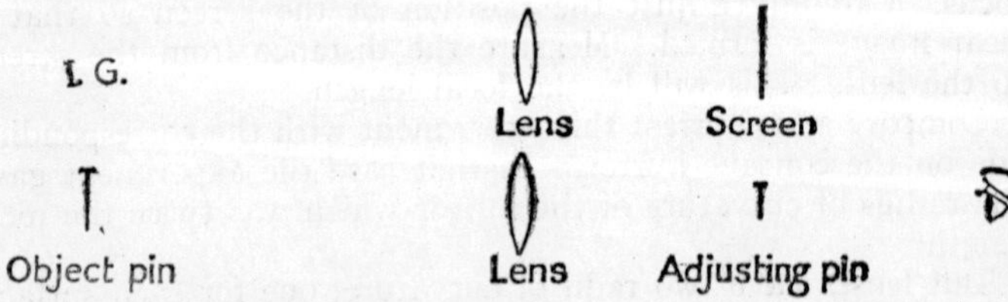

FIG. 187.

(*a*) Fix up the illuminated gauze IG at a distance from the lens equal to about three or four focal lengths. Adjust the screen S for a clear image.

(*b*) Use a long pin as object and adjust the position of a shorter pin so that there is no parallax between it and the image of the first pin.

Note that each adjustment serves to give two readings, for, by the principle of conjugate foci, when the adjustment is made, image and object can be interchanged. Thus if $u = -20$ and $v = +10$, then $u = -10$ and $v = +20$ will be another reading. Substitute the values of v and u in the formula and calculate f.

The Convex Lens as a Magnifying Glass. You will probably have learnt by experience that the best way to use a reading glass is to put it close to the print and then gradually withdraw it until the magnification is a maximum. By carefully studying Case (5) above, you will understand the reason for this procedure.

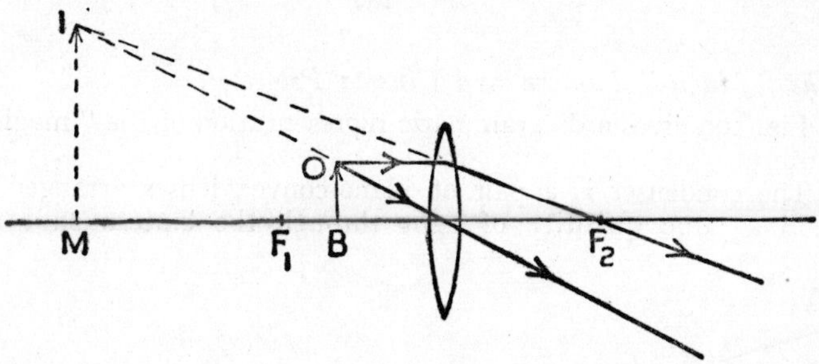

FIG. 188.

Maximum magnification is obtained when the object is between F_1 and the lens and as near to F_1 as possible (fig. 188). But we shall learn later that the *best* position for the object depends also on the observer's eyesight.

The Convex Lens in a Camera. On examining Cases (1) and (2), we see that when the object is situated anywhere between infinity and $2f$, a real inverted diminished image is formed on the other side of the lens. When a screen is placed there to receive the image, and the space between screen and lens is enclosed by a box or bellows, we have a *camera*.

When the object is distant $2f$, the image is distant $2f$ on the other side, real, inverted and equal to the object. The bellows of the ordinary camera will not rack out as far as this, but in some cameras the bellows are twice as long. We then have what is known as a *double extension* camera which can be used for copying photographs (fig. 189).

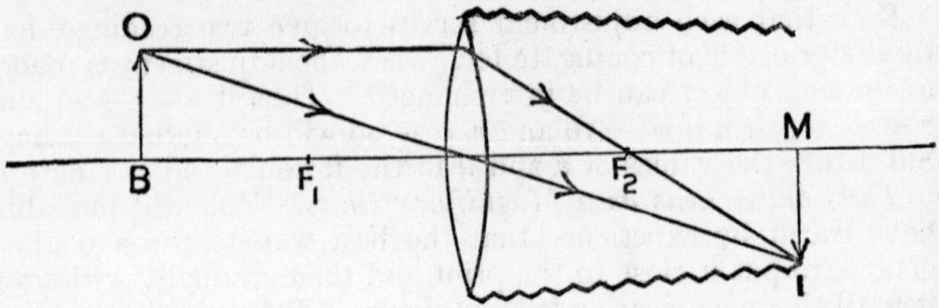

Double Extension Camera.

FIG. 189.

The "Magic" Lantern and Cinema Projector.

Fig. 190 gives a diagrammatic representation of the "magic" lantern.

The condenser is a pair of plano-convex lenses arranged to send a large quantity of light through the lantern slide *ab*.

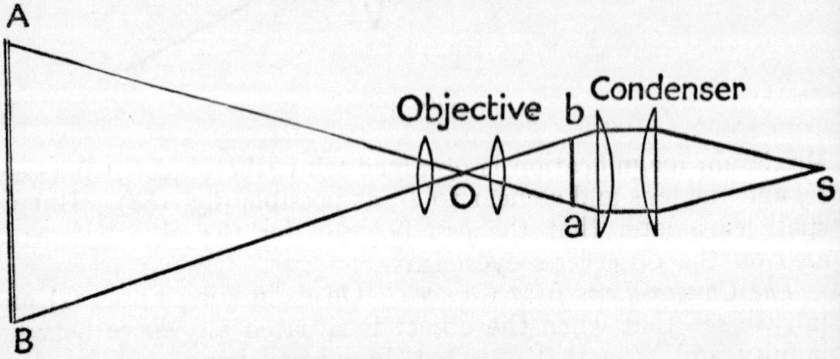

FIG. 190.

Without the condenser, very few rays from S, the source of light, would pass through the slide.

The focusing lens or objective generally consists of two or more lenses so arranged that the image AB shall be free from colour. The point O represents the optical centre of this combination and, as usual, rays through this point are undeviated. If the slide *ab* is inverted, it is clear from the figure that the image AB will be the right way up.

As far as the objective is concerned, the magic lantern is an application of Case (3) above, in other words, the slide must be at a greater distance than *f* from the objective.

The Double Concave Lens. Experiments with a concave lens will show that only one kind of image can be obtained—an erect diminished image. The farther the object is from the lens, the smaller does the image become.

Let us try to account for these results by a carefully drawn diagram. A ray close to and parallel to the principal axis will be bent towards the circumference of the lens, and will appear to diverge from a focus on the same side as the object. If a ruler or a piece of thread is passed through the optical centre and made to rotate round that point, we shall see that the image is always virtual, erect, and diminished.

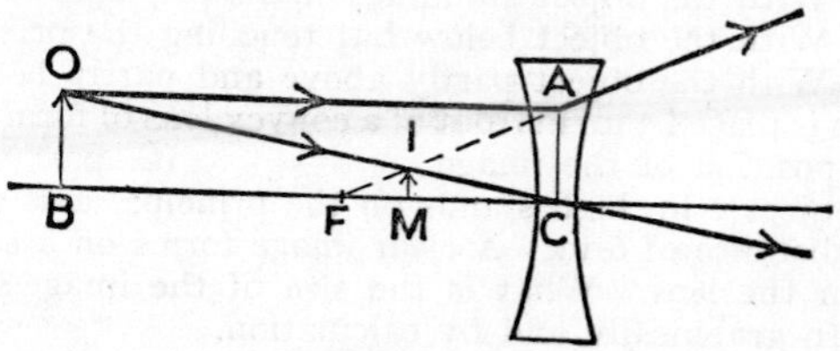

FIG. 191.

The lens formula is easily proved by reference to a concave lens. In fig. 191

$$\frac{IM}{AC} = \frac{FM}{FC} = \frac{f-v}{f}$$

also

$$\frac{IM}{OB} = \frac{CM}{CB} = \frac{v}{u}$$

but

$$AC = OB$$

$$\therefore \frac{FM}{FC} = \frac{CM}{CB}$$

$$\therefore \frac{f-v}{f} = \frac{v}{u}$$

Cross multiply and divide by uvf

then $$\frac{1}{v} - \frac{1}{u} = \frac{1}{f}$$

which is the standard formula for lenses. Note also that the magnification formula arises out of the same proof and we have

$$\frac{\text{Size of Image}}{\text{Size of Object}} = \frac{v}{u}.$$

QUESTIONS

1. A thin convex lens has a focal length of 8 cm. An object 2 cm. high stands on the principal axis at a distance of 16 cm. from the lens. On a diagram drawn to scale illustrate the behaviour of the three rays from the top of the object which travel (*a*) parallel to the principal axis, (*b*) through the optical centre, (*c*) through the first principal focus. Find the position and size of the image.

2. Draw five diagrams illustrating the properties of a convex lens :

   (*a*) With the object standing on the principal axis.

   (*b*) With the object below but touching the principal axis.

   (*c*) With the object partly above and partly below.

3. A pin is placed 3 in. in front of a convex lens of focal length 2 in. Find the position of the image. (C. part question.)

4. An object 1 in. high stands on the principal axis of a convex lens at a distance of 6 in. A clear image forms on a screen 12 in. away from the lens. What is the size of the image? Find the focal length graphically and by calculation.

5. A convex lens has focal length 4 in. An object $\frac{1}{2}$ in. high stands on the principal axis 3 in. away from the lens. Find graphically and by calculation the position and size of the image.

6. A converging lens is placed 6 in. away from a luminous object 1 in. long. A clear image is formed on a screen 24 in. away from the object. What is the size of the image? Find f graphically and by calculation.

7. A camera has a lens of $4\frac{1}{2}$ in. focal length. How far must the bellows stretch,

   (*a*) to photograph landscape;

   (*b*) to copy photographs exact size;

   (*c*) to make copies double length and width?

8. Explain why the slide is always inverted before being put into a magic lantern. Illustrate your answer by a diagram.

9. A magic lantern makes a picture on a screen 13 ft. away. If the focal length of the objective is 6 in. and the slide $3\frac{1}{4}$ in. each way find the position of the slide and the size of the picture.

10. A convex lens of focal length 6 in. forms an image twice the length of the object. Where must the object be if the image is (*a*) real, (*b*) virtual?

11. An object is placed 4 in. away from a convex lens of focal length 10 in. Find the magnification produced.

12. A convex lens of focal length 12 in. produces an erect image three times as high as the object. Where is the object?

13. How far from the object must a magnifying-glass ($f=$ 2 in.) be placed to produce an image 10 in. away? What magnification is produced?

14. An object is placed 6 in. away from a lens. An inverted image is formed 24 in. from the lens. Find the focal length.

15. An object is situated 10 in. from a lens. An image is formed 20 in. from the lens on the same side. What kind of lens is it and what is its focal length?

16. A printed page is held 10 in. from an old gentleman's eye, but he can only read by holding the book at arm's length, say 24 in. away. What sort of lens held close to the eye will produce an image at the required distance?

17. An object is situated 10 in. from a lens. An image is formed 6 in. from the lens on the same side. What kind of lens is it and what is its focal length?

18. A printed page is held 10 in. from a man's face, but, being very short-sighted, he can only read print at a distance of 5 in. What sort of lens held close to the eye will produce an image at the required distance?

19. A cinema film measures 1 in. $\times \frac{3}{4}$ in., the projector lens has a focal length of 10 in. and the screen picture is 12 ft. $\times$ 9 ft. Calculate the distances from lens to film and lens to screen.

CHAPTER XXI

OTHER IMPORTANT OPTICAL INSTRUMENTS

The Eye. The eye is in many respects similar to the photographic camera. Fig. 192 shows the horizontal section of a

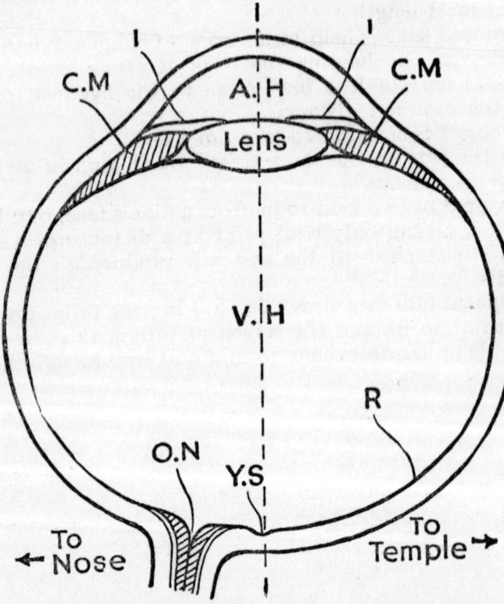

FIG. 192.

right eye. The transparent *horny* membrane which forms the front covering of the eye is called the **cornea** from Latin *cornu*, a horn. Between this and the lens is a watery liquid called the **aqueous humour.** On the other side of the lens is another watery fluid, the **vitreous humour,** in contact with a membrane called the retina. CM is the **ciliary muscle.**

The retina is sensitive to light and corresponds to the film, plate or focusing screen of the camera. The light impressions are carried to the brain by the **optic nerve.** The area occupied by the optic nerve is not itself sensitive to light and forms what is known as the *blind spot.* To the right of it in a right eye and to the left of it in a left eye is the most sensitive part of the retina, called the **yellow spot.** This is where the image forms when we fix our attention on some small object.

It is quite an easy matter to pass an image across the retina from one side to the other and thus prove the existence of a blind spot.

Experiment. Close the left eye and gaze perpendicularly at the dot in fig. 193. Vary the distance of the book from the eye. At most positions the cross can also be seen by means of slanting rays, but at one position these oblique rays strike the blind spot and the cross disappears. Moving the book nearer or

Fig. 193.

farther causes the rays to strike left or right of the spot and the cross reappears. The experiment can of course be repeated with the left eye.

The fact that there is a blind spot in each eye does not cause us any inconvenience because it is not situated in the middle of the retina but rather on the nasal side. Rays, therefore, do not fall on both blind spots at the same time.

There is one great difference between the camera lens and the eye lens. The latter has normally a focal length of about 15 mm., and when at rest it brings rays from a distant object to a sharp focus on the retina. The camera lens does the same when set at the "infinity" catch. To focus nearer objects, the camera lens moves forward, but to achieve the same result in the eye, the ring of muscle round the lens acts in such a way as to thicken the lens and thus shorten the focal length. This power of *accommodation* is very marked in children's eyes, but with age the lens loses its elasticity, so that while young children can focus on very close objects, "grandfather" holds things at arm's length.

You probably know that the camera lens has a *stop* to vary the size of the aperture. In very bright light only the centre of the lens need be used and this improves the definition of the image. In the eye there is also a stop which serves the same purposes, but instead of being black as in the camera, it may be of various colours.

For this reason the stop is called the **iris**, from Latin and Greek words meaning " a rainbow." Popular taste leans towards brown or blue, but some of us have to be content with a green or yellow iris! What we know as the **pupil** of the eye is the circular opening in this iris. The iris of a kitten and that of the adult cat have striking features with which you are probably well acquainted.

Very little thought enables us to realize the advantage of having *two* eyes. One eye gives a flat picture while two eyes give us a solid or *stereoscopic* view. When we use one eye, all objects a little way off appear to be at the same distance. One-eyed people have to do parallax experiments daily as a matter of routine! But with two eyes we have a sort of base line 3 in. long with the distant chimney forming the vertex of the triangle. This " triangulation " experiment may be only rough, but it is nevertheless very serviceable.

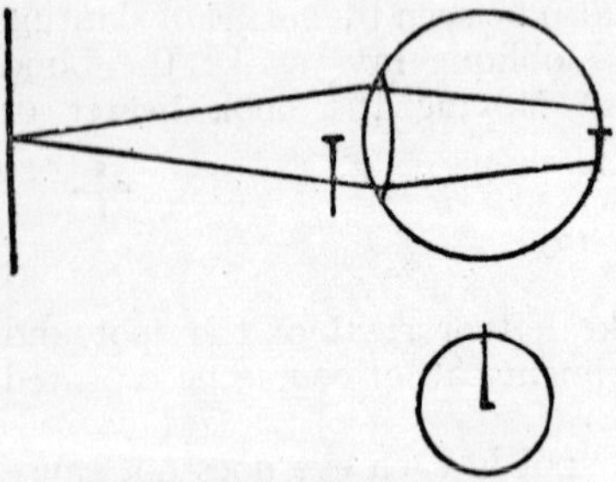

Fig. 194.

You will remember that when a lens forms a real image on a screen, the image is inverted. Images formed on the retina must therefore also be inverted. Why, then, do we not see all objects upside down? The answer is that the brain from long experience has learnt to read these *inverted* images as *erect* objects. There is an interesting little experiment which illustrates this peculiarity.

Experiment. Hold an erect pin close to the eyelashes (fig. 194) and look at the sky or a light through a pinhole placed about 2 or 3 in. away. Move the pin slowly up and down and left to right. An inverted pin will be seen.

The explanation is quite simple. A diverging beam of light travels from the pinhole to the eye. The pin obscures the light and causes a sharp *erect shadow* to be thrown on the retina. But the brain follows its usual practice and we get the idea that it is an inverted pin which is on view.

When an image is flashed on to the retina and then off, the impression remains for about $\frac{1}{10}$ sec. Therefore if images are flashed on at the rate of 10 per second or faster, they blend. It is for this reason that if the glowing end of a stick is whirled

FIG. 195.

FIG. 196.

round, we do not see a multitude of glowing ends, but a bright circle of light due to the blending of the images.

There is an old scientific toy called the **thaumatrope**, the idea of which is illustrated in figs. 195 and 196. On one side of the card a head is drawn, on the other a hat. The card is twirled until the strings are very much twisted. When the strings are now quickly pulled, the two impressions blend and the hat appears to be on the head.

Boys sometimes amuse themselves by drawing on the corners

of an exercise book two men in various boxing attitudes. Sometimes we meet little booklets of pictures such as a seal in all stages of diving into water. Running the pages rapidly forwards or backwards produces the illusion of continuous motion.

The fact here illustrated is known as the **persistence of vision** and is the basis of cinema pictures. The cinema camera takes snapshot photographs at 16 per second on a long film. This is accomplished by having a shutter which opens and closes at that rate. The film is developed and printed to form a positive on another film.

The positive film is drawn through the magic lantern or projector, and a shutter operates at the same rate as before to cut off the light while one snap moves off and the next gets into view. The film being of celluloid or some such material is highly inflammable, and since the light used is very powerful each little snap gets warm. But unless the film gets jammed, it does not get hot enough to catch alight.

Curious tricks are often performed on the cinema. Natural processes can be accelerated, retarded, or even reversed. Photographs of the planting and growth of a seed can be taken at intervals over a comparatively long period of time on a single film. When this is shown at the ordinary rate, we get the illusion of very rapid growth. On the other hand, in the making of a "slow motion" picture, the snaps are taken at 160 per second and then shown at the ordinary rate of 16 per second. This makes possible the careful study of such things as high jumping, and strokes in cricket, tennis or golf. Again, a film depicting the preparation and eating of a Christmas dinner makes a very amusing spectacle when reversed.

Can you explain why we occasionally see on the pictures a cart moving rapidly forward while the spokes of the wheel appear to be travelling backwards? You will meet applications of this idea in more advanced physics.

Defective Eyes. We have already learnt that the normal eye at rest forms a sharp image on the retina when the object is at infinity, and that for nearer objects "accommodation" takes place, the lens thickening to shorten its focal length. This thickening cannot go on indefinitely, and normally it ceases when the object is 10 in. or 25 cm. from the eye. At this distance the image has its maximum clearness. It is called the *minimum distance of distinct vision* and is indicated by the letter D.

In some cases the focal length is too great for the eyeball, and rays from a distant object come to a focus behind the retina. Accommodation has to be used even for distant objects and the thickening is perhaps at a maximum when the object is still 30 in. away; this person cannot see near objects clearly. He is said to have **long sight**; in this case D is greater than 10 in. The eye lens is not sufficiently convergent; it is not thick enough at the centre. What is the remedy? He must use an *additional* lens which is thick at the centre, in other words **convex spectacles.**

In other cases the focal length is too small for the eyeball; parallel rays come to a focus in front of the retina even when no accommodation is used. The image only forms on the retina when the object has approached to within, say, 6 ft. of the lens. Then when accommodation comes into play the eye is able to focus on points perhaps only 5 or 6 in. away. In other words, D is much less than 10 in. Distant objects cannot be seen because the eye lens is too thick at the centre. This trouble is known as **short sight** and the remedy is to use an *additional* lens which is thin at the centre; **concave spectacles** are prescribed.

In problems on long sight and short sight you are generally given two distances, at one of them the object is situated, while the other is the distance to which the person can see. The method is to *place an image of the object where he can see it.* The first distance is obviously u and the second one v, so that an application of the usual lens formula will give the nature and focal length of the lens necessary. You have already done some problems like this (Nos. 15–18, Chap. XX) and you are recommended to work them again in the light of your new knowledge.

The Magnifying-Glass or Simple Microscope. Very little experience with convex lenses will prove that the most powerful magnifying-glasses have short focal lengths. Why is this? Let us consider the following problem.

"Mr. Brown is using a magnifying-glass of 2 in. focal length. His eye is normal, *i.e.* $D = 10$ in. Where should the object be?"

Evidently things must be so arranged that the image is where

Mr. Brown can see it best, therefore $v = -10$ in., and since $f = 2$ in. we have

$$-\frac{1}{10} - \frac{1}{u} = \frac{1}{2}, \quad \therefore u = -1\tfrac{2}{3} \text{ in.}$$

The magnification is

$$\frac{v}{u} = \frac{10}{1\frac{2}{3}} = 6.$$

By drawing a diagram to scale it is quite easy to show that the magnification depends on the focal length.

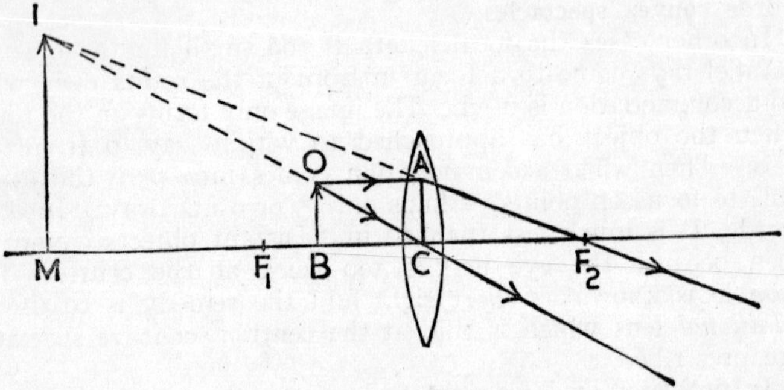

FIG. 197.

In fig. 197 magnification =

$$\frac{\text{IM}}{\text{OB}} = \frac{\text{IM}}{\text{AC}} = \frac{F_2\text{M}}{F_2\text{C}} = \frac{D+F}{F} = 1 + \frac{D}{F}$$

From this result it is easy to see that the smaller F is, the greater is the magnification.

The Compound Microscope.

Problem. A small object $\frac{1}{5}$ in. long is placed $1\frac{1}{5}$ in. from a convex lens of focal length 1 in. Find by means of squared paper and by calculation the size and position of the image.

This real image now acts as object to another convex lens of focal length 3 in. placed 2 in. farther away. On the same diagram find the size and position of the final image.

The above problem illustrates roughly the principle of the compound microscope. A real magnified image is formed by the object glass, and this image is then further magnified by the eyepiece. For great magnification the lenses should both be of short focal length.

Experiment. Take two lenses of short focal length, say 2 or 3 in. On a burette stand or other convenient holder set up one of them above a printed page, so that the latter is more than one but less than two focal lengths away.

Fix up the second lens as an eyepiece (fig. 198) and adjust it so that it magnifies the real image formed by the objective.

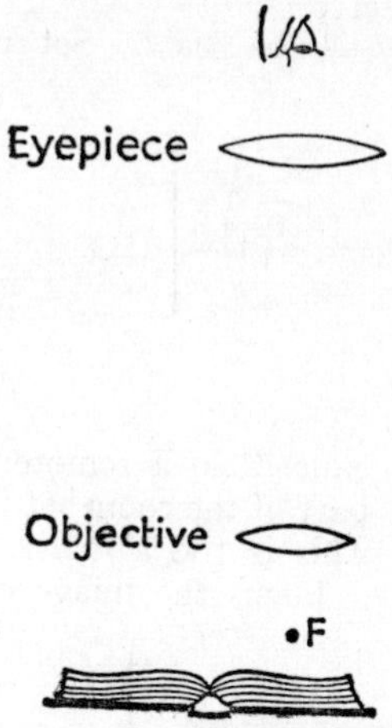

FIG. 198.

The Astronomical Telescope.

Problem. An object 10 in. high is placed 100 in. away from a convex lens of focal length 20 in. Find by means of squared paper and by calculation the size and position of the image.

This image now acts as object to another convex lens of focal length 4 in. placed 3 in. farther away. On the same diagram find the size and position of the final image.

The above problem is only a very rough illustration of the principle of the astronomical telescope because 100 in. is such a tiny distance. It will be obvious that if the object were a star or some really distant object, then we could not make a scale drawing. The objective forms, at or near the focus, a small inverted image of the distant object. This image is then magnified by the eyepiece.

The distance between the lenses is generally equal to $F + f$ where F is the focal length of the objective and f that of the eyepiece. For great magnification $\frac{F}{f}$ should be large. The objective should therefore be a long-focus lens and the eyepiece one of short focal length. The objective should also have a large aperture to ensure that a large quantity of light is taken in.

The fact that the final image is inverted, laterally and actually, is no disadvantage in astronomy, but for ordinary work such an instrument would be a nuisance. In the *terrestrial telescope* an extra convex lens is therefore inserted behind the eyepiece lens to produce a second inversion, thus making the final image erect.

Experiment. Set up a lighted candle or the "illuminated

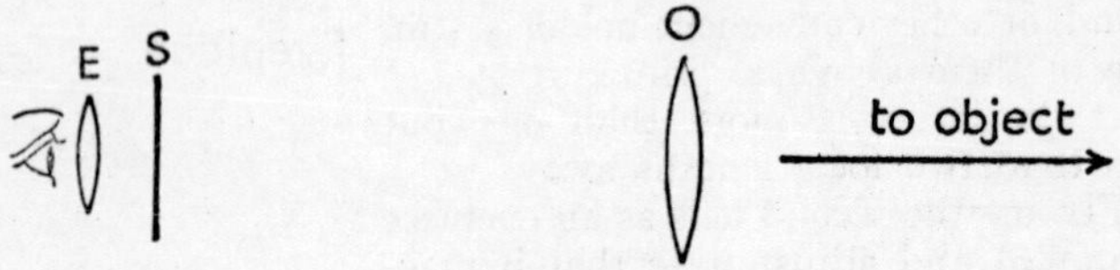

FIG. 199.

gauze" in a remote corner of the room. In the most shaded part of the room set up a long focus lens with its axis horizontal. This is the *objective.*

Focus the image on a piece of frosted glass or on a screen made by sticking a piece of thin paper on a slip of glass.

Fix up a short-focus lens on the other side of the screen (fig. 199). This lens acts as the *eyepiece.* Having set it for maximum magnification, remove the screen. The two lenses now form an astronomical telescope.

In fair sunlight an object on the sky-line may be used, the screen and lenses being placed as before in the most shaded part of the room. If desired, the lenses can be fitted into cardboard tubes blackened on the inside and sliding one into the other.

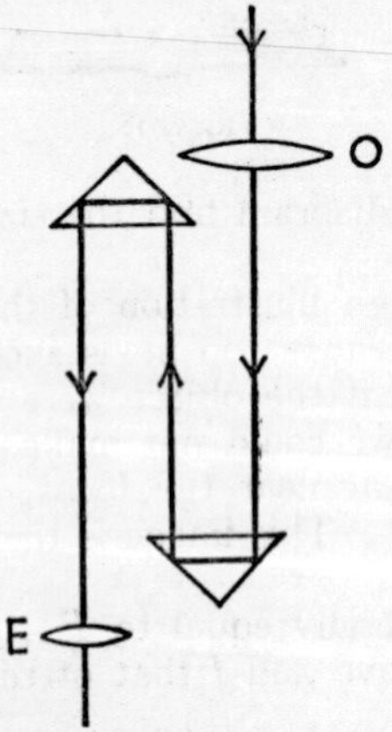

FIG. 200.

Prism Binoculars. Since the magnification in an astronomical telescope depends on F being large and the distance between the lenses is practically $F + f$, the instrument tends to be very long. In prism binoculars (fig. 200) this long length is folded up into three parts by the use of two right-angled prisms. Moreover, the lateral inversion produced by the objective is corrected by the first prism (see p. 205) and the actual inversion is corrected by the second prism. There is thus no need of an erecting lens. Note that the second prism is really set with its refracting edge at *right angles* to that of the first.

QUESTIONS

1. Write an account of the resemblances and differences between a photographic camera and the eye.

2. An object travels up from infinity to a glass lens. Show by diagrams how the position of the image changes. Explain what happens if the lens is the eye lens of a child.

3. Illustrate by diagrams what happens to parallel rays in the case of (*a*) long sight, (*b*) short sight.

4. A certain man can read print best when it is 15 cm. away from his eye. What glasses will he need to enable him to read a book at a distance of 30 cm.?

5. In the case of Mr. X. the value of D is 30 in. What spectacles must he use to make him normal in this respect?

6. A person cannot see clearly beyond a distance of 8 ft. What lenses must he use to recognize his friends on the opposite pavement 20 ft. away?

7. What magnification will be obtained when a person with normal eyesight uses convex lenses of the following focal lengths: 5 cm., 8 cm., 10 cm., 15 cm., 20 cm.?

8. A person whose *minimum distance of distinct vision* is 20 cm. uses a magnifying-glass of 5 cm. focal length. Find graphically or by calculation how far a book should be from the lens.

9. Point out the resemblances and differences between a compound microscope and an astronomical telescope.

CHAPTER XXII

DISPERSION AND COLOUR

When dealing with the prism (p. 214) we observed a band of colour on a piece of white paper held vertically across the emergent beam. The colours were most distinct when the prism was in the position of minimum deviation.

A similar experiment was done on sunlight by Sir Isaac Newton in the seventeenth century. He distinguished the following colours, Red, Orange, Yellow, Green, Blue, Indigo, Violet, and called the band a *spectrum* (fig. 201).

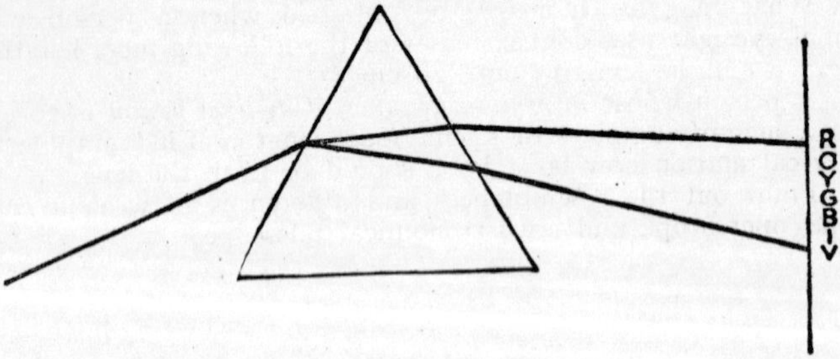

FIG. 201.

This splitting up of white light into different colours is called dispersion.

We have already learnt (p. 211) that refraction is caused by a reduction in speed when light enters a denser medium. These dispersion experiments indicate that the greatest reduction takes place in the case of violet light, for this is the light which is bent most from its original path. In other words, red light travels faster in glass than violet light. Therefore the "speed ratio" or "refraction ratio" or refractive index is greater for violet light than for red light.

You will now understand why, in stating Snell's Law, we said, "For the same two media and *for light of the same colour*, sin i divided by sin r is always a constant."

Ether Waves. According to the modern idea of considering light to be a sort of wave motion, red light consists of waves which are longer than the waves which produce violet light. The wave length of red light is roughly double the wave length of violet light. Short waves are thus more retarded and therefore more deviated by glass than longer waves.

Now the velocity of light is 300,000,000 metres per second and the wave length of red light is 0·00008 cm. Imagine a source giving out red light. How many waves would it put into that length of 300,000,000 metres? If you work this out, you will find it to be 375 followed by 12 noughts, a number which is more conveniently written $3{\cdot}75 \times 10^{14}$.

This number is obviously the number of waves sent out per second or what is called the *frequency*, and we have just been using the well-known fact about wave motion that

$$\text{Velocity} = \text{Frequency} \times \text{Wave Length.}$$

The frequency of violet light is double that of red light, viz. $7{\cdot}5 \times 10^{14}$. Colour in light may be compared with *pitch* in sound; violet light corresponds to a high note, red to a low one.

These frequencies are sometimes stated as $7{\cdot}5 \times 10^{11}$ and $3{\cdot}75 \times 10^{11}$ *kilocycles*. Have you met kilocycles before? If not, look at the broadcasting programmes in a daily paper. Opposite the National programme you may see 200 kilocycles per second and 1500 metres. Multiply these two numbers together. Does the result come to anything like the velocity of light? What is the explanation? Is there any connection between light waves and wireless waves?

Modern science says that there is a very close relation between them, in fact they are both waves in the same medium—ether. Our eyes act as detectors for these short ether waves, but nature does not provide us with a detector for the long waves; we must make or buy a "wireless set."

The table below shows that there is a long range of these ether or electromagnetic waves available to man and useful for widely different purposes.

Kind of Wave.	*Wave Length.*	*Frequency in kilocycles.*	*Detector.*
Wireless . . .	20,000 metres to 5 metres	$1{\cdot}5 \times 10^4$ to 6×10^7	Aerials and wireless sets.
Infra Red . .	0·04 cm. to 0·00008 cm.	$7{\cdot}5 \times 10^{11}$ to $3{\cdot}75 \times 10^{14}$	Heating effect on the skin.
Red, Orange, Yellow, Green, Blue, Indigo, Violet } The Visible Spectrum	0·00007 cm. to 0·00004 cm.	$4{\cdot}3 \times 10^{14}$ to $7{\cdot}5 \times 10^{14}$	The eye.
Ultra Violet .	0·00004 cm. to 0·000002 cm.	$7{\cdot}5 \times 10^{14}$ to $1{\cdot}5 \times 10^{16}$	Photographic plates, and fluorescent screens coated with barium platinocyanide or cadmium tungstate
X-rays . . .	0·000005 cm. to 0·0000000006 cm.	6×10^{15} to 5×10^{19}	
Gamma Rays (from Radium)	0·000000014 cm. to 0·0000000001 cm.	2×10^{18} to 3×10^{20}	

A few remarks may be helpful in explaining the fluorescent screens used in detecting the band of high-frequency waves. A fluorescent substance is one which absorbs short waves and converts them into longer waves of visible light. If the light continues to be emitted even after the short waves are cut off, then the substance is not only fluorescent but also *phosphorescent.* The sulphides of calcium and barium used in painting the figures and hands of luminous watches, possess this property of phosphorescence.

The most efficient fluorescent substances are two expensive chemicals called barium platinocyanide and cadmium tungstate. When a piece of paper is coated with either of these and held near an X-ray tube, the paper emits a yellowish-green light. If a duster containing a key is held between the tube and the screen, a dark shadow of the key is plainly seen. The bones of the hand may be seen in a similar way.

To Produce a Pure Spectrum. In our prism experiment the beam of light was almost parallel and the colours were fairly well separated. In other words, the spectrum was fairly *pure.*

If the beam is divergent, we obtain so much overlapping that colour is only seen at the two edges, red at the top and blue at the bottom ; the spectrum is *impure* (fig. 202).

Experiment. Set up a convex lens of focal length about 12 in. at a distance of about 14 in. from an illuminated slit. Where will the image be? Focus it carefully on a white screen. Both distances will depend on the power of your source of light. Why? Place the prism close to the lens with its refracting edge parallel to the slit. The prism may be on either side of the lens. Move the prism until the colourless image entirely

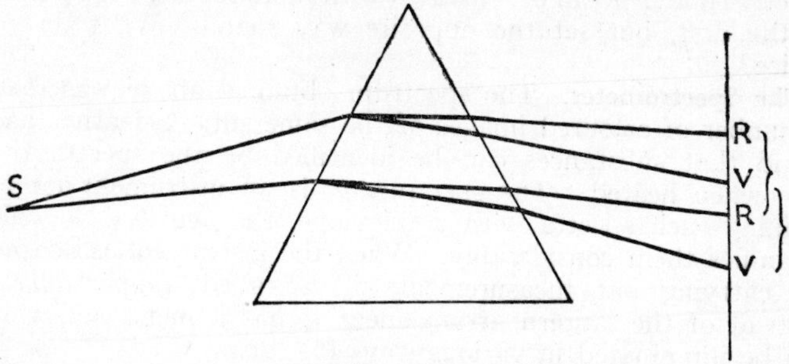

FIG. 202.

disappears. A pure spectrum will be formed on the screen. Rotate the prism until it is set at minimum deviation. The colours are then brightest (fig. 203).

Having obtained this *real* spectrum on the screen, look into the prism for a *virtual* spectrum.

If the aperture of the lens happens to be larger than the prism face, it can be stopped down with four strips of black adhesive

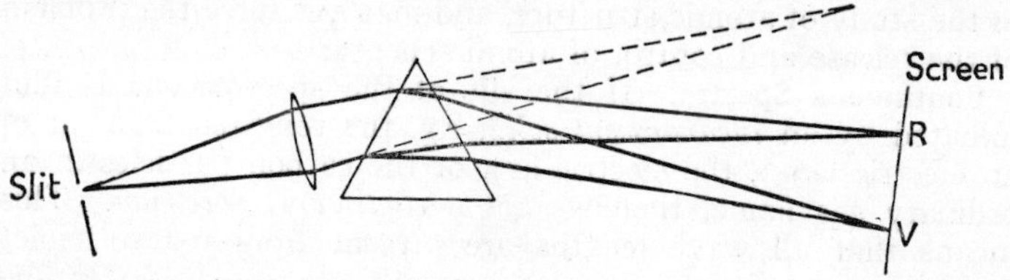

FIG. 203.

paper, stuck on the lens in such a way as to leave a square aperture of the desired size.

If a small magic lantern is available, an illuminated slit can easily be fixed up; remove the objective and cut a disc of cardboard large enough to cover the hole. In the disc cut a slit 1 in. × $\frac{1}{16}$ in. Around the circumference stick a piece of paper. This now serves as a cap to slip on to the lantern. With such a lantern, a reading glass and a glass "lustre" the whole experiment can be done at home.

Hold different coloured pencils or skeins of wool in various parts of the spectrum. Record your observations. Use another exactly similar prism or "lustre" with its refracting edge parallel to the first, but set the opposite way round. What do you notice?

The Spectrometer. The spectrum obtained above was really a number of coloured images of the same slit. Scientists have found that substances can be identified by the spectra they give when heated. The spectro*scope* is an instrument for examining such spectra with a telescope, the eyepiece of which magnifies them considerably. When the instrument is adapted for carrying out measurements it is called a spectro*meter*. Instead of the lantern arrangement it has a metal slit which can be illuminated in various ways (fig. 204A).

The method of analysis here indicated was first used by the German scientists Bunsen and Kirchhoff in the latter half of the nineteenth century. It enabled them to discover two new elements of the sodium family, namely Rubidium and Cæsium. By this same method Sir Wm. Crookes discovered the metal Thallium and definitely proved the rare gases of the atmosphere to be really distinct elements, and not merely different sorts of nitrogen.

To-day the method of spectroscopy is playing a great part in the study of atomic structure, and may yet solve the problem of the release and control of atomic energy.

Continuous Spectra. If the slit of the spectroscope is illuminated by an *incandescent solid, e.g.* the tungsten filament of an electric lamp, the electric arc, or the carbon particles in an ordinary gas flame, then we get a *continuous spectrum.* This means that all wave lengths are present from red to violet inclusive.

Bright Line Spectra. When the slit is illuminated by an *incandescent gas or vapour,* then the spectrum is no longer continuous; only certain wave lengths are present. Gases give *bright line* spectra, no two of which are alike. If common salt is held on a platinum wire or ordinary wire gauze in the non-luminous bunsen flame, we get a bright line in the yellow region from the incandescent sodium vapour.

Similarly from incandescent lithium vapour we get a red line and a yellow line. The yellow lithium line corresponds to a longer wave length, lower frequency, or "lower pitch" than that of sodium, therefore it will be slightly nearer to the red end of the spectrum. The positions of these lines can easily be distinguished by reflecting a graduated scale into the telescope

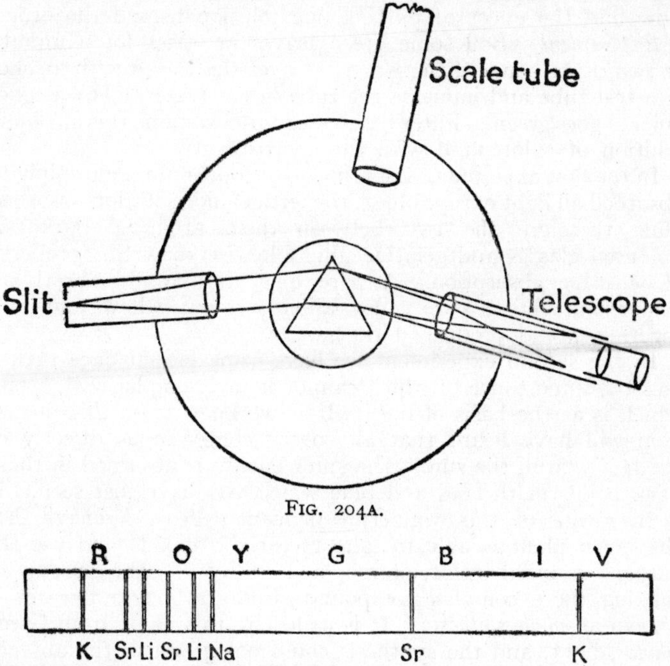

FIG. 204A.

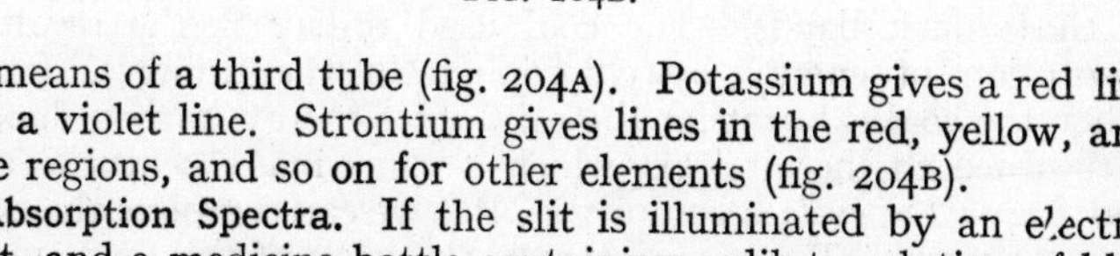

FIG. 204B.

by means of a third tube (fig. 204A). Potassium gives a red line and a violet line. Strontium gives lines in the red, yellow, and blue regions, and so on for other elements (fig. 204B).

Absorption Spectra. If the slit is illuminated by an electric light, and a medicine bottle containing a dilute solution of blue litmus is held in front of the slit, some of the light will be absorbed. But the action of the liquid is not to absorb a little light of *all* wave lengths, it takes mainly wave lengths from the yellow. In other words, the absorption is not *general* but *selective*; there will be a dark band in the yellow.

Experiment. To a 10% solution of copper sulphate add ammonium hydroxide until the precipitate which first forms just dissolves. Test this liquid for selective absorption, diluting if necessary. Repeat with a solution of potassium ferricyanide. Now find the effect of putting one solution behind the other.

Experiment. Boil some green leaves in water for a minute or two, then pour off the water. Cover the leaves with alcohol in a test-tube and immerse the tube in hot water. The alcohol quickly goes green. Filter if necessary and examine this alcoholic solution of chlorophyll with the spectroscope.

In the first experiment the solution of copper ammoniosulphate absorbed all light except blue; the ferricyanide solution absorbed blue, therefore the two between them produced darkness. Coloured glasses and gelatine films likewise show this property of selective absorption. A pure blue glass would absorb all colours but blue, a pure yellow all colours but yellow, and both together would produce darkness.

In the second experiment we have come face to face with a fact the importance of which cannot be over-emphasized, a fact which is at the basis of life itself as we know it on this planet. You will have heard that all energy comes to us directly or indirectly from the sun. The sun's energy is absorbed in those dark bands in the red and blue which you have just seen. It is by means of this wonderful pigment called *chlorophyll* that the green plant is able to take in carbon dioxide and use the carbon to build sugar, starch, and cellulose. The process of making these complex compounds from carbon and water is known as *photosynthesis*. It is called by this name from Greek *photos*, light, and the synthesis could not go on in the absence of light, that is, without the absorption of energy from the sun in those dark bands. The coal used to-day is the result of absorption of energy by chlorophyll in the primeval forest. When the coal is burnt for the sake of its energy, carbon dioxide is returned to the air from which it came many centuries ago, and the *carbon cycle* is complete. But we can complete the cycle in other ways. The green plant is the basis of the food supply of all animal life including man himself. The working ox derives his energy from the green plant, but he may also serve as the unfortunate connecting link between the green plant and the tiger! In both cases the slow combustion of the carbon in the body causes the energy of the sun to reappear as heat and work, and carbon dioxide is restored to the air. We may sum up the matter from the energy point of view by saying—

Carbon + Oxygen → Carbon dioxide (Energy given out)
Carbon dioxide → Carbon + Oxygen (Energy taken in).

Other substances giving interesting absorption spectra are potassium permanganate solution of various dilutions, iodine vapour, chlorine, and nitrogen peroxide.

All the spectra dealt with in this chapter can be very nicely observed with a handy little instrument called the *direct vision* spectroscope, which consists of prisms and lenses mounted in a single brass tube.

Chemistry of the Sun and Stars. When sunlight is examined with a spectroscope, a large number of dark lines is seen running transversely across the spectrum. A few of them were observed by an English doctor and scientist, W. H. Wollaston, in 1802, but the German physicist Fraunhofer in 1814 counted 576 of these lines and lettered them off in groups A, B, C, D, etc.

The cause of these "Fraunhofer lines" was an absolute mystery until 1848 when Foucault in France made a most remarkable discovery.

It had been noticed that two of these *dark* lines were situated in the yellow exactly where sodium vapour gives two *bright* lines. These were called the D lines. Foucault showed that if a very powerful light from an electric arc was made to pass through a flame coloured yellow by a sodium salt, the spectroscope showed two dark lines in the exact position of the D lines.

The mystery was further investigated at Heidelberg by Kirchhoff, and in 1859 he was able to give a clear explanation of the whole question.

Kirchhoff soaked the wick of a spirit lamp in sodium chloride solution and then dried it. On examining the flame through a spectroscope, the bright D lines were seen as usual. But when strong sunlight was made to pass through this flame into the spectroscope, the bright D lines of the sodium flame were exactly replaced by the dark D lines of sunlight, and *they were darker than usual*.

From this strange result, Kirchhoff reasoned that if sodium

vapour could *darken* these lines, then it might have *caused* them in the first place.

He now passed limelight through the sodium vapour, and there again on the ordinary red to violet background, dark D lines were produced! On cutting off the limelight, the D lines were bright again and these results could be repeated at will. With lithium in the flame similar results were obtained.

The most reasonable explanation of all this is that the incandescent lime corresponds to the sun's nucleus, the sodium flame to sodium vapour in the sun's glowing atmosphere or *photosphere*. In both cases the sodium absorbs its own wave lengths. Since the rest of the light gets through unweakened, there is in each case a bright background on which the *less bright* D lines look dark by contrast.

As a result of all his experiments, Kirchhoff came to the conclusion that **a glowing gas or vapour absorbs its own wave lengths from light sent out by a hotter source.**

To-day his experiments are often repeated with an arc light as the hot source and a bunsen flame containing vapours of the compounds of sodium, potassium, calcium, strontium, etc., as the absorbing "photosphere."

Kirchhoff's work thus cleared up the mystery of the Fraunhofer lines. If the brilliant background of the sun's nucleus could be for an instant cut off, then those dark lines would become bright as in the limelight experiment. Since the time of Kirchhoff the work has gone on steadily, and to-day we know that the sun's atmosphere contains more than thirty of our terrestrial elements, the most prevalent being hydrogen, magnesium, iron, sodium, potassium, calcium, and carbon.

The same methods have been applied to stars, and here we meet another wonder of spectroscopy. By its aid astronomers have been able to measure the speed of stars which happen to be travelling towards or away from the earth. When you are standing on a railway platform, an engine sometimes passes through while giving out a shrill whistle. The pitch of the whistle is higher than the true pitch while the engine is approaching and drops suddenly below the true pitch when the engine is receding. Now *pitch* in sound corresponds to *colour* in light. Similarly, the lines in star spectra move towards the violet or region of higher pitch when the star is approaching, and towards the red when the star recedes. By measuring the shift in the spectral lines it is possible to measure the speed of the star. This change of pitch in sound and light was explained by an Austrian physicist Johann Christian Doppler (1803–53).

The Invisible Parts of the Sun's Spectrum. When a solid is *white* hot it is giving out light of all wave lengths. When it is merely *red* hot it is only giving out *red* waves. If the cooling is continued, it becomes invisible in the dark. Is it still giving out waves? Yes, it is now giving out heat waves or the so-called **infra-red rays.**

The fact that these heat waves are similar to light waves was discovered in 1800 by the elder Herschel, who had already made himself famous by the discovery of the planet Uranus.

Sir William Herschel put a thermometer with a blackened bulb into the sun's spectrum. He found that the temperature steadily rose in passing from the violet to the red. Moreover, the rise was still more marked in the dark space beyond. The sun evidently sends out waves which are longer than red waves.

These infra-red rays have since been carefully investigated by the American physicist Langley. Like light waves they can be reflected and refracted. In fact, the difference between them and light waves is simply a question of *wave length.*

About the same time as Herschel's discovery of the infra-red rays, Johann Wilhelm Ritter, a scientist of Munich, was busy exploring the other end of the visible spectrum.

Ritter found that the action of light in blackening photographic silver salts increased as one passed through the sun's spectrum from red to violet. Moreover, in the dark space beyond the violet, the action was greater still. In exploring this region photographic plates are used.

These short waves of **ultra-violet light** have since been found to have important health-giving properties, but unfortunately they are stopped or absorbed by smoke and clouds. Ordinary window glass is also opaque to practically the whole band of ultra-violet wave lengths.

Quartz glass transmits down to very short waves and certain rooms in hospitals are now being fitted with window-panes of this material. But in the manufacture of this, a temperature of about 1700° C. is required to soften the quartz crystals, a temperature about three times higher than that necessary for ordinary glass-making. This makes the cost high.

Considerable research has been carried out in several countries with the object of making a glass which would transmit a fair proportion of the rays and yet be not too expensive for general use. Several glass materials are known which satisfy these conditions, but some of them are acted upon by the atmosphere. In 1925 an Englishman, Lamplough, discovered that glass containing 2% boric acid and no iron oxide went a long way towards satisfying all three conditions. This glass is now on the market under the name "Vitaglass." A short time ago the skylights of the monkey-house at the London Zoo were glazed with this material to the great joy of the inmates.

It will be obvious that all lenses and prisms used in the investigation of the properties of these rays must be of quartz glass since this transmits almost the whole wave band. With regard to the ordinary properties of reflection and refraction, it has been found that ultra-violet rays like infra-red rays are similar to the waves of the visible spectrum; the difference is just a matter of wave length.

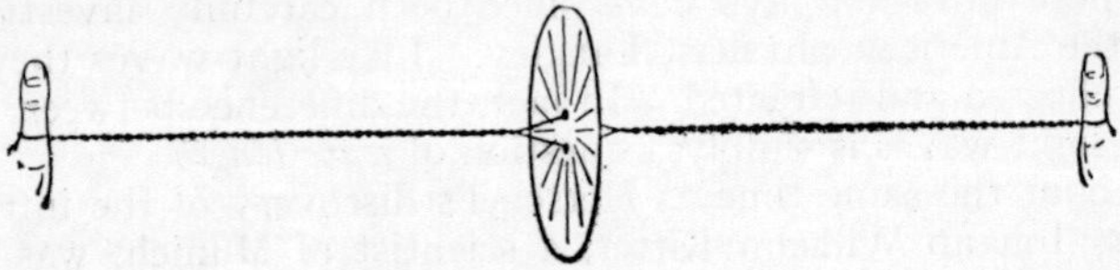

FIG. 205.

Recomposition of White Light. In our experiments with a pure spectrum, we finally placed two prisms with their refractive edges in opposite directions. We found that the image of the slit returned to its old position and was free from colour. This experiment was first done by Sir Isaac Newton.

Another experiment of his on the recomposition of white light is the well-known colour disc experiment. A disc of white cardboard was divided into fourteen sectors. These were painted with the seven colours in order and then the colours were repeated. The disc was then rapidly rotated.

We may imitate his experiment by means of a well-known toy (fig. 205). The disc when spun will be approximately *white*. The fact that it is not quite white is due to the fact that pigments are never as pure as the colours of the spectrum, *e.g.* blue always contains a little green.

The Colour of an Object. When we held a coloured object in our pure spectrum, we found that the apparent colour depended upon the part of the spectrum in which it was held. A pure red article held in the red would look red, but in any other part of the spectrum it would look black. An article described as "red" in daylight reflects red wave lengths but absorbs most of the rest. A *pure* red would absorb *all* the remaining wave lengths.

A dead-black object absorbs all wave lengths so that strictly speaking we do not see it, but we infer its existence because we are receiving light from its surroundings; it is the white linen collar which tells us where the black coat starts!

Why does a blue suit look darker in artificial light? Because such light is deficient in blue and *the cloth cannot reflect what it does not receive.*

A pure blue glass, when held up to daylight, *transmits* blue wave lengths and absorbs the rest. Similarly a pure yellow glass transmits only yellow. When both are held one behind the other no light is transmitted; the result is *black.*

Here we have the key to a well-known optical puzzle. The difficulty is to reconcile the following three facts:

(*a*) If blue light and yellow light are sent from two lanterns on to a white screen, the result is *white.*

(*b*) If a disc is painted partly blue and partly yellow, then spun, the result is *white.*

(*c*) Yet if blue pigment is mixed with yellow pigment the result is *green.*

The last fact is an accident due to the impurities of the pigments. If the pigments were pure, the effect would be the same as with the blue and yellow glasses, namely black. For when white light strikes the paper, the blue pigment would send back blue and absorb all other colours. But this blue light has to get through a yellow pigment which absorbs everything but yellow. Thus yellow absorbs blue and blue absorbs yellow, so no light would be sent back at all and the result would be black. Actually blue and yellow pigments are impure and each sends back some green, so this is the resulting colour.

There is thus a great difference between mixing lights and mixing pigments.

In (*a*) we meet the fact that blue and yellow are complementary colours (see below). In (*b*) we are again mixing lights and not pigments, for when using the colour disc, blue has not to pass through yellow nor yellow through blue; the lights are mixed on a "screen"—the retina of the eye. The result of course is not a perfect white owing to the slight green in the pigment.

To sum up, we may say that in (*a*) and (*b*) we are mixing lights (addition) and in (*c*) we are mixing pigments (subtraction).

Primary and Complementary Colours. Experiments with the colour disc show that any other colour may be obtained by mixing in the right proportions the three colours **Red, Green,** and **Blue.** For this reason they are called the **Primary Colours.** To make white we should need some of all three.

Two colours which together produce white are called **Complementary Colours.** The relation between primary and complementary colours can easily be remembered by means of the following scheme—

Yellow (Red + Green)   Peacock Blue (Green + Blue)

Red + Green + Blue = White

Magenta (Red + Blue)

Therefore:

Red + Peacock Blue = White
Green + Magenta = White
Blue + Yellow = White

To mix colours or lights, two methods have already been mentioned, namely, the colour disc and the method which uses two lanterns. There is a third which may be tried.

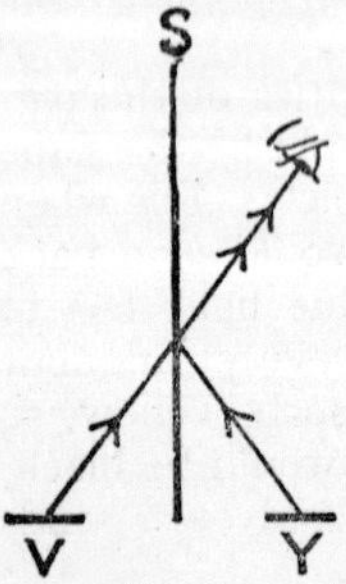
Fig. 206.

In fig. 206 V and Y are strips of violet (or blue) and yellow paper standing on a sheet of black paper. S is a sheet of glass which may be a photographic quarter plate with the film removed. The eye sees both papers at once, and the result is approximately a white strip. Other colours may be combined in a similar way.

Colour Vision. Since all the other colours of the spectrum may be produced by mixing red, green, and blue, Thomas Young in England and Hermann von Helmholtz (1821–94) in Germany suggested that there were three different sets of nerves in the eye corresponding to the three primary colours. But although they were both medical men as well as physicists, they were unable to confirm this theory by dissection of the optic nerve. Nevertheless, the theory is quite useful in explaining many of the known facts relating to colour vision.

Experiment. Place a slip of bright red paper in the middle of a sheet of white paper. Gaze at it steadily for about 20 sec., then allow it to slide off. The area now looks peacock blue —the complementary colour. The "red nerves" are tired and only the "green and blue nerves" are responding to the white light received from the paper. The eye is for the moment "colour blind" with respect to red.

Repeat with other coloured slips and try to make up a list of complementary colours.[1]

Scattering of Light in Nature. A street lamp seen through a fog looks red like the setting sun. The explanation is the same in both cases. The shorter the waves, the more easily they are scattered or irregularly reflected by small obstacles. The light from the lamp and from the sun has been deprived of a large proportion of its short blue waves by this scattering; the light which gets through is therefore redder. Light has to travel a longer distance through the atmosphere at sunset than at other times of the day.

The motorist in a fog is also affected by this scattering effect. Approaching lamps look red, but this is not his chief trouble; his own lamps throw out all wave lengths from red to violet, but the blue-violet waves are reflected back from the particles of the fog giving the appearance of a bluish-white blanket in front.

To get over this trouble he uses an "antiglare" lamp with a yellow glass. The useless blue-violet waves now do not get out. A red glass would serve the same purpose except that red is the recognized colour for rear lights.

This scattering of blue light is responsible for the light blue colour of smoke and the blue sky is thought to be due to the same cause. The colour of the setting sun can be imitated in a very simple way.

Experiment.—Take half a beaker of 1% "hypo" solution and add the same volume of dilute hydrochloric acid (the usual 10 to 1 reagent). Hold this in front of a milky electric globe. In a minute or so there will be a fine precipitate of sulphur, the lamp

[1] "Colour" is fully dealt with by Mr. E. G. Savage, C.B., in *The School Science Review*, Parts 49, 50, 51, 66.

will look yellow, then orange, then red, and finally will become invisible.

Or, if an optical lantern is available, throw a disc of light on to a white screen. Place in front of the lantern, or better, just in front of the condenser, a flat-sided glass vessel containing one of the liquids. Add the other liquid, and the screen will show the sun reddening slowly from the bottom upwards.

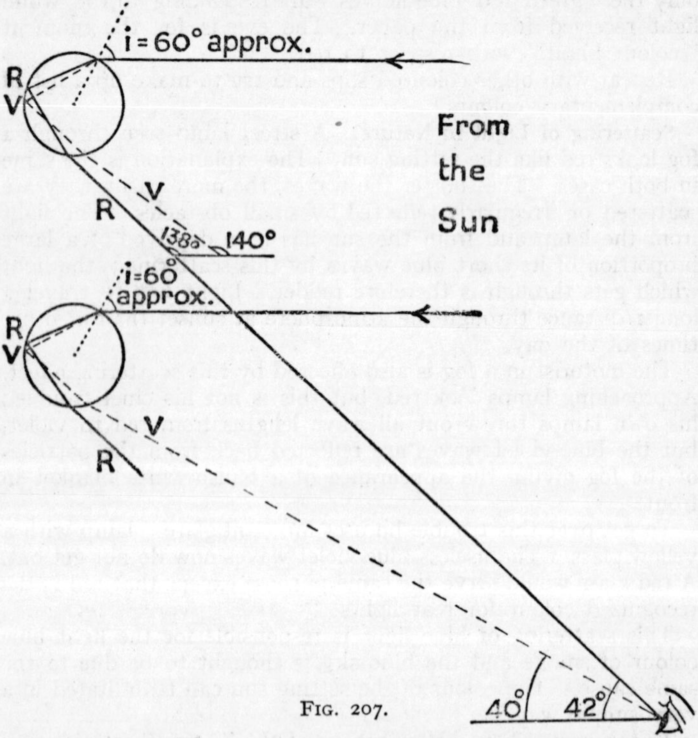

FIG. 207.

The Rainbow. The most wonderful example of dispersion in nature is undoubtedly the *rainbow*.

In order to obtain a rough idea of the cause of the rainbow, let us consider what happens when a ray of light strikes a spherical drop of water (fig. 207). The ray will bend towards the normal on entering the drop, but will also be *dispersed*. Some of the light will then be reflected at the back surface of the drop, and when it comes out it will be still more dispersed.

It can be proved that when $\underline{|i}$ has any value within a few degrees of 60°, the rays coming out of the drop will form a strong beam of dispersed light, the violet making an angle of 140° with the original direction and the red an angle of 138°.

If $\underline{|i}$ has any value outside these limits, then the emerging beam will be too divergent to affect any single observer. Even when $\underline{|i}$ is within the limits, the red and violet from the same drop will not reach the same observer because they are diverging;

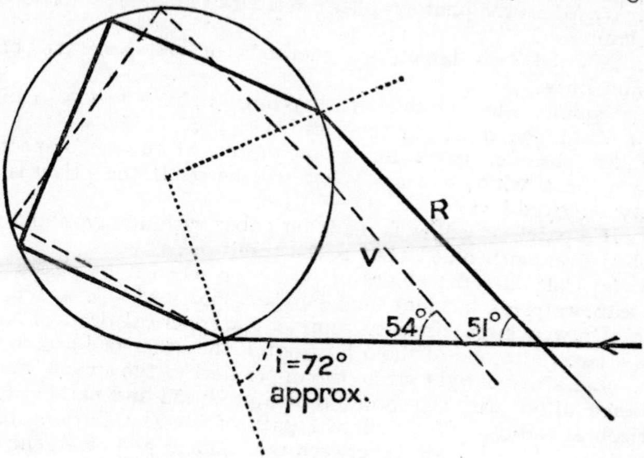

FIG. 208.

the red forms the top of "Mr. Brown's" rainbow while the violet forms the bottom of the rainbow seen by our neighbour "Mr. Robinson" who is standing some distance farther back.

But the red from one drop and the violet from another farther down will converge to a single observer, while other colours arrive from drops situated between these two. The observer will then see the *primary bow* forming the rim of a cone whose semi-vertical angle varies from 40° to 42°.

Outside this bow will be drops of water which send no light to our observer and there he will see a dark patch.

But farther out still will be drops of water giving a spectrum formed by two internal reflections (fig. 208). These produce the *secondary bow*.

From the above reasoning it will be seen that the rainbow is caused by dispersion of sunlight in raindrops and that the observer must have his back to the sun.

QUESTIONS

1. Can you justify the statement that coal is "bottled sunshine"?

2. Since a lens is partly made up of prisms, should it disperse light like a prism? Give reasons for your answer and illustrate by a diagram.

3. Why does the photographer use a dark red glass in his developing lamp?

4. Describe two laboratory methods of *reversing* the bright sodium lines.

5. Explain the statement "White light − yellow = blue." How could you illustrate the fact?

6. An observer gazes for 20 or 30 sec. at the sun's spectrum thrown on a white screen. What will he see if the prism is suddenly removed?

7. If a patch of yellow is made on paper with a crayon and then rubbed over with blue, what is the result? Why?

8. (*a*) Calculate the angles of refraction when light passes from air into water at incident angles of 55°, 60°, 65°. [$\mu = 1{\cdot}33$.]

(*b*) Draw a large circle to represent a spherical drop of water. Draw two radii, one of them horizontal, the other inclined to it at 60°. Let a ray of light strike the upper part of the sphere, making an angle of 60° with the second radius produced and parallel to the horizontal radius. Work out the path of the ray allowing it one reflection. Find the angle between the incident and emergent rays.

(*c*) On the same diagram repeat exercise (*b*) using an angle of 55° instead of 60°.

(*d*) On the same diagram repeat exercise (*b*) using an angle of 65°

9. A trade poster consists of letters printed, some in green and others in red, on a white background. Describe and explain the effect of illuminating it with (*a*) green light, (*b*) red light, (*c*) both lights at once. (C. part question.)

10. Give an explanation of the cause of the colour of (1) a piece of red cloth, (2) a piece of red glass when viewed in daylight. Describe experiments you would make to justify your answer. (L.)

CHAPTER XXIII

PHOTOMETRY OR LIGHT MEASUREMENT

It is common experience that some sources give out much more light than others, *e.g.* a 40-watt lamp gives more light than a candle. The object of the present chapter is to study some of the simpler methods of comparing sources of light.

Suppose there is a point source of light at O (fig. 209). It is

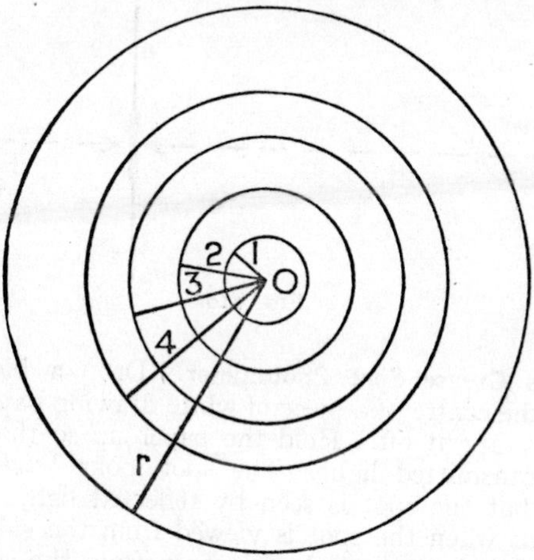

FIG. 209.

clear that the farther you are away from this light, the more difficult it will be to read by it. But let us try to get a more precise statement than this.

Imagine spheres of radii 1, 2, 3, 4 . . . r ft. described round the source of light and let L units of light be sent out from the source every second. The areas of the spheres will be $4\pi \times 1^2$, $4\pi \times 2^2$, $4\pi \times 3^2$, $4\pi \times 4^2$ . . . $4\pi r^2$ sq. ft.

The quantity of light falling on 1 sq. ft. of each sphere will be

$$\frac{L}{4\pi 1^2} \quad \frac{L}{4\pi 2^2} \quad \frac{L}{4\pi 3^2} \quad \frac{L}{4\pi 4^2} \cdots \frac{L}{4\pi r^2}$$

or

$$\frac{L}{4\pi} \quad \frac{L}{16\pi} \quad \frac{L}{36\pi} \quad \frac{L}{64\pi} \cdots \frac{L}{4\pi r^2}$$

or $1 : \frac{1}{4} : \frac{1}{9} : \frac{1}{16}$ and so on.

We see then that the intensity of the illumination falls off very rapidly; when we double the distance it is four times weaker or four times more difficult to read. When we treble the distance the intensity is nine times weaker.

To sum up, we may say that **the intensity of illumination is inversely proportional to the square of the distance from the source.** This is called the *Law of Inverse Squares.* You will often meet this law in physics.

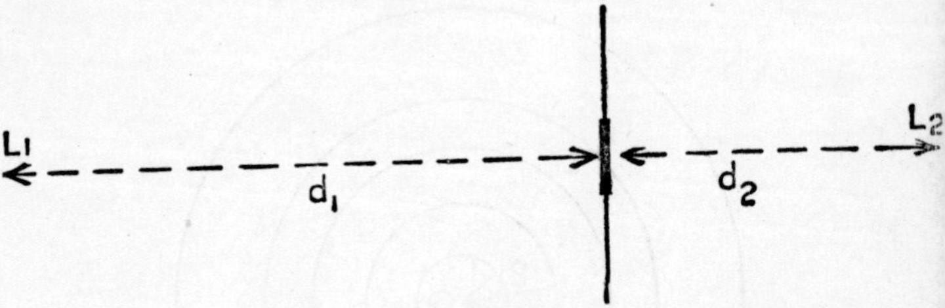

FIG. 210.

Bunsen's Grease Spot Photometer. Drop a blob of candle grease on the centre of a piece of white drawing paper. When it solidifies, scrape it off. Hold the paper up so that the spot is seen by transmitted light. The spot looks *bright.* Hold the paper so that the spot is seen by reflected light. The spot is *dark.* Thus when the spot is viewed from the side of stronger illumination it is dark, and when seen from the side of weaker illumination it appears bright. If the intensity is the same on each side, then either the spot disappears or it will look the same from each side.

Next suppose that we have two sources of light, one on each side of the grease spot. Let one give out L_1 units of light per second and the other L_2 units per second. It will be possible to arrange the distances d_1 and d_2 of the two sources so that the intensity of illumination is the same on each side (fig. 210). Now the spot can be regarded as being a small part of a sphere radius d_1 and also part of a sphere radius d_2. From our previous reasoning the intensity on one side will be $\frac{L_1}{4\pi d_1^2}$ and on the other $\frac{L_2}{4\pi d_2^2}$. But we have just arranged matters so that the intensity is the same on each side

$$\therefore \frac{L_1}{4\pi d_1^2} = \frac{L_2}{4\pi d_2^2}$$

$$\text{or} \quad \frac{L_1}{L_2} = \frac{d_1^2}{d_2^2}.$$

Now the **Candle-power** of a source is proportional to the quantity of light given out per second.

Therefore we may rewrite the above equation thus—

$$\frac{\text{Candle-power of Source (1)}}{\text{Candle-power of Source (2)}} = \frac{d_1^2}{d_2^2}.$$

The above arrangement of the grease spot is not very convenient, and in practice things are generally managed so that

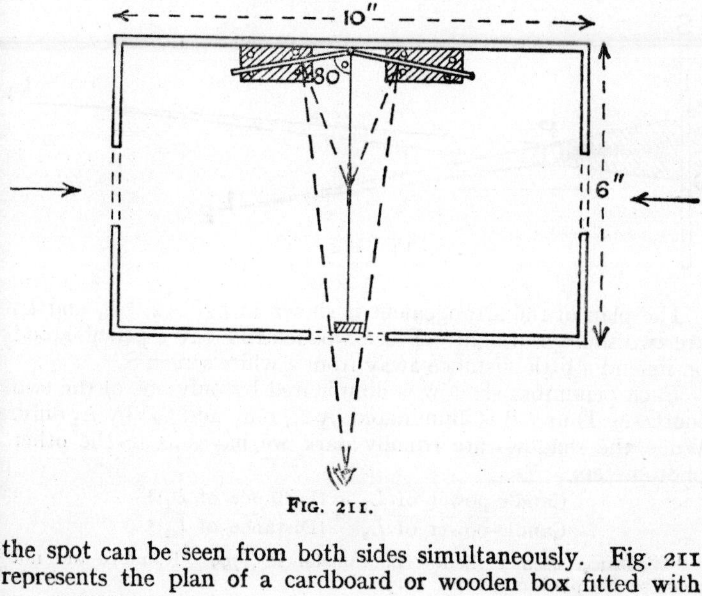

FIG. 211.

the spot can be seen from both sides simultaneously. Fig. 211 represents the plan of a cardboard or wooden box fitted with

two mirrors and a grease spot. It is convenient to enclose the paper carrying the grease spot in a sort of picture frame made of strips of cardboard. This and the mirrors can be fixed in an erect position in slots formed between bits of wood nailed to the bottom of the box.

The apertures may be $1\frac{1}{2}$ in. wide, either circular or rectangular. The two mirrors, $4\frac{1}{2}$ in. × $3\frac{3}{4}$ in., can be cut with a steel cutter from a sixpenny mirror obtainable at a well-known popular store. Such an apparatus can easily be made in the school workshop.

It is an improvement if the inside of the box has a coat of dead-black paint.

For practice the two sources may be four candles stuck on a wooden block, and one candle similarly mounted. During the experiment the top of the box should be covered with a lid or an exercise book.

The Rumford [1] Shadow Photometer. One of the earliest photometers, and still interesting, is that generally credited to Count Rumford, whose name you met in studying heat.

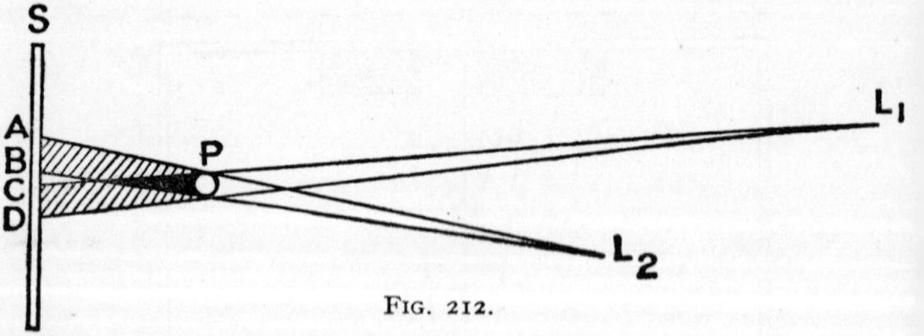

FIG. 212.

The plan of the arrangement is shown in fig. 212. L_1 and L_2 are two sources of light. P is a wooden rod, say a pencil, stood on its end a little distance away from a white screen S.

Each penumbra shadow is illuminated by only one of the two sources. Thus AB is illuminated by L_1 only and CD by L_2 only. When the shadows are equally dark we have, as in the other photometers,

$$\frac{\text{Candle-power of } L_1}{\text{Candle-power of } L_2} = \frac{(\text{Distance of } L_1)^2}{(\text{Distance of } L_2)^2}.$$

[1] Wollaston used a shadow photometer in 1799. Rumford did not describe his photometer till 1813.

QUESTIONS

1. A source of light consisting of four candles mounted close together is situated 50 cm. from a grease spot. A single candle is fixed on the other side of the spot, so that there is equal illumination. Find the distance of the single candle.

2. State the Law of Inverse Squares. Show how it could be verified for two sources of light.

3. Two men are reading evening papers, one at 10 ft., the other at 30 ft. from a street lamp. Compare the intensity of illumination in each case.

4. If a gas-light print has to be held for half a minute 12 in. away from a 20-candle-power lamp, how far should it be held from a 30-candle-power lamp?

5. Describe the apparatus and method you would use to compare the candle-powers of two light sources.

Two lamps A and B are placed so as to give equal illuminations on a surface. A is replaced by a lamp of twice its candle-power. How must B be moved to give equal illumination? (L.)

MAGNETISM AND ELECTRICITY

CHAPTER XXIV

MAGNETISM

Early History of Magnetism. The ancient Greeks were acquainted with a peculiar kind of black stone found round the town of Magnesia,[1] near Smyrna in Asia Minor. They called it *magnēs*. To-day we call this ore "magnetite." The shepherds of Asia Minor found that pieces of this rock clung to their iron-shod crooks.

In later times many legends and superstitions grew up round this fact. Sailors said that islands were known which were made entirely of this strange material. To approach such an island was very dangerous, for the nails and the ironwork in the ship would be so strongly attracted that they would fly off and the ship would break up!

Sometimes a dangerous wizard would take up his dwelling near one of these rocks and when the mail-clad knight approached to attack, not only was he held fast to the rock by the attractive force, but his sword, spear, and dagger suffered a like fate (fig. 213).

In more modern fairy tales the villain is made to stand straight out from the rock, held fast by his hobnailed boots.

About the eleventh century the sailor's superstitious dread of this rock became tempered by the discovery of another property valuable in navigation; it was found that a piece of this same rock suspended by a thread or allowed to float on a cork in a dish of water pointed north and south. This was the first mariner's compass. The rock was now called "loadstone" or "leading stone" because it helped to lead the way.

The next advance was to rub a strip of steel with the loadstone. The steel acquired the property of pointing north and south when suspended by a thread or floated on a piece of wood.

It has been claimed for the Chinese that they knew the attractive and directive properties of loadstone as far back as 2000 B.C.

[1] Now called Manissa.

From the chemical point of view loadstone is ferroso-ferric oxide Fe_3O_4. This oxide can be made in the laboratory and it is the oxide which scales off iron in a blacksmith's shop. It is also called "magnetic oxide of iron." As a mineral the oxide is widely distributed. It is always attracted by a magnet, but only rarely is it a magnet itself.

FIG. 213.

The next great stride forward in our knowledge of magnetism was made by William Gilbert (1540–1603) of Colchester. Gilbert was Court physician under Queen Elizabeth and for a short time acted in the same capacity for James I. In his spare time he studied electricity, magnetism, and chemistry. His experiments in magnetism are described in his book, *De Magnete, Magneticisque Corporibus, et de Magno Magnete Tellure—Concerning the Magnet, Magnetic Bodies, and the Great Magnet the Earth.*

Dr. Gilbert showed that if a bar of iron was placed in the north and south direction and hammered, it became a magnet. A red-hot bar of steel treated in the same way also became a magnet. He was the first to point out that, in any magnet natural or artificial, there were two points where the attractive force was strongest. These he called the *poles* of the magnet. When the magnet was suspended, one of these poles pointed to the north and was called the " north-seeking pole " or " north pole " while the other was called the " south-seeking pole " or " south pole." If two of these magnets were suspended, it was found that **Like poles repel and unlike poles attract each other.**

Gilbert further pointed out that the observed facts relating to magnetic needles could be explained by supposing that the earth was itself a magnet having two poles close to the north and south geographical poles. He conjectured that magnetism and electricity were intimately related, a guess which was in later times amply justified by the experiments of Oersted in Denmark and Faraday in England.

Simple Experiments with Magnets.

1. Sprinkle iron filings on a bar magnet. They cling mainly at the ends—the poles are at or near the ends. Sprinkle the filings on a smooth piece of paper. Hold a bar magnet underneath with one pole in contact with the paper. The filings can be made to stand up, lie down or march along in life-like fashion.

2. Suspend a bar magnet in a stirrup of paper by means of unspun silk. It will point north and south. Bring up another bar magnet. It can be shown that like poles repel and opposite poles attract each other.

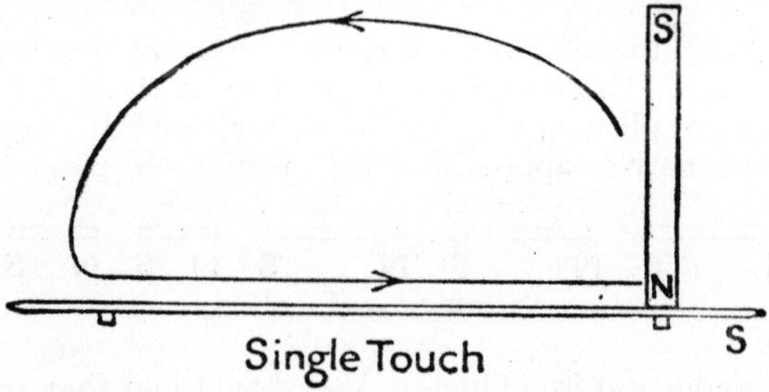

FIG. 214.

3. Stick two small bits of plasticine to the bench. Press a steel knitting-needle on them. Gently stroke the needle with

the north end of a bar magnet. Repeat several times in the same direction (fig. 214). Apply the end last stroked to the south end of a compass needle. It should be repelled. Note that repulsion is a surer test of magnetization than attraction. Why?

This method of magnetizing is known as *Single Touch*.

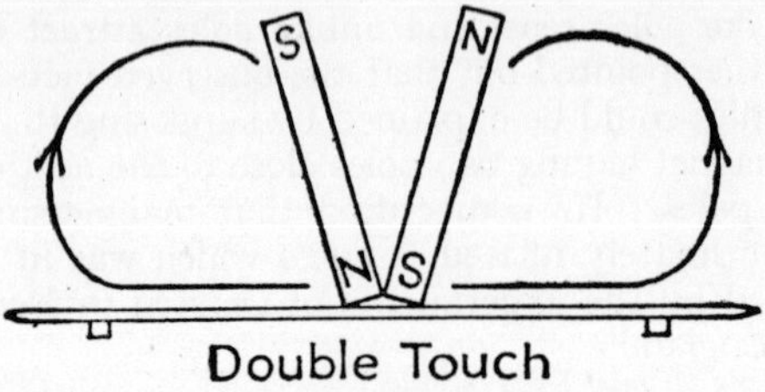

FIG. 215.

Stroke the needle with two magnets as shown in fig. 215. You should find that the needle becomes more strongly magnetized.

This is the method of *Double Touch*. Note that the stroking magnets have opposite poles in contact. If the stroking magnets

FIG. 216.

have like poles together you will get a *consequent* or *intermediate* pole (fig. 216). The filings will then cling at three places.

By means of pliers and a vice, break the correctly magnetized needle into halves approximately. Test each piece with a

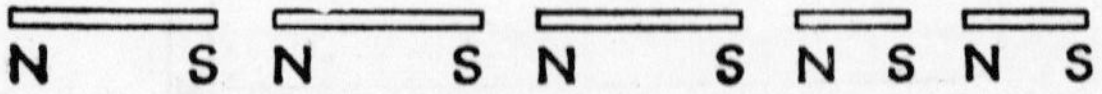

FIG. 217.

compass needle and iron filings. You should find that you now have two magnets. Break the needle into quarters and test again. Break off about an inch and test this small bit. In all cases the piece is a complete magnet having north and south poles (fig. 217).

Take one of the quarter lengths and make it red hot in the bunsen flame. When cold test it with filings and compass needle.

4. Fill a test-tube with steel filings. Close the tube with a cork cut as short as possible. Lay the tube on the bench and magnetize by Double Touch, rolling the tube gently through a small angle between each few strokes, so that all filings near the surface shall be affected. Test for magnetization. Shake the tube and test again.

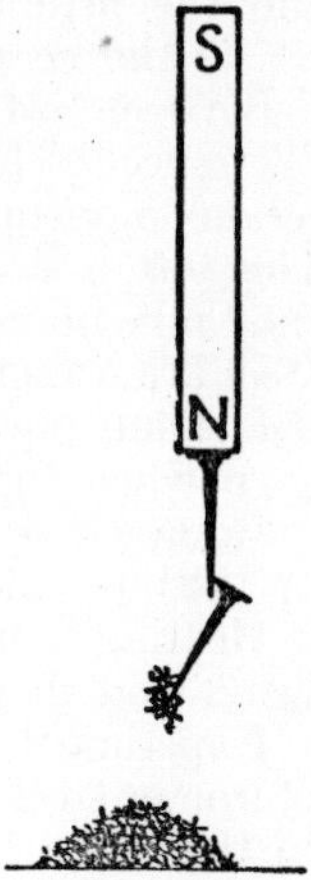

FIG. 218.

5. Use a bar magnet and a few small wire nails as shown in fig. 218. The bottom nail readily picks up iron filings. Remove the top nail from the magnet and the whole system collapses.

Each nail became magnetized by *induction,* a south pole being *induced* at one end and a north at the other. In other words, for the time being, each nail becomes itself a magnet, and since the filings to a great extent stand end to end they also become magnets.

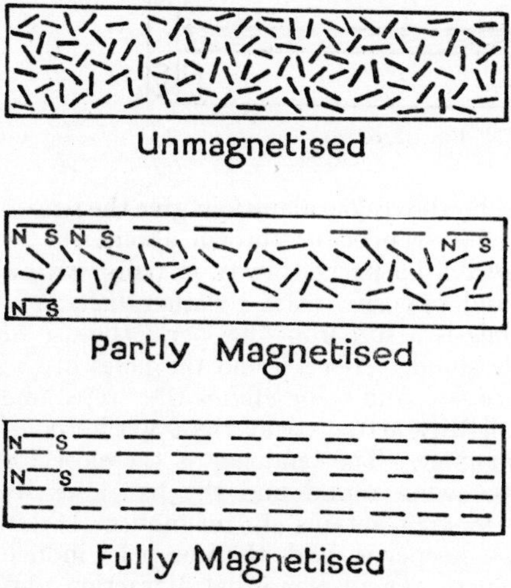

FIG. 219.

Molecular Magnets. According to Ampère in France, Weber in Germany, and Ewing in England, the above experiments have a very simple explanation. In a piece of unmagnetized iron each molecule is a magnet, but the molecules are generally so thoroughly mixed up with their axes in all directions that they neutralize one another (fig. 219).

The stroke of a bar

magnet acts like the order "from the right in twos—number," and the little molecules near the surface number off "NS., NS., NS.," and so on.

Between soft iron and steel there is here a very important difference. The former is more easily magnetized, but the latter retains more magnetism when the magnetizing force is removed. The soft iron molecules quite readily obey the command, but they mix up as soon as they get the chance. The molecules in steel are a more disciplined crowd but a little hard of hearing; one shout, provided it is loud enough, and they all "stay put" even when the influence is removed.

Hammering a bar of iron or steel lying north and south shakes up the molecules, and the earth's magnetism then lines them up.

Heating a magnetized needle causes the molecules to move faster and they get mixed up again.

Experiment shows that there is a limit beyond which a piece of iron or steel cannot be magnetized. This fact is well explained by the above theory, for obviously when all the molecular magnets are in alignment, nothing further can be done.

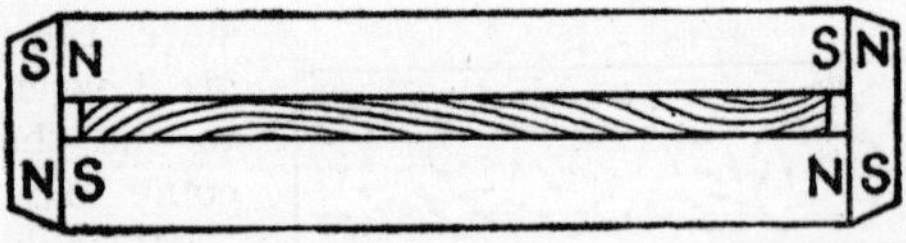

FIG. 220.

The Care of Magnets. The above considerations give the reason why magnets should not be dropped or thrown about.

Bar magnets should always be packed away in pairs, with a piece of wood between and opposite poles together (fig. 220).

Against each pair of ends is a soft iron "keeper," the use of which may easily be understood. At each end the poles of the tiny molecular magnets are *free*, and being all *like* they repel one another. They are also slightly attracted by the opposite poles at the other end of the magnet. The tendency is therefore for the molecular magnets to swing round and the bar loses its magnetism. A *long* bar magnet retains its magnetism better than a short one. When a keeper is used, the free poles induce opposite poles in the keeper. There is mutual attraction and the poles of the tiny molecular magnets are no longer free.

A horseshoe magnet retains its magnetism better than a bar magnet because the poles of the molecular magnets being attracted by their neighbours across the way are not so free and the tendency to swing round is less. The addition of a keeper, across the ends, still further diminishes this tendency.

When using a magnet, you should remember that its condition is unnatural and very unstable without a keeper. But these precautions are not so necessary with the modern *cobalt steel* magnets.

To make a really powerful horseshoe magnet, several thin horseshoe magnets are screwed together. This is because during magnetization it is the molecules near the surface which are most affected. These powerful horseshoe magnets may be seen in the magneto of a car or motor-cycle.

To find the Poles and Axis of a Bar Magnet.

The *poles of a magnet* are the points in the magnet where the attractive force is strongest. The *magnetic axis* is the straight

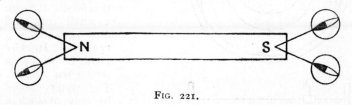

FIG. 221.

line joining the two poles ; it may or may not coincide with the geometrical axis.

The poles and magnetic axis can be found with the aid of a "plotting compass" which consists of a very short compass needle pivoted in a round box generally having glass faces. The north end of the needle is usually coloured blue.

Place a bar magnet on a sheet of paper and make a pencil-mark round it. Place the plotting compass near one end of the magnet and *close to the geometrical axis* (fig. 221). Put pencil-marks opposite the two ends of the needle. Join the points by a straight line. Repeat on the other side of the geometrical axis and do the same at the other end of the magnet. Produce all four lines into the rectangular trace of the magnet. The poles and magnetic axis are then found.

Magnetic Fields and Lines of Force.

A magnetic field may be defined as **the region round a magnet where its influence may be detected.** At every point near a magnet, the north pole of another magnet is acted upon by a force, and if this north pole were isolated and free to move it would trace out a definite line. Such lines were called by Faraday "lines of force."

It is of course impossible to obtain an isolated north pole, that is a north pole without a south pole, but we can illustrate the idea fairly well as follows.

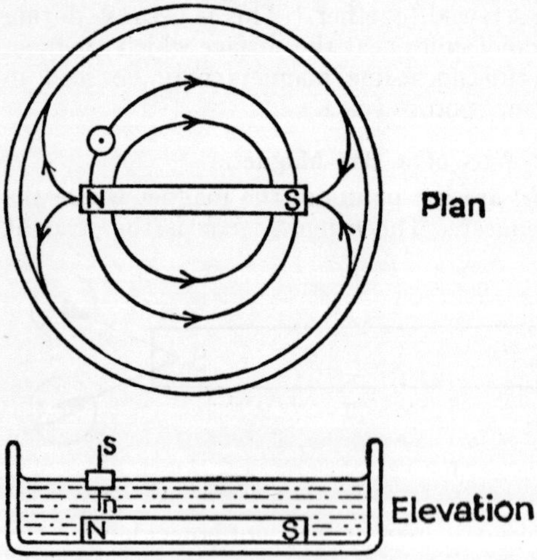

FIG. 222.

Experiment. Magnetize a sewing needle by means of a bar magnet or by pulling it across one pole of a strong electromagnet. Stick the needle through a small cork and float on water in a trough. In the trough place a strong bar magnet. The water should be only of such a depth that the bottom end of the needle may clear the magnet. This bottom end will be practically an isolated pole and it can be made to describe lines of force round the magnet (fig. 222).

A line of force is made up of a number of tangents, each tangent being the direction of the magnetic field at a certain point.

Experiment. To map a magnetic field with a plotting compass.

Place a bar magnet on a sheet of drawing paper with its north pole pointing north. Draw a pencil-line round the magnet and fix the paper to the bench. Place the plotting compass near the north pole of the magnet. Mark a dot on the paper at each end of the needle. Move the compass so that *the near point is over the far dot.* Make a third dot opposite the far pole. Repeat this process until the line traced out either returns to the magnet or goes off the paper.

Now start again at a different point near the north pole of the magnet and trace out another line of force. Repeat the process until the whole field is mapped out as shown in fig. 223. Each line of force indicates the path which would be traced out by a single isolated north pole.

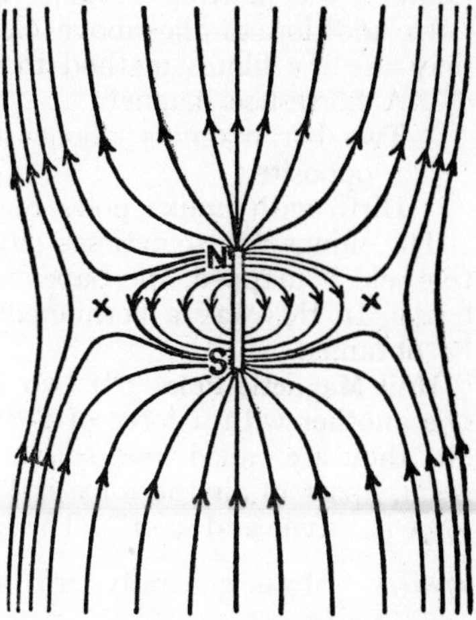

FIG. 223.

In the regions indicated by a X the earth's magnetic field just neutralizes the field due to the bar magnet. Here the plotting is rather more difficult. The method should be slightly varied; move the compass so that *its centre point is over the far dot.* In this way the neutral points are more easily located.

If you have time, it is interesting to map the fields in the following cases:

South pole pointing north;
North pole pointing east.

Experiment. To map a magnetic field with iron filings.

Place a bar magnet between two similar exercise books. Over the top lay a piece of white blotting paper (fig. 224). By means of a paper tray perforated with the points of a pair of dividers, sift a small quantity of iron filings over the blotting-paper.

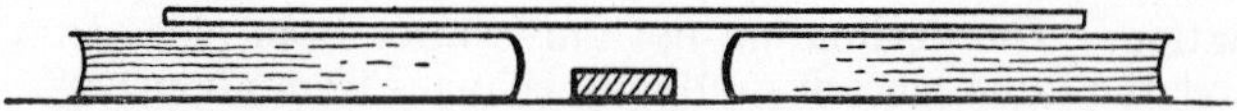

FIG. 224.

Touch the paper with one finger on the middle of the magnet to prevent violent movement, then tap gently with a pencil. The iron filings act like a large number of plotting compasses and the field is instantly mapped out.

This method is quick, but since there is naturally more friction between a filing and the paper than exists in the bearings of a plotting compass, the method is not very sensitive. The earth's field is not powerful enough to make iron filings point north and south, therefore to investigate the earth's field or to find "neutral points" the plotting compass must be used.

In addition to the above case of a single bar magnet, you may use the filings method to map the following fields.

A horseshoe magnet;

Two bar magnets about an inch apart with like poles opposite;

Ditto with unlike poles opposite.

The filings are sometimes sifted on to waxed paper. When the field is mapped, the paper is carefully held over a source of heat. In this way a permanent record of a magnetic field can be obtained.

Unit Magnetic Pole. If two like poles of equal strength repel one another with a force of 1 dyne when placed 1 cm. apart in air, they are called *unit poles.* If these same poles are placed 2 cm. apart in air the force is $\frac{1}{4}$ dyne, if placed 3 cm. apart the force is $\frac{1}{9}$ dyne and so on. The force thus obeys the *law of inverse squares.* More generally we may say, *force* $= \frac{m_1 m_2}{d^2}$ *dynes,* where m_1 and m_2 are the pole strengths and d cm. is the distance apart in air. If the poles are unlike then the force will be attractive.

Terrestrial Magnetism. The statement that a compass needle points to the north is only roughly true. If a pen is fixed vertically on a horizontal sheet of paper in a good light, the direction of the shortest shadow, *i.e.* at 12 noon by sun time, gives the geographical N. and S. or geographical meridian. The angle between the geographical meridian and the magnetic meridian obtained with a compass needle is called the **declination** or **variation.** The declination not only varies from place to place, but at the same place it gradually changes from about 24° E. to 24° W. in the course of centuries.

If a knitting-needle is suspended at its centre of gravity and then magnetized, it will point towards the magnetic north, but at most places on the earth it will also **dip.** In England it will dip through about 67°.

While this is a good way of showing the fact of dip, the measurement of the **angle of dip or inclination** is best made with a *dip circle* (fig. 225). The instrument is rotated on its base until the needle takes up a vertical position. When this is so, the horizontal component of the earth's slanting magnetic force is having no effect and the needle must be swinging in the E. and W. plane. Therefore rotating the instrument 90° from this position must put it accurately into the magnetic meridian, when the angle of dip can be read off.

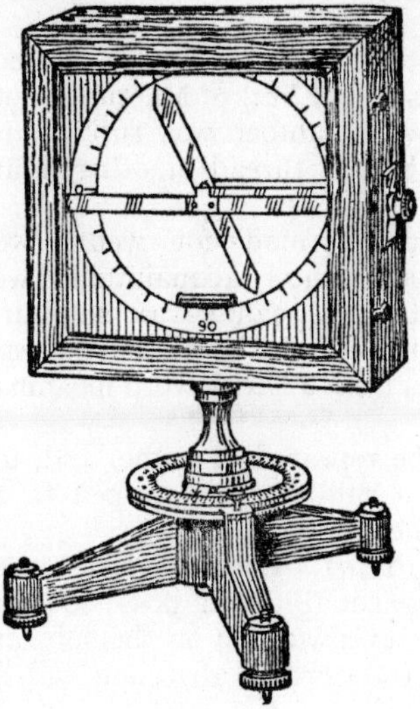

FIG. 225.

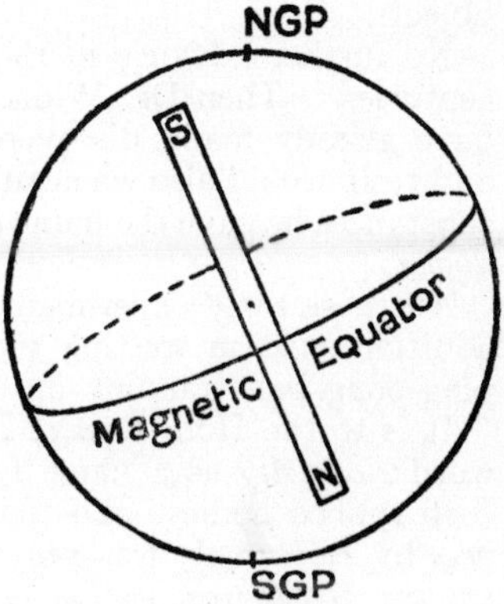

FIG. 226.

Declination and Dip might be explained by supposing that there is a huge magnet buried in the earth with its S.-seeking end somewhere in the Arctic Circle and its N.-seeking pole in the Antarctic (fig. 226). But although this gives a very convenient mental picture, it must not be regarded as the real explanation. No thoroughly satisfactory theory to account for the earth's magnetism has yet been found.

CHAPTER XXV

ELECTROSTATICS

THE earliest recorded experiments in electricity were carried out by the Greek philosopher Thales (*Thay'leez*) of Miletus about 600 B.C. Thales discovered that when amber was rubbed, it acquired the power of picking up bits of thread or other light objects.

No further advance in the subject was made for twenty-two centuries. Then Dr. William Gilbert, whose acquaintance we have already made, discovered that glass, sealing-wax, sulphur, and resin would also when rubbed attract light bodies. To these substances he gave the name **electrics** from a Greek word meaning *amber*.

All these early experiments can be repeated at home, and, in addition, it is interesting to apply a rubbed fountain-pen to a ping-pong ball standing on a polished table.

It is to the Hon. Robert Boyle (1627–1691), that we owe the word *electricity* as a name for the peculiar power possessed by such rubbed bodies. The first book ever written on the subject was by Boyle. It was published at Oxford in 1676 and called *On the Mechanical Origin or Production of Electricity.*

Although Gilbert made a decided advance in the subject, he made one important mistake; he came to the conclusion that metals could not be endowed with this power of attracting light bodies, or in other words, that a metal could not be "electrified" or given a "charge of electricity." He called metals, and any other substances which he could not electrify, by the name "Non-electrics."

More than a hundred years elapsed before Gilbert's mistake was corrected and even then it was only done by slow and sometimes accidental steps. In 1729 Stephen Gray (1696–1736), a Fellow of the Royal Society, was surprised to find that, if a glass tube fitted with a cork at each end was rubbed, the corks as well as the glass attracted light bodies; electricity had therefore travelled to the corks. He then fastened a fir rod into one of the corks and fixed an ivory ball to the free end of the rod. On rubbing the glass, the ivory ball picked up feathers! The electricity had therefore travelled from glass to cork to wood to ivory ball. Between the ball and the wood he next interposed still another body, namely a length of pack-thread (fig. 227). Electricity again travelled to the ball. The pack-thread was then lengthened and hung from the balcony of his house. The experiment was again successful.

His next effort was to make electricity travel horizontally. He suspended a long piece of pack-thread by loops of *metal* wire,

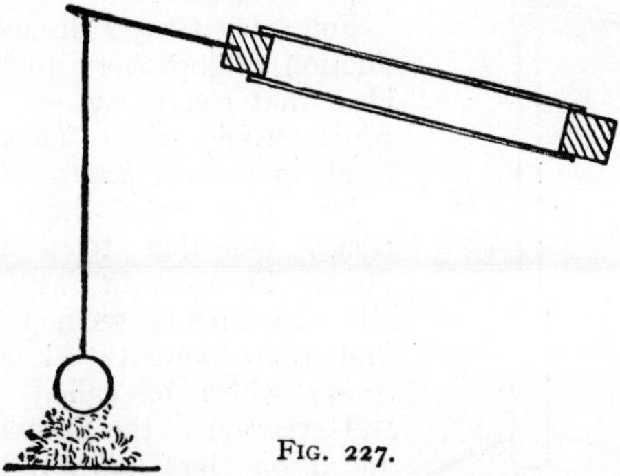

FIG. 227.

but now electricity did not travel to the ivory ball. A friend, Dr. Granville Wheeler, suggested *silk* loops. This was carried out at Wheeler's house and the experiment was a success with the pack-thread extending horizontally to a distance of 886 ft.! On replacing the silk loops by loops of *pack-thread*, the ivory ball again failed to attract feathers.

The experimenters came to the conclusion that the electricity leaked away through the supports when these were of metal or pack-thread but not when they were made of silk. Gray had thus distinguished between **conductors and non-conductors**; pack-thread and metals were conductors, while silk was a non-conductor or insulator (Lat. *insula*—an island).

Gray's discovery of conduction was the first step in the correction of Gilbert's mistake. The next step was carried out by

Jean Théophile Desaguliers (1683–1744). Desaguliers showed that Gilbert's "non-electrics" were the best conductors; the charge leaked away from them as rapidly as it was formed. He found that if a metal was mounted on an insulator, it could be electrified quite easily. In other words,

"non-electrics" = conductors
"electrics" = insulators.

You will probably find in your laboratory a rod made partly of brass and partly of glass. With this you can easily illustrate Desaguliers's discovery, for, holding the glass end, it is quite easy to electrify the brass and pick up bits of paper or feathers.

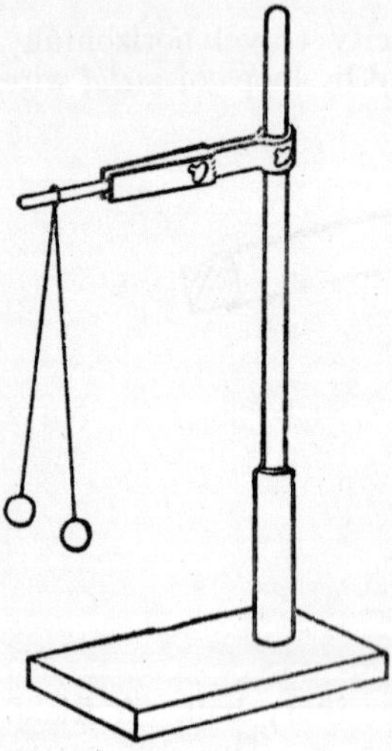

FIG. 228.

Following Gray's discovery of conduction, philosophers quickly got the idea that electricity was something which would *flow*. They began to think of it as a *fluid*.

The next great discovery in electricity was due to a Frenchman, Charles François du Fay (1699–1739). His experiments seemed to indicate that there were two kinds of electricity which he called "vitreous" and "resinous," the former being produced on glass (*vitrum*) by rubbing with silk, the latter on resin, sealing-wax or amber by rubbing with flannel. Two bodies charged with the same kind of electricity would repel one another, while bodies carrying unlike charges would be attracted to one another. This was the so-called *two-fluid* theory.

These ideas of du Fay can be illustrated by the **pith-ball electroscope.** It consists essentially of two balls of elder pith on a piece of thread tied at the middle to an insulating support.

Experiment. Tie the thread connecting the two pith balls to a rod of glass or ebonite fixed in a wooden burette stand (fig. 228). Rub a glass rod with silk, then hold the rod near the pith balls. They are attracted, but after contact with the rod they are repelled. They also repel each other.

Now rub a rod of ebonite with dry warm flannel or catskin.

Bring the rod near the pith balls. They are attracted, but after contact they are repelled by the ebonite and attracted by the rubbed glass rod.

The first pith-ball electroscope was made by an Englishman, John Canton (1715–72). A piece of wood 12 in. long, 1 in. wide and $\frac{1}{4}$ in. thick was sawn in two and then joined by a hinge of linen (fig. 229). Two pith balls were connected by 12 in. of thread and fastened at the middle to the end of one of the pieces of wood. Hemispherical holes were cut in the wood to take the pith balls when the arrangement was folded up and carried in the pocket. When in use the electroscope was placed on a drinking glass near the corner of a table.

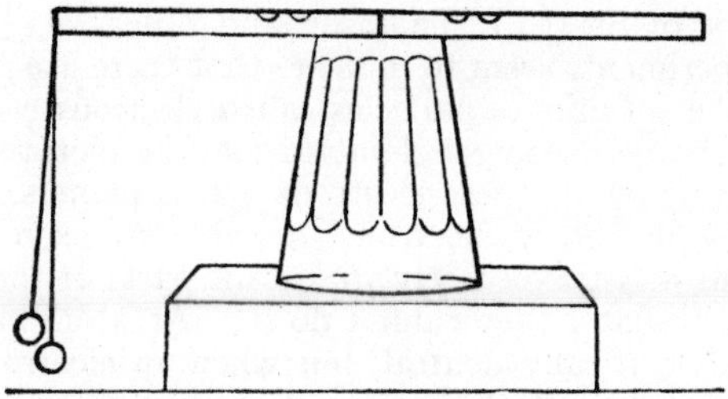

FIG. 229.

To make the instrument more effective, Henry Cavendish recommended that the thread should be dipped once in salt water, then no matter how dry the weather, the thread would still be a good conductor.

Among other discoveries made by John Canton was the fact that the kind of electricity generated on a body by friction depends not on the material but on the surface of the material. Thus a glass rod half smooth and half rough developed both kinds of electricity when excited by the same rubber.

The two-fluid theory of du Fay was elaborated by an Englishman, Robert Symmer, about 1759. His mental picture of electrification was as follows: A body in its natural state contained the two fluids. When it was electrified, it gained a certain amount of the one fluid and lost an equal quantity of the other.

Just before this time another English scientist, Sir William Watson, F.R.S. (1715–87), had propounded a one-fluid theory.

This one-fluid theory was amplified by Benjamin Franklin (1706–90), an American scientist and statesman of Philadelphia. Franklin's idea was that a rod of glass and a piece of silk both possessed a certain amount of the electric fluid. When they were rubbed together, some of the fluid passed from the silk to the glass. The glass became *positively* electrified, while the silk having less than the normal amount of fluid was said to be *negatively* electrified. Thus according to Franklin

vitreous electricity = positive electricity
resinous electricity = negative electricity.

Although it may be a little out of place from the historical point of view, it is better perhaps to give here a brief account of the modern view of electrification arising out of the experimental work of Sir J. J. Thomson and others.

These experiments seem to indicate that there are in all bodies a vast number of minute particles called **electrons** each carrying a negative charge. Any single atom may be pictured as a tiny solar system in which these electrons act as planets. In a conductor these planetary electrons are able to leave their own solar systems and travel freely to distant parts of the body, but in a perfect insulator they cannot do so. An atom in its normal condition is electrically neutral, but when an electron leaves it, the residue being short of negative electricity becomes positively charged.

According to this view, a positively charged body is deficient in electrons, while a negatively charged body has received an extra number from some outside source.

Why does an ebonite rod become negatively charged when rubbed with flannel ? Because the flannel gives extra electrons to the ebonite. But electrons do not travel freely on an insulator, so it is not much use touching just one spot of the ebonite. To make sure that the rod is properly charged, we must touch all points on it. In other words, we must try to bring into contact the surface atoms of the rod and those of the rubber. This is why we *rub* the rod.

But if the flannel really parts with electrons, it should now have atomic residues each carrying a positive charge. The fact that the rubber actually is charged can easily be proved with an electroscope.

It will now be seen that Franklin got very near to the modern idea. He thought that only one thing moved about and that a state of electrification was due to an excess or deficit of this something. We agree with this. To him the movable something was that which collected on a rubbed glass rod, but we say the movable something is that which resides on ebonite. He pictured a moving *fluid* producing a *positive* charge. We picture moving *particles* producing a *negative* charge.

We will now apply the modern theory to a phenomenon first discovered by Stephen Gray. This discovery was at least as important as his experiments on conduction.

Having suspended a boy horizontally by silken cords, he held an electrified glass tube *near* the boy's feet. He found that the

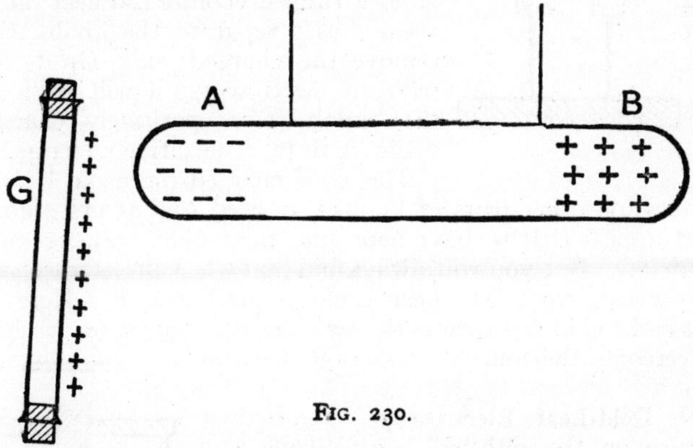

FIG. 230.

boy's nose would then pick up feathers! Likewise when the tube was held near the boy's head, the feet would pick up light bodies.

This phenomenon which is perfectly general with conductors is called *electrostatic induction.*

On the electron theory it is explained as follows: In fig. 230 the long conductor AB represents the boy. The positively charged glass tube G, being deficient in electrons, attracts those in AB and some of these accumulate at A. At B there are atomic residues which have lost electrons. There is at B therefore a positive charge. The end B would therefore attract light bodies.

But there is also another curious fact; if we touch AB with the finger and then remove *first the finger, then the glass rod,* we find that AB is charged negatively. This is because electrons have travelled from the earth through the finger to make up the deficiency at B, in other words, to neutralize the positive charges on the atomic residues at B. We have charged the conductor by *induction*.

An interesting variation of this can be carried out by using a conductor divisible at the centre.

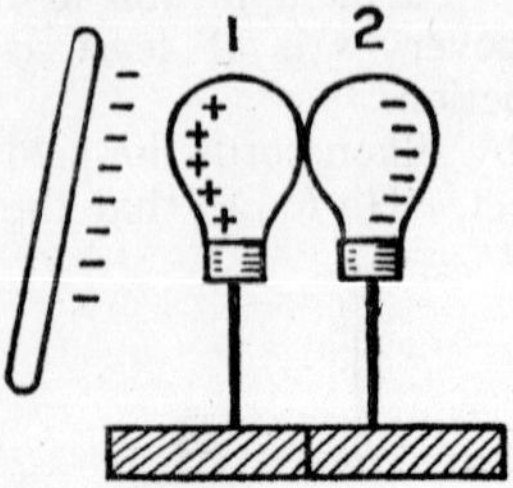

FIG. 231.

Experiment. Fix two door knobs or bedstead knobs on sticks of ebonite or sealing-wax. Fit a pair of wooden feet and place the knobs in contact (fig. 231). Hold a rubbed ebonite rod near one of the knobs. Separate the knobs, then remove the charged rod. On testing with an electroscope, it will be found that knob (1) is positively charged, while knob (2) is negatively charged.

The same charged rod could be used with several other pairs of knobs if desired, and at first sight it might appear that we have here some miraculous way of *creating* electricity. But you will always find that when an electric charge is produced, work has been done in producing it. Here the work is done in separating the two charged knobs, for we have to overcome the mutual attraction between them.

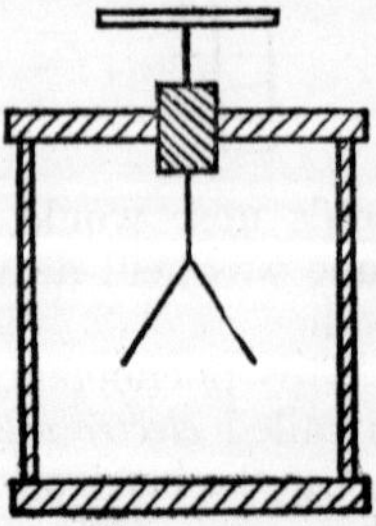
FIG. 232.

The Gold-Leaf Electroscope. A distinct advance on the pith-ball electroscope was made by a clergyman of Wirksworth in Derbyshire. The Rev. Abraham Bennet, F.R.S. (1750–99), conceived the idea of using two slips of gold leaf instead of the pith balls. These slips when electrified would repel one another just like the pith balls, but being lighter the arrangement would be more sensitive.

A modern form of the *gold-leaf electroscope* can easily be made. The apparatus in fig. 232 consists of a wooden box having the front and back replaced by two $\frac{1}{4}$-plate glasses to serve as windows, a farthing soldered to a stiff brass wire passing through a sulphur stopper and two slips of aluminium leaf.

To make the sulphur stopper, stick the brass wire through

an ordinary cork, then wrap a piece of drawing paper round the cork so as to make a cylindrical extension. Into this pour sulphur just above the melting-point. When the sulphur has cooled, the paper can be removed and the ordinary cork cut away.

A small charge given to the disc from a rubbed glass rod or ebonite rod causes the leaves to diverge on account of mutual repulsion.

The electroscope can also be charged by induction.

To Charge the Electroscope Negatively.

Hold a rubbed glass rod near the disc. A certain number of electrons are attracted to the disc which therefore becomes negatively charged. The leaves are now short of electrons and therefore, being positively charged, repel one another (fig. 233A).

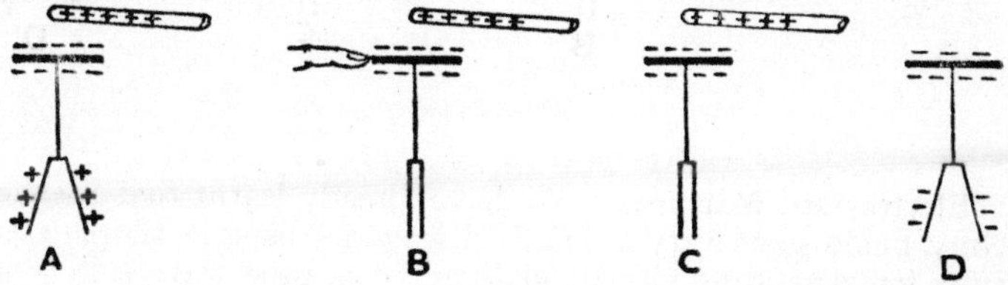

FIG. 233.

Touch the disc with the finger. Electrons pass from the earth to neutralize the positive charge on the leaves. The leaves therefore collapse (fig. 233B).

Remove the finger—the leaves remain collapsed (fig. 233C). Remove the glass rod—electrons spread from the disc to the leaves which now diverge, and the instrument is negatively charged (fig. 233D). It can be used to test the sign of the charge on any approaching body. What will happen if a negatively charged body approaches? What will the leaves do when a positive charge approaches?

To Charge the Electroscope Positively.

Hold a rubbed ebonite rod near the disc. A certain number of electrons are repelled into the leaves. The leaves become negatively charged and repel one another, while the disc being short of electrons becomes positively charged (fig. 234A).

Keeping the ebonite rod in position, touch the disc with the finger. The electrons which were repelled to the leaves are now able to get away still farther, namely to earth. The leaves therefore collapse (fig. 234B).

Remove the finger—the leaves remain collapsed (fig. 234C). Remove the ebonite rod—electrons from the leaves partly neutralize the positive charge on the disc. In this way, disc and leaves are left with a positive charge (fig. 234D).

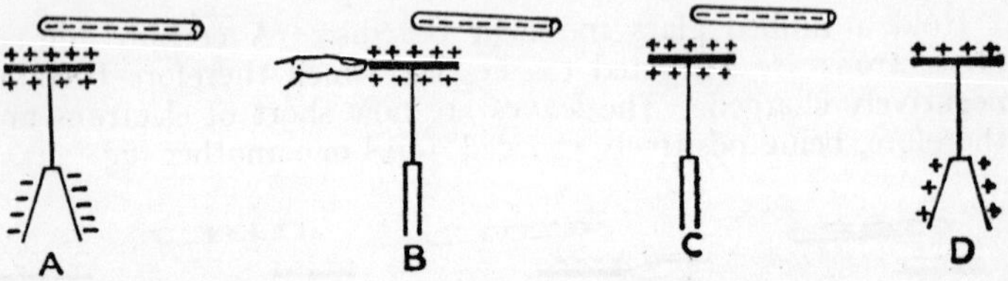

FIG. 234.

Electrostatic Machines. We have already learnt that Stephen Gray made some very valuable discoveries using a simple glass tube for generating electric charges. His tube was $3\frac{1}{2}$ ft. long, just over an inch in diameter, and closed with corks to keep out the dust.

It is rather strange that Gray never seems to have used anything more elaborate, although Otto von Guericke (1602–86) had already, before Gray was born, discovered a much better method of generating electricity. Guericke allowed molten sulphur to cool in a glass globe, then broke off the glass. The sulphur sphere was mounted on an axle and revolved while an assistant pressed dry hands against it. In this way the sulphur would become negatively charged, while the positive charge on the hands would be neutralized by electrons from the earth.

Sir Isaac Newton, and later Francis Hawksbee, found that a glass sphere gave still better results. A German scientist, Professor Bose of Wittenberg, fitted a " prime conductor " to collect and store the charge. This was a long tin tube suspended by silk threads and making contact with the globe by means of a hanging chain (fig. 235). Further improvements were the use of a leather rubber and the substitution of a glass cylinder for the globe.

Using one of these friction machines, a most important discovery was accidentally made by two men independently in the years 1745 and 1746. One was a monk called von Kleist living in Pomerania. The other, Petrus van Musschenbroek (1692–1791), was a member of a Dutch family of physicists and instrument makers.

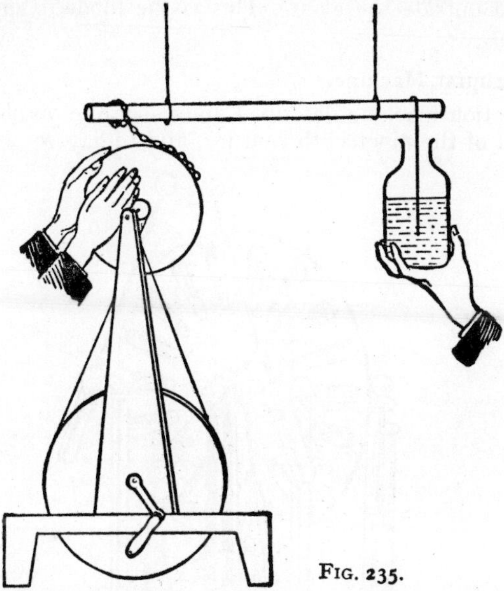

FIG. 235.

Musschenbroek, then professor of physics at Leyden, had noticed that bodies soon lost their electricity in *damp* air. He thought that if he surrounded some *water* with an insulator, the water would be able to collect and hold a considerable quantity of electricity. He accordingly put some water in a glass bottle, hung a nail to the prime conductor of an electric machine, and got his pupil Cunæus to hold the bottle so that the nail dipped into the water (fig. 235).

After the machine had been worked for some time, Cunæus tried to take the nail out of the water. He received a violent shock in the arms and chest; and thus was the "Leyden phial" or "Leyden jar" discovered.

This discovery made a great stir amongst the scientists of the time and the Leyden jar soon became a very popular scientific toy. Sir William Watson suggested that the electricity was stored or "condensed" by means of the two conductors, water inside and the hand outside. He further showed that both these conductors could be replaced by layers of tinfoil stuck inside and outside the glass. This is the modern form of the instrument.

The Wimshurst Machine.

The friction machine described above became obsolete in the latter half of the nineteenth century, and to-day we use instead

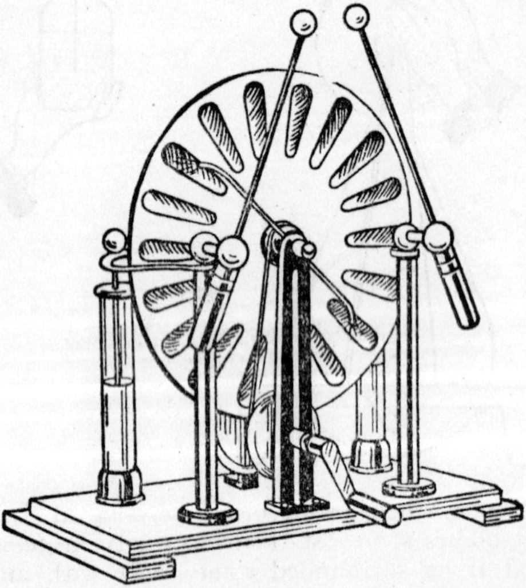

FIG. 236.

a machine invented by James Wimshurst about 1878. It is one of these that you will probably meet in your physics laboratory (fig. 236).

The full explanation of the working of a Wimshurst machine is a little beyond the scope of the present book. It must suffice here to point out that it depends not upon friction but upon induction. It has the advantage over the friction machine that its success is not so dependent on the weather.

With this instrument it is possible to repeat all the experiments carried out by the old philosophers and with more certainty of success. Thus we may **charge a Leyden jar** by putting its knob in contact with one of the discharging knobs of the Wimshurst and giving the handle a few turns. The inner coating becomes charged and this charge induces an equal and opposite charge on the outer coating.

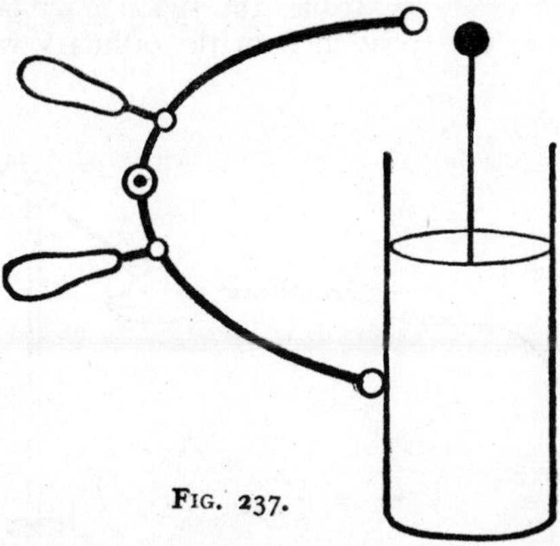

FIG. 237.

After removing the discharging knob by its ebonite handle we may **discharge the condenser** by means of a pair of tongs specially made for the purpose. These discharging tongs consist of two brass rods terminating in knobs and joined by a hinge to one or two glass handles. One knob is held against the outer coating of the jar and the other is brought near the knob of the jar (fig. 237). A plump spark passes, the two opposite charges neutralizing one another.

A small jar may safely be discharged through a row of boys holding hands, one end touching the outer coating and the other end touching the knob. It is a little less comfortable if the hands are perspiring, as the charge will more readily pass to earth through that person.

A boy may be placed on a stool with glass legs and instructed to hold one of the discharging knobs of the Wimshurst. After a few turns of the handle his hair, if dry, stands up. He will be able to light the gas with his knuckle. When he presents his knuckle to a boy on the ground, both receive a shock.

It is quite easy to **ignite ether** by sparks from one of the knobs. Copper wire is wound round a clean metal spoon and the other end twisted round a clean gas jet or joined to any other good "earth." Ether is poured into the spoon and the knob is brought to within half an inch of the liquid (fig. 238).

When the ether has burnt away, the spoon will be quite warm and **methylated spirit** is easily ignited in the warm spoon. If ether is not easily available, the spoon may be warmed by burning some of the spirit in it in the ordinary way, and then

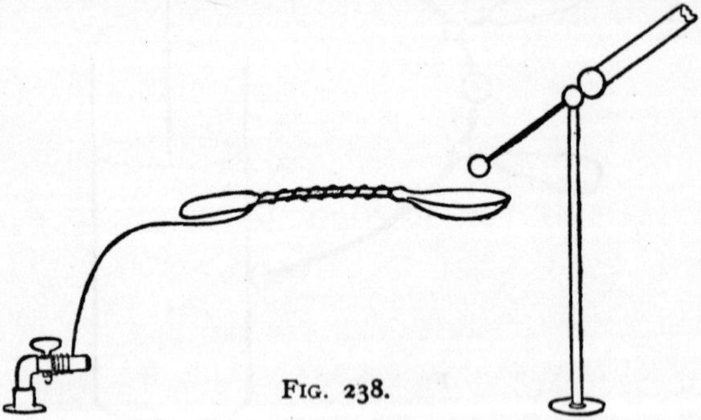

FIG. 238.

a fresh supply of spirit is easily ignited by the sparks. Without some preliminary warming, the ignition of methylated spirit is rather uncertain.

It will probably be noticed that in each case the liquid in the spoon piles up in a heap. Try to explain this by induction.

If a drop of liquid is allowed to form on the knob, a depression will appear on the liquid in the spoon, as if a powerful draught is acting downwards. The reason for this you will understand later.

Distribution of Charge.

Experiment. Obtain two insulated conductors of the shapes shown at A and B (fig. 239). Such conductors can be made by sticking tinfoil on wood with seccotine. Solder a farthing to the nib of a pen and replace the wooden holder by a rod of glass.

This will serve as a **proof-plane** (fig. 240). Charge the sphere by contact with one of the knobs of the Wimshurst. Having broken contact, touch the proof-plane against any part of the sphere, then against the disc of the gold-leaf electroscope. Note the

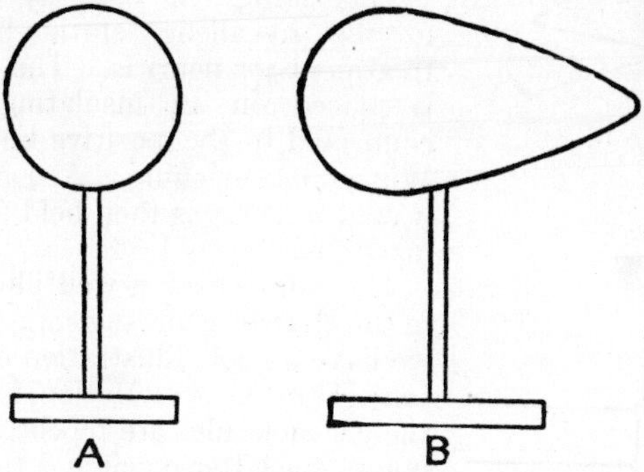

FIG. 239.

FIG. 240.

divergence of the leaves. Discharge electroscope and proof-plane by touching them with the finger. Touch the proof-plane against some other part of the spheres and repeat.

The divergence should be the same no matter which part of the sphere is touched. *The distribution of charge on a sphere is uniform.*

Repeat the experiment with the conductor B. The greatest divergence will be found after the proof-plane has touched the pointed end. *Electricity collects on edges and points.*

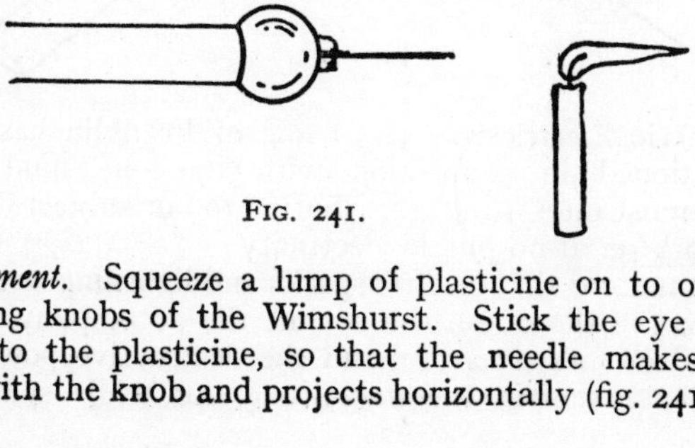

FIG. 241.

Experiment. Squeeze a lump of plasticine on to one of the discharging knobs of the Wimshurst. Stick the eye end of a needle into the plasticine, so that the needle makes metallic contact with the knob and projects horizontally (fig. 241). Work the machine and hold one hand a few inches away from the needle point. Hold a lighted candle in the same position.

A decided draught is produced. This is because electricity, collecting at the point, charges the gas molecules and then repels them.

FIG. 242.

This draught is used by doctors in the so-called "static breeze" treatment for neuritis. The patient is placed on an insulating stand connected to the positive knob of a Wimshurst machine. A point connected to earth is then held towards his skin.

The point effect is well illustrated in the **electric whirl** (fig. 242). Here we have a good illustration of Newton's Third Law of Motion, for while the gas molecules are repelled by the points, the latter recoil and the whirl spins backwards.

Experiment. Stick a needle on one of the knobs so that its point is about half an inch from the other knob (fig. 243). On working the machine, there is no visible spark. The electricity is discharging peacefully.

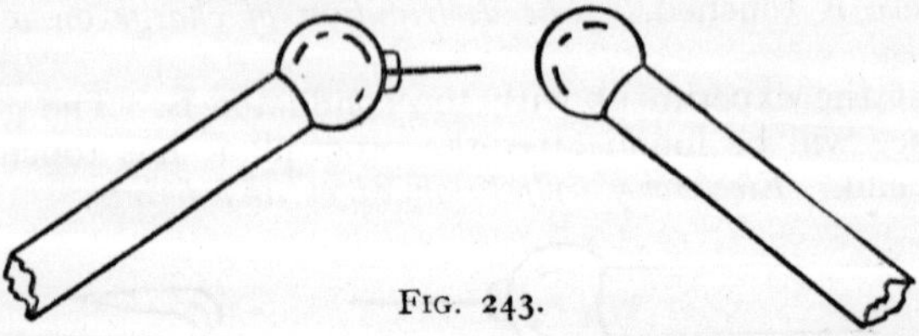

FIG. 243.

Atmospheric Electricity. The name of Franklin has already been mentioned in connection with the one fluid theory, Franklin's most interesting contribution to our subject, however. was his work on atmospheric electricity.

Franklin noticed that electric sparks and lightning were similar in many ways—the noise, the colour, the accompanying smell, the crooked or forked nature, and the destructive power. The only difference was in the magnitude, for while sparks were measured in inches a flash of lightning would be a few miles long. A simple experiment carried out in 1752 confirmed his idea that an electric spark was a flash of lightning on a small scale.

He had already shown that electricity passed off readily and peacefully from points. He conceived the idea that if a pointed conductor connected to earth could be sent up under a thunder cloud, the point would "draw the electric fire."

His pointed conductor was a sharp-pointed wire fastened to a kite (fig. 244). The kite was made of two light cross-pieces of cedar wood and a silk handkerchief, silk being chosen instead of paper so that the kite would be better able to withstand the wind and rain. The pointed wire projected about a foot from the vertical cross-piece. To the kite was attached the usual long piece of twine with a piece of silk ribbon attached to the bottom end. At the junction of the string and silk was a key. The person operating the kite stood inside a doorway holding the silk.

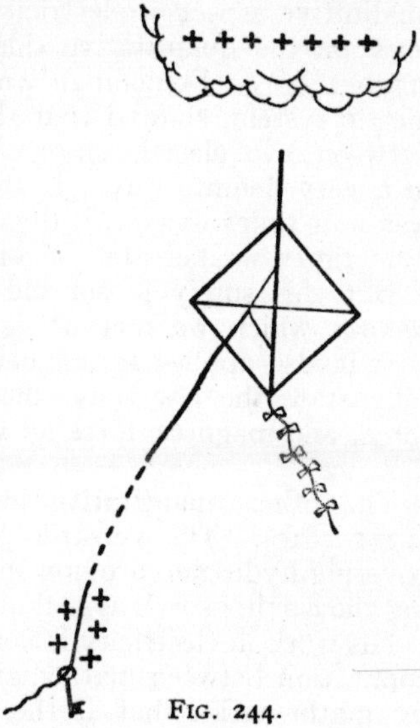

FIG. 244.

When a thunder cloud appeared over the kite and the string got wet, its separate strands were seen to stand out, and sparks could be obtained by presenting a knuckle to the key.

Franklin's kite experiment led to the use of lightning conductors for the protection of buildings. The modern explanation is this. If, say, a positively charged cloud appears over the conductor, the latter becomes charged by induction, the pointed end negatively and the bottom end positively. But no very great charge can accumulate at the point because as fast as it forms, it discharges and neutralizes the charge on the cloud. At the lower end a similar peaceful discharge takes place due to electrons coming in from the earth.

By means of the key attached to his kite, Franklin was able

to charge Leyden jars, ignite spirit and carry out all the experiments usually associated with electric machines. He thus confirmed his idea that the "electric fire" of the atmosphere was exactly the same as laboratory electricity but on a much larger scale.

The Beginnings of Quantitative Work. Until the late eighteenth century our philosophers had mainly dealt with the qualitative aspect of electricity. Now we find two men getting busy on the quantitative side. Charles Augustin de Coulomb (1736–1806), a Frenchman who took part in the making of the metric system, showed that the force of attraction or repulsion between two electric charges depended on the distance apart in a very definite way. If the distance was doubled, the force was four times weaker, if the distance was trebled, the force was nine times weaker, and so on.

But this surely is our old acquaintance, the *law of inverse squares* which we met in light and sound. Coulomb showed that it also applied to magnetic attraction and repulsion, so we may state the law thus—**the intensity of light, sound, electric force, and magnetic force all vary inversely as the square of the distance.**

The other quantitative investigator was Henry Cavendish (1731–1810). This versatile philosopher amused himself by discovering hydrogen, proving the composition of water and weighing the earth, as well as making many other scientific discoveries.

His work in electricity is very striking as showing the intimate connection between mathematics and physics. He first showed by mathematics that if the inverse square law was true for electric charges, then the charge on any hollow conductor must be entirely on the outside. He then proceeded to show by experiment that there *was* no charge on the inside of a hollow conductor. This fact was also proved later by Michael Faraday (1791–1867) in his famous ice-pail experiment described later on.

Although Cavendish had such varied scientific interests and was extremely wealthy, he seems to have been very unsociable, and it has been said that "he probably uttered fewer words in the course of his life than any other man who ever lived to four score." Communication with his housekeeper was maintained by notes left on the hall table!

Potential. The word "potential" was first used by Cavendish. Let us try to get some idea of its meaning. The word potential in electricity roughly corresponds to the word "temperature" in heat.

Suppose that a bar of iron is heated at one end with a bunsen burner; heat will pass from one end to the other. If heat passes from a point A to a point B we say that A is at a higher temperature than B. Likewise if electricity passes from a point A to a point B we say that it is because the potential at A is higher than the potential at B. There is a **potential difference** between A and B.

Again, we talk of heating a body *to a certain temperature.* So also we speak of charging a conductor *to a certain potential.* Suppose we have two kettles of water on a gas stove and that one is much larger than the other (fig. 245). Let both be warmed

FIG. 245.

with equally slow burners. After, say, one minute, what can we say about the quantities of heat absorbed? Which will be at a higher temperature? What will be the result of emptying the small kettle into the large one?

Next suppose that we have two insulated spherical conductors, one much larger than the other (fig. 246). Let charges be carried to each from the knob of a Wimshurst by means of a proof-plane. When each has received the same number of visits from the proof-plane, how will their charges compare? Which will be at a higher potential? What will be the result of joining them by a copper wire?

The large kettle has the greater *thermal capacity.* The large sphere has the greater *electrical capacity.* The small kettle had the higher temperature and the small sphere the higher potential.

The result of mixing in the case of the kettles was that heat passed from the small kettle to the large because the former had the higher temperature. Likewise electricity passed from the small sphere because it had the higher potential. Ultimately

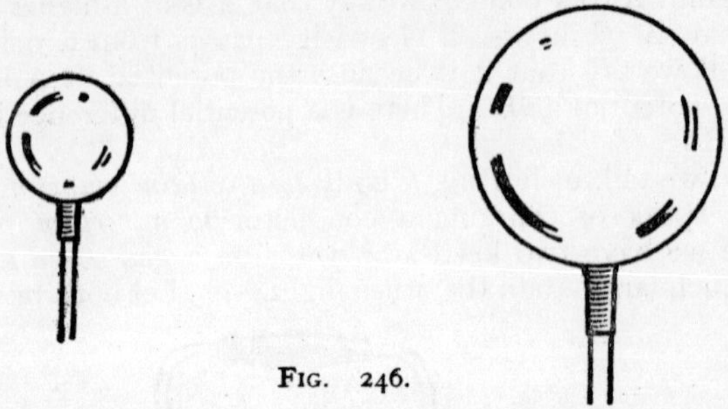

FIG. 246.

the kettles will be at the same temperature and the spheres at the same potential. Thus temperature and potential, not quantity, decide the transfer of heat and electricity.

The idea of potential is also somewhat like that of "water level" in hydrostatics. Suppose we have a small cylinder and

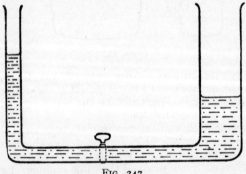

FIG. 247.

a large cylinder connected by a tap (fig. 247). Let both cylinders be charged with water in tablespoonfuls while the tap remains closed. When each cylinder has received the same number of tablespoonfuls, they correspond to two insulated conductors of different capacity charged to different potentials.

On opening the tap, water flows from the high level to the low level because there is a **difference of water pressure.** From analogy with flowing water, a potential difference is often described as a **difference of electrical pressure.**

Experiment. To show that all parts of a charged conductor are at the same potential.

Connect a proof-plane with the disc of a gold-leaf electroscope by means of very thin copper wire, say 36 d.c.c. Charge the pear-shaped conductor by touching it for a moment with the knob of a Wimshurst. Touch the blunt end of the conductor with the proof-plane (fig. 248). The leaves diverge. Move the proof-plane along the surface to the sharp end of the conductor. The divergence remains the same.

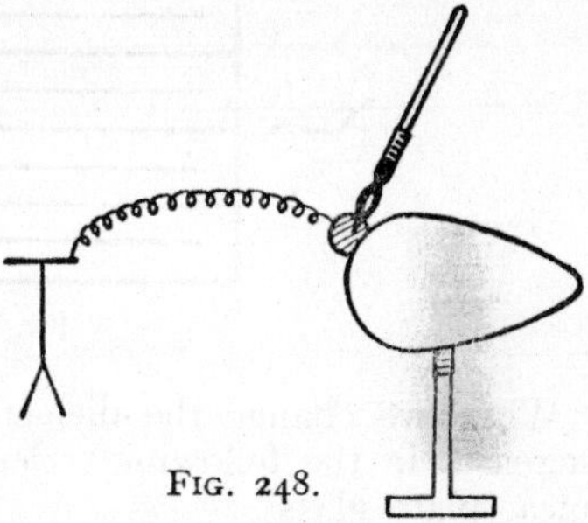

FIG. 248.

Compare and contrast this with a former experiment where we tested the same conductor for density of charge.

Condensers. We saw on a former page that a Leyden jar was an instrument which stored or "condensed" electric charges on its two coatings. Between these two coatings there is a difference of potential, and this causes a sudden flow of electricity when the coatings are connected by any conductor.

What is the essential difference between a large jar and a small jar? The case is similar to that of the two heated kettles; the large one has the greater capacity. In other words, when there is the same potential difference between the coatings, the large jar contains more electricity than the small one. The greater the **area** of the coatings, the greater the capacity becomes.

The capacity also depends on the material between the coatings and the thickness of this material. The substance between the coatings is called the **dielectric.** The **thinner** the dielectric, the greater the capacity.

Again, we may have more than two coatings or plates and the dielectric may be air, mica, or paper soaked in paraffin wax.

In wireless tuning condensers the dielectric is air and there may be dozens of plates. The capacity is directly proportional to the **number of plates.**

The fixed condensers of a wireless set generally have mica as the dielectric. In the base of a sparking coil you will find that there are numerous sheets of tinfoil, and sheets of waxed paper serve as the dielectric. The conventional diagram for such a condenser is shown in fig. 249, the lines representing the plates and the layers of dielectric being left blank.

FIG. 249.

When we change the dielectric of a condenser the capacity increases in the following order—air, waxed paper, turpentine, mica, plate glass.

Experiment. To show that positive and negative electricity are produced simultaneously and in equal quantities by friction.

Obtain an ebonite rod and a flannel cap which fits tightly on one end and has a silk thread attached (fig. 250). To make

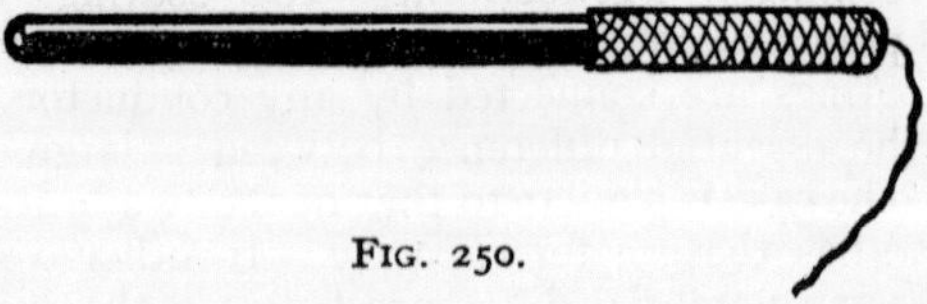

FIG. 250.

sure that the rod is not already charged, pass it quickly through a bunsen flame. Fit the cap and twist it round a few times. Then

(*a*) Hold the rod and cap near a charged gold-leaf electroscope.
(*b*) Take off the cap and hold it near the electroscope.
(*c*) Hold the rod near the electroscope.

These three tests should prove the proposition.

Faraday's Ice-pail Experiment.

Place a deep calorimeter or other metal can on the disc of an electroscope. Suspend a brass ball by a long silk thread. Charge the ball, say, positively. Hold the ball well inside the can.

There is now an induced negative charge on the inside of the can and an induced positive charge shared between the outside and the electroscope. The leaves diverge with positive electricity (fig. 251A). Note the divergence.

Earth the electroscope with a finger. The leaves collapse and the only charge on the can is the induced negative charge (fig. 251B).

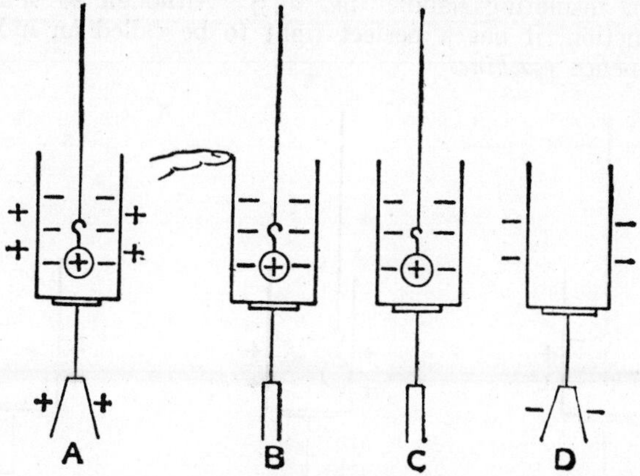

FIG. 251.

Remove the finger (fig. 251C) *then* the ball. The leaves diverge to the same extent as before, but now with negative electricity (fig. 251D). This shows that

Induced negative charge = Induced positive charge.

Again hold the charged ball well inside the can. As before, the leaves diverge (fig. 252A).

Touch the can with the ball. The leaves remain diverged (fig. 252B). The ball can be shown to be *completely discharged* by holding it near another electroscope. Therefore

Inducing charge = Induced charge.

But why is it that the ball after touching the can and neutralizing the induced negative charge did not bring away some of the positive charge? This can only be explained by assuming that the positive charge was entirely on the outside (fig. 252C). The same result would be obtained if you touched the inside of the can with a proof-plane and then held the proof-plane near an electroscope. The electroscope would not be affected. **There is no charge on the inside of a hollow conductor unless there is a charged body inside.**

The Electrophorus. The electrophorus was invented by the Italian physicist Volta in 1775. It consists essentially of a circular *cake* of ebonite, sealing-wax, or sulphur, a metal *disc* and an insulating handle (fig. 253). Although so simple in construction, it has a perfect right to be called an induction or influence ***machine.***

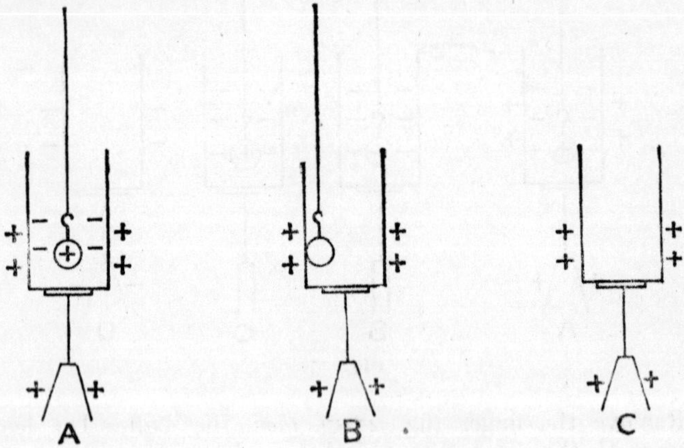

FIG. 252.

When the surface of the cake is rubbed with flannel it becomes negatively charged. If the disc is now placed on the cake, touched with the finger and then removed by the insulating handle, it will have a positive charge. On a dry day a bunsen may be lighted with a spark from the disc. Further charges may be obtained *without again rubbing the cake.* A Leyden jar can be charged up by repeatedly touching the knob with the charged disc.

At first sight this seems quite miraculous, because we are tempted to think that the cake is giving an endless supply of electricity. A little thought, however, will convince us that it is nothing like "the widow's cruse of oil." In the first place it can be proved that the disc carries a **positive** charge by bringing it near a positively charged electroscope. But the cake has a **negative** charge, so it is not a case of conduction. Moreover, the cake is not a conductor and the points of contact between disc and cake are very few.

The explanation is rather to be sought through induction. The negative charge on the cake induces a positive charge on the lower face of the disc and a negative charge on the upper face (fig. 253). When the disc is touched with the finger, the negative charge goes to earth. We now have a positive charge on the disc and the original negative charge is still on the cake ready for the next operation. Nor is the instrument a contradiction of

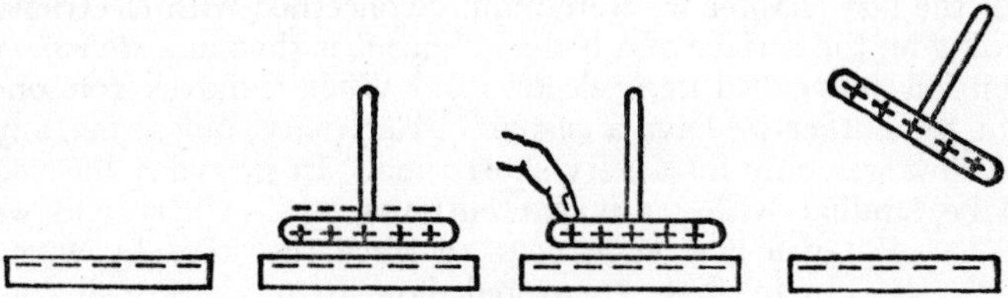

FIG. 253.

the Law of Conservation of Energy, for the electrical energy obtained is produced by the work we do in lifting the disc against the electrical attraction between the two opposite charges.

Simple electrophori can easily be made by using small metal lids filled with molten sulphur, pennies and sticks of sealing wax.

QUESTIONS

1 and 2. What contributions were made to our knowledge of electricity by the following men—

William Gilbert, Robert Boyle, Stephen Gray, du Fay, John Canton, J. J. Thomson, Abraham Bennet, von Guericke, Coulomb, Cavendish ?

3. What are the advantages of using aluminium leaf in a " gold "-leaf electroscope ?

4. Explain the action of a lightning conductor.

5. Given an electrophorus, how would you charge an insulated conductor (*a*) positively, (*b*) negatively ?

6. A copper calorimeter standing on a slab of paraffin wax has been given an electric charge. How could you find out the sign of the charge and its distribution ?

7. You are given a small charged conductor. How could you discharge it completely without earthing it ?

CHAPTER XXVI

CURRENT ELECTRICITY: MAGNETIC, HEATING AND CHEMICAL EFFECTS. ELECTROLYSIS

In the last chapter we were mainly concerned with electricity residing on the surface of a body. Since it is then in a *stationary* condition, it is called *static* electricity. When it moves from one point to another we have a *current* of electricity, but so far, any such flow was only for a very short time. In everyday life you will be familiar with *continuous* currents of electricity and we will now endeavour to trace the steps by which man first discovered how to produce such continuous currents.

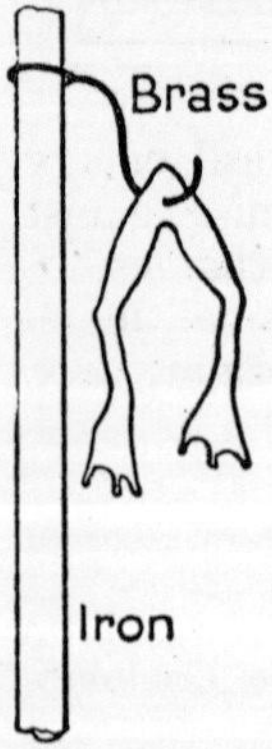

FIG. 254.

The first step in current electricity was made in 1786 by an Italian physiologist and anatomist, Luigi Galvani (1737–98). Galvani was born at Bologna and became professor of anatomy there in 1762. For some years he was busy studying the effect of electricity on the nervous and muscular systems of animals. It was while engaged in this work that he made his celebrated discovery.

There are many stories as to how the first observations were made. One is that a *brass* hook was thrust through a pair of frog's legs and then hung on *iron* railings (fig. 254). Every time the legs touched the iron, the muscles contracted as if they had received an electric shock. Galvani thought that the electricity was generated by the frog's leg.

The next step in the development of the subject was due to the Italian physicist, Alessandro Volta (1745–1827). Volta was professor of physics at Padua and at one time paid a visit to England where he met Joseph Priestley of oxygen fame.

To Volta it seemed highly improbable that electricity should be generated by a dead frog's leg. He thought the observed muscular contraction was rather due to the contact of two dissimilar metals. While carrying out experiments to confirm this point of view, he discovered what is now known as the "Voltaic cell" which consisted of a piece of zinc and a piece of copper immersed in salt solution or dilute acid. To-day we realize that these are the essential conditions, namely, that two dissimilar metals must be immersed in a suitable liquid. In Galvani's experiment the liquid was the fluid in the frog's leg.

The Simple Voltaic Cell. If a piece of zinc and a piece of copper are immersed in dilute sulphuric acid (fig. 255) there is a **difference of potential** between the two plates.

What will happen if we connect the two plates by a piece of wire? Modern science says that electrons travel from the zinc through the wire to the copper. There is thus a flow of negative electricity from zinc to copper. Most people, however, still have the old mental picture—they imagine positive electricity flowing through the wire from copper to zinc. Since the final result is the same in either case, it is convenient to adopt this way of looking at things, being always ready, however, to switch over to the other picture whenever necessary. We shall therefore think of positive electricity travelling through the wire from the copper or positive pole to the zinc or negative pole, being driven by the difference of potential between the two plates.

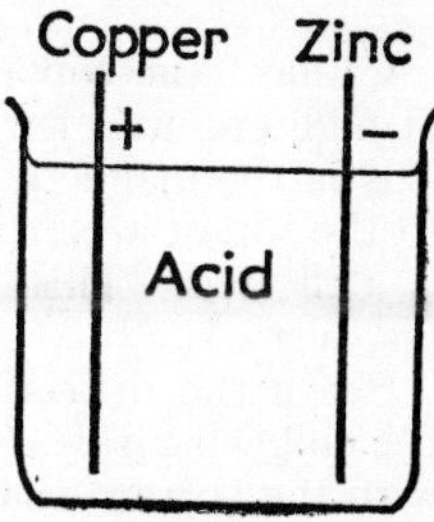

FIG. 255.

This difference of potential is often referred to as the "P.D." Because this difference of potential puts *electricity* in *motion*, it is also called the electromotive force or **E.M.F.** Again, since electricity is regarded as something which flows like water, we frequently use the term **electrical pressure.** Finally, P.D. is measured in units called "Volts" after Volta, so it often goes by the name of **Voltage.**

Thus Difference of Potential or P.D. = Electromotive Force or E.M.F. = Electrical Pressure = Voltage.

But the healthy-minded sceptic will ask, "How do you know that this copper wire connecting the zinc and copper plates is different from any other piece of odd wire lying on the table?"

To answer this question let us repeat an experiment first

carried out in 1819 by the Danish physicist, Hans Christian Oersted (1777–1851), professor of physics at Copenhagen.

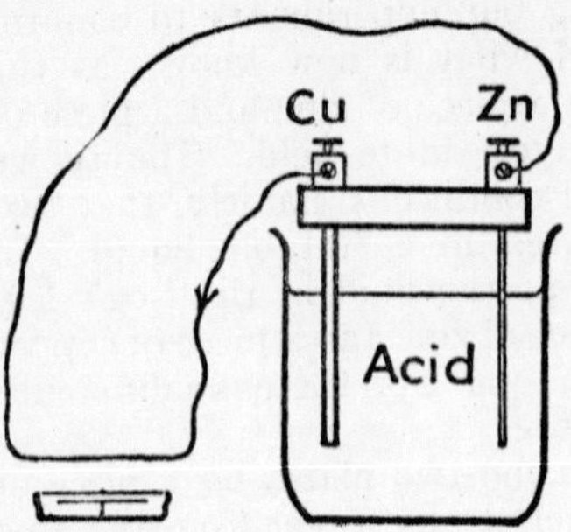

FIG. 256.

Experiment. Oersted's discovery of electro-magnetism. Fasten a strip of copper and a strip of zinc to a piece of wood by means of screws. Fix two "telephone terminals" into the wood and connect them by short pieces of wire to the metal strips. Immerse in a beaker of dilute sulphuric acid. We now have a convenient simple cell (fig. 256).

Connect the copper and zinc by about a yard of copper wire. Straighten out a few inches of this wire so that it is in the magnetic meridian and hold it close to the top of a plotting compass. The needle is deflected. This was Oersted's important discovery.

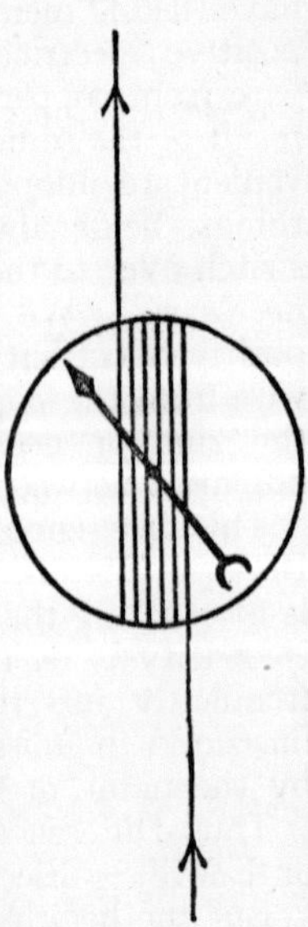

FIG. 257.

See if the deflection is in accordance with the following rule. **Imagine a man swimming with the current and facing the compass needle, then the N. end of the needle will be deflected towards his left hand.** This rule is due to the French physicist and mathematician, André Marie Ampère (1775–1836). Ampère was a professor at Lyons and later at Paris. He did a considerable amount of research on the relation between magnetism and electricity.

Let us now wind the copper wire several times round the plotting compass (fig. 257). The deflection is increased, for each time that the current passes over or under the needle it exerts its magnetic force. This idea was first carried out in 1822 by Schweigger. His "multiplier" was the first **galvanoscope** or **galvanometer.**

When the wires form a circular coil set vertically round a compass, we have what is known as a

Tangent Galvanometer (fig. 258). The compass needle is generally very short with an aluminium pointer at right angles. The reason for the name you will readily appreciate if you understand the principle of moments. The coil is always set so that it is in the meridian. When a current passes through the coil, we have two forces acting on each end of the needle (fig. 259), the deflecting force F due to the current and the controlling force H due to the earth's magnetism. The needle will set so as

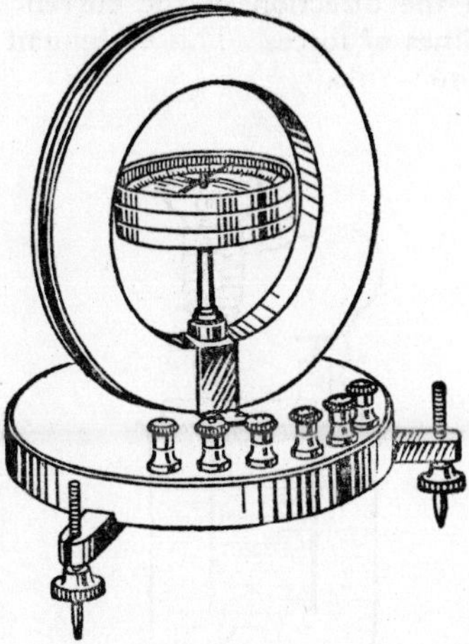

FIG. 258.

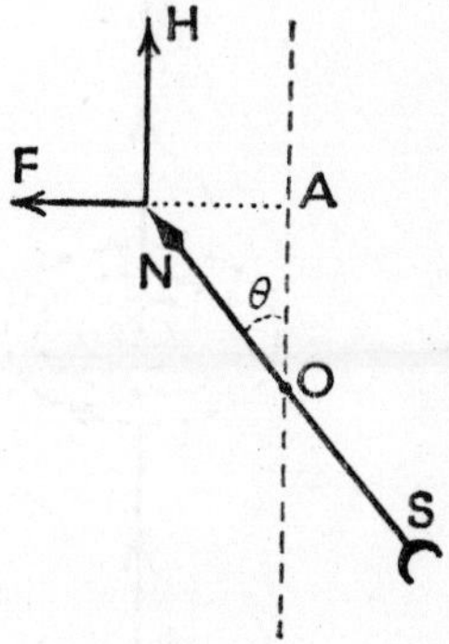

FIG. 259.

to be in equilibrium under the action of these two forces. Then by the Principle of Moments

$$F.\text{AO} = H.\text{NA}$$

or

$$F = H.\frac{\text{NA}}{\text{AO}} = H.\tan\theta.$$

Now H the earth's controlling force is constant, so if we double F then it is not the angle θ which will be doubled but $\tan\theta$. If F is trebled, $\tan\theta$ is trebled, and so on. In other words, the Deflecting Force is directly proportional to the Tangent of the angle of deflection. This is the reason for the name.

It will now be evident that the wire joining the zinc and copper plates of the simple cell certainly has at least one property not possessed by any odd piece of wire lying on the table—it has a magnetic field! Can we plot this magnetic field with iron filings or a plotting compass as we did in the case of other magnetic fields? In a later experiment (p. 319), using a stronger current, it will be shown that we can, and that the lines of force form circles round the wire (fig. 260).

This magnetic field is therefore conveniently described by what is called the *right-hand rule*—**Grasp the conductor with the right hand with the thumb pointing in the direction of the current, then the grasping fingers indicate lines of force.** This statement serves as an alternative to Ampère's rule.

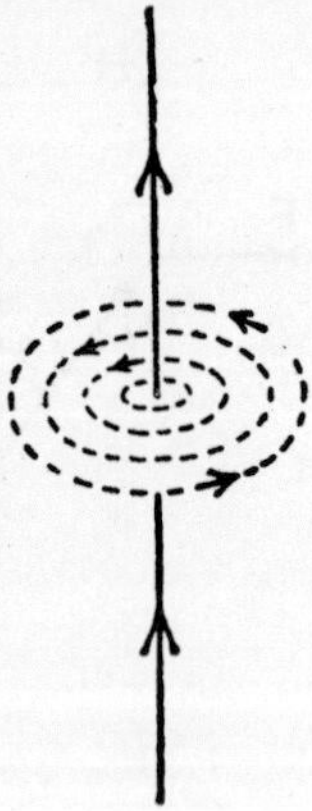

FIG. 260.

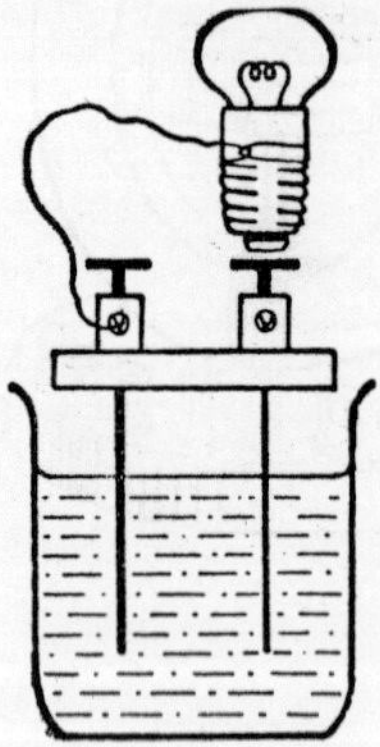

FIG. 261

Having shown that the electric current has a magnetic effect we will next show that it has another important property.

Experiment. Take about a foot of thin copper wire, say 26 d.c.c., and a bulb from a pocket flash lamp. Bare the ends of the wire and wrap one of them round the brass part of the lamp, doubling the wire back on itself and threading through the loop to secure it in position (fig 261). Fasten the other end to one of the poles of the simple cell. Bring the lead stud of the lamp into contact with the other pole. The lamp lights up, then fades away.

The lighting up is of course caused by the heating of the fine wire through which the current passes. Thus in addition to the magnetic effect the current also has a heating effect!

But why did the light fade away?

Polarization. If you watch the copper plate of the simple cell, you will find that as long as the external circuit is "open" nothing is happening there, but as soon as the circuit is "closed" bubbles appear, some coming off and some remaining on the plate. These bubbles are hydrogen gas.

Close the circuit again by means of the lamp. Rub the copper plate with a slip of cardboard or take out the plates and wipe the copper with a duster. When the plates are once more immersed the lamp lights up again but quickly fades as the layer of hydrogen forms.

This defect of the simple cell is called **polarization** because the hydrogen layer forms a *new pole* between the copper and the zinc. This layer of hydrogen weakens the current in two ways.

(*a*) The hydrogen layer is a bad conductor of electricity.

(*b*) A back E.M.F. is set up. This *back E.M.F. of polarization* tends to send a current in the reverse direction.

We shall meet other cases where one or both of the existing poles become modified in this way. We shall also learn that what is a nuisance in the simple cell is actually made use of in that valuable piece of apparatus, the accumulator or secondary cell. At present we must study methods of overcoming the trouble in simple cells.

The Daniell Cell. This cell was invented in 1836 by John Frederick Daniell (1790–1845). Daniell was a meteorologist and chemist. In connection with his work on meteorology he invented a hygrometer which you have probably met in school. He became F.R.S. in 1814 and Professor of Chemistry in King's College, London, in 1831. He was contemporary and friendly with Michael Faraday.

The main reaction in a Daniell cell is exactly the same as in the simple cell, namely,

$$Zn + H_2SO_4 \rightarrow ZnSO_4 + H_2.$$

To get rid of the layer of hydrogen, a saturated solution of copper sulphate is used as a "depolarizer." This acts on the hydrogen according to the following equation

$$H_2 + CuSO_4 \rightarrow H_2SO_4 + Cu.$$

The layer of hydrogen is therefore replaced by an extra film of copper on the copper plate. The copper sulphate is separated from the zinc and acid by a porous pot.

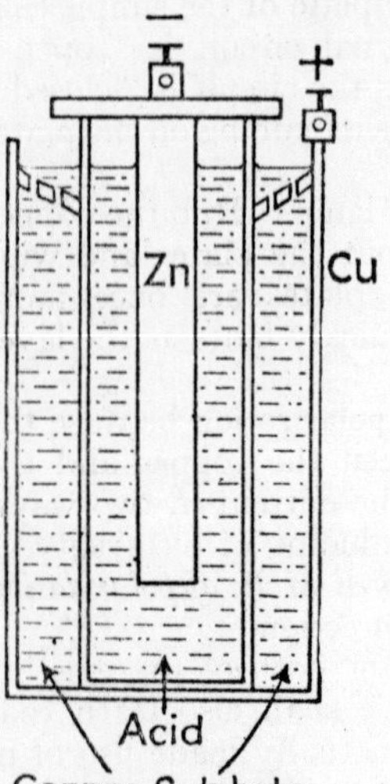

FIG. 262.

In one form of the cell (fig. 262) the copper plate forms the outer containing vessel. It is fitted with a perforated shelf to carry crystals of copper sulphate to maintain the strength of the solution. Inside is a porous pot of unglazed porcelain to contain the zinc and acid.

When putting a Daniell cell away after use, the outer vessel should be washed out and the porous pot left to soak in water. If a porous pot is left to dry with copper sulphate solution in its pores, crystallization will take place and this causes cracking and chipping.

The Leclanché Cell. This cell (fig. 263) was devised by Georges Leclanché in 1868.

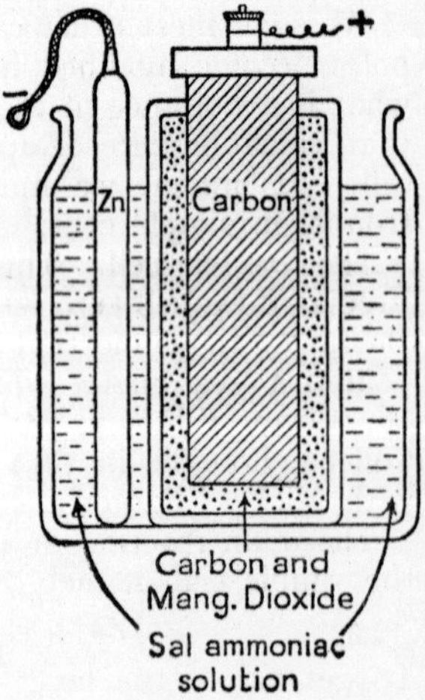

FIG. 263.

The positive pole is a flat carbon plate packed round with granulated carbon and granulated manganese dioxide. The negative pole is a zinc rod immersed in a concentrated solution of sal ammoniac. Like the Daniell cell the Leclanché has a porous pot, but here it serves not to separate two liquids but as a convenient holder for the carbon and manganese dioxide. The granulated carbon increases the effective area of the positive pole, thereby decreasing the internal resistance of the cell. It also prevents the manganese dioxide forming a cake.

The main reaction in the cell is indicated by the following equation—

$$Zn + 2NH_4Cl \rightarrow ZnCl_2 + 2NH_3 + H_2.$$

The material in the porous pot is held in position by a layer of pitch which has a small vent to allow the escape of the ammonia and hydrogen. Some of the ammonia dissolves in the moisture present, the rest escaping through the vent. Any hydrogen collecting on the carbon and polarizing the cell is oxidized by the manganese dioxide thus—

$$2\,MnO_2 + H_2 \rightarrow Mn_2O_3 + H_2O.$$

The manganese dioxide is a slow depolarizer but acts quite well if given time. The cell is therefore best suited for intermittent work, *e.g.* bell batteries.

The glass outer vessel is always made square so that there shall be no wastage of space when a number of cells have to be used simultaneously. The top of the glass vessel is painted to stop the creeping of the liquid.

The "dry" cell is really a Leclanché containing a paste made of plaster of Paris, zinc chloride and a solution of sal ammoniac.

Local Action. When the copper and zinc of a simple cell are joined through an external circuit, we think of positive electricity travelling from copper to zinc or negative electricity travelling from zinc to copper. What happens *inside* the cell? Modern opinion says that here both kinds of transfer take place, the hydrogen carrying positive electricity to the copper while the SO_4 part of the sulphuric acid molecule carries negative electricity to the zinc. This transfer of electricity maintains a difference of potential between the two plates.

It is as well to bear these modern opinions in mind, even if we actually find it more convenient to picture a "one-way traffic," namely, from copper to zinc outside and zinc to copper inside.

What happens to the zinc when the SO_4 part of the acid molecule arrives? It is converted into zinc sulphate ($ZnSO_4$). But if you have done any chemistry you will say, "Surely zinc sulphate is *always* formed when zinc is put into sulphuric acid whether there is any electric current or not?" The answer is that pure zinc does *not* dissolve in the acid except when a current is passing. In chemistry you probably used commercial zinc and here also the dissolving of the zinc is really an electrical effect. Commercial zinc contains an impurity of lead and we have a number of small *local* cells consisting of zinc, acid, and lead. If therefore we use in the simple cell a plate of commercial zinc, it will dissolve wastefully even when the cell is not giving a current. This *local action* can of course be avoided by using pure zinc, but this is rather expensive.

William Sturgeon, an English electrician and lecturer in science, in 1830 discovered another way out of the difficulty. He coated the commercial zinc with mercury. The zinc then, only dissolves when the cell is giving a current. Sturgeon's process is called *amalgamation* ; whenever mercury unites with another metal the resulting substance is called an *amalgam*.

To amalgamate a zinc rod or plate it is dipped into dilute hydrochloric or sulphuric acid to clean it, then mercury is poured over it and rubbed in with a piece of rag tied to a stick.

Amalgamation is essential in Daniell cells, but in those of the Leclanché type it is not so necessary because sal ammoniac does not act much on zinc except when a current is passing.

Series and Parallel. If we have several voltaic cells available, there are two ways of arranging them. The first method (fig. 264) is called "cells in series." Here the positive pole of one cell is joined to the negative of the next and so on through the whole series. In the diagram positive poles are indicated by long strokes and negative poles by short strokes.

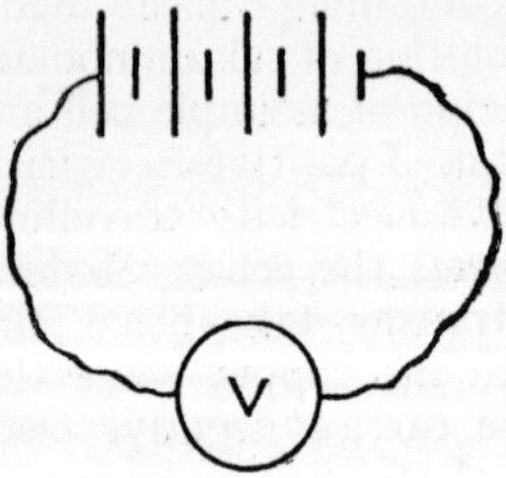

Cells in series.

FIG. 264.

In this series arrangement the separate electrical pressures are added together. Instruments for measuring electrical pressure are called voltmeters. They work on various principles the consideration of which must be postponed for the present.

If the voltmeter is connected to a simple cell, it will probably register "1 volt." Four such cells in series would give a voltage or electrical pressure of 4 volts. A Daniell cell gives a constant voltage of 1·1 volts especially after connecting its two poles for a short time by a thick piece of copper wire. This is called *short circuiting* the cell. It must never be done with any other kind of electric cell. Four Daniell cells in series will give a pressure of 1·1 × 4 = 4·4 volts. A single Leclanché cell gives about 1·5 volts. Four of these in series will give about 6 volts.

In the second arrangement of cells shown in fig. 265 we have what is called "cells in parallel." Here all the positives are joined to one common point and all the negatives to another common point. The result is now that we have one large cell and the electrical pressure is that of a single cell. Each arrangement is called an electric "battery."

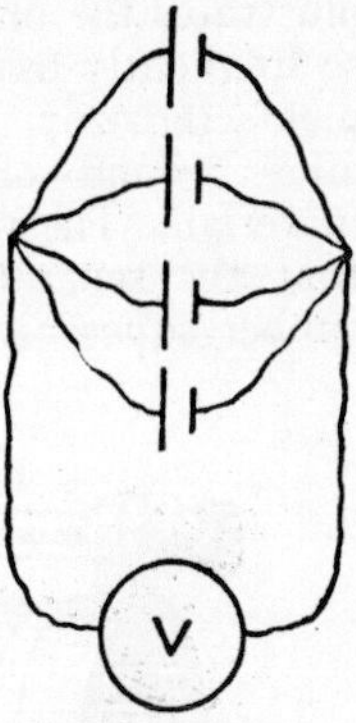

Cells in parallel.

FIG. 265.

Resistance. It can easily be shown that the current flowing from a battery through a wire depends on (*a*) the length, (*b*) the thickness, and (*c*) the material of the wire.

Experiment. It will be convenient to use as our source of current either four Daniell cells or two accumulator cells. Arrange the cells in series with one another and with a pocket flash lamp and plug key with plug out (fig. 266). Across the terminals of the plug connect in turn

(*a*) 8 yd. of 26 d.c.c. copper wire,
(*b*) 8 yd. of 36 d.c.c. copper wire,
(*c*) 1 yd. of 36 German silver wire,
(*d*) 2 yd. of 36 German silver wire (an alloy of copper, nickel, and zinc 5 : 2 : 2).

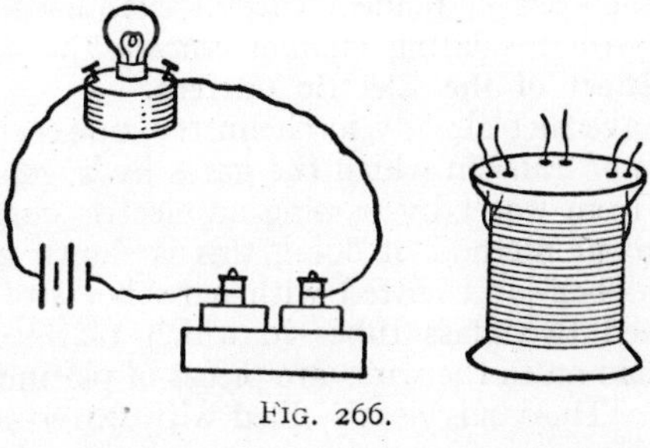

FIG. 266.

These wires are conveniently wound on a cotton reel having holes bored in the top to receive the ends (fig 266.). The effect of length, thickness, and material will be plainly seen by the variation in the light of the lamp.

The Rheostat or Variable Resistance. The above experiment illustrates the principle of the "rheostat" or variable resistance so frequently used in controlling the current in electrical experiments (fig. 267). The wire is of German silver or some similar alloy wound on slate or other non-inflammable insulating material. The wire is either covered with enamel or wound so that the separate turns are not in contact. Only where the rubber squeezes on the wire is the enamel worn off and there

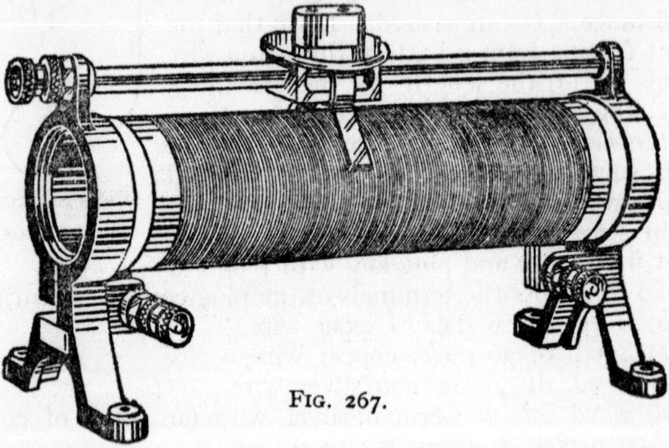

FIG. 267.

only is metallic contact made; careful examination will show that there is still insulating enamel *between* the wires.

Chemical Effect of the Electric Current.

You may have met already in chemistry an experiment called the *electrolysis of water* in which the gases hydrogen and oxygen are obtained from water by passing an electric current through it. A convenient method of doing this is shown in fig. 268.

An inverted bell-jar is fitted with a rubber stopper through which are fixed two glass tubes in which platinum wires are sealed. Welded on to the wires are pieces of platinum foil called the *electrodes*. The jar is nearly filled with water acidified with a little sulphuric acid. From the projecting ends of the platinum wire, copper leads pass to a plug key, rheostat, tangent galvanometer, and a battery of three accumulator cells.

The electrode next to the positive pole is called the positive electrode or *anode* ; the other is called the *kathode*. Over the electrodes are placed two test-tubes also filled with the same

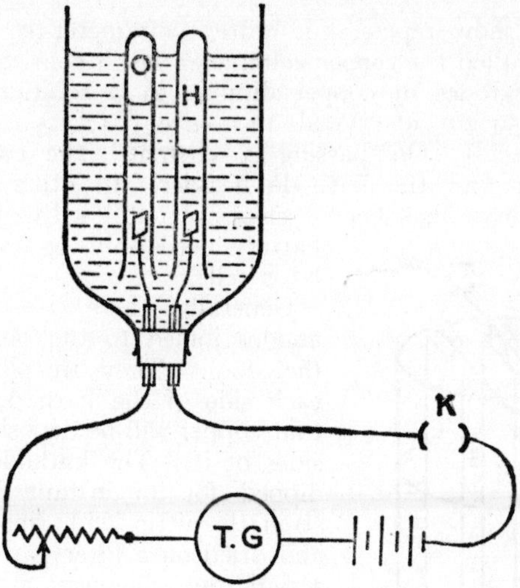

FIG. 268.

acidulated water. These tubes should be calibrated in c.c.s. This can be done with the aid of a burette and a sharp file. The jar with its fittings is called a water or hydrogen *voltameter*, a name which means " current measurer."

Adjust the rheostat so that the bubbles come off at a convenient rate, then place the tubes in position. If this adjustment cannot be made with the rheostat, pull the glass tubes farther down through the cork. It will be found that two volumes of hydrogen appear at the kathode and one volume of oxygen at the anode.

Allow the current to run for 5 min., keeping it constant by watching the galvanometer and altering the rheostat if necessary. Read the volume of each gas. Repeat the observations for time intervals of 10, 15, and 20 min.

It should be possible to prove that the volume of either gas is proportional to the time during which the current has flowed. This is an illustration of Faraday's first law of electrolysis which says: "**The quantity of substance liberated at either electrode is proportional to the quantity of electricity which passes.**"

We may now replace the water voltameter by a piece of apparatus called the **copper voltameter** which consists essentially of two electrodes of copper dipping in a solution of copper sulphate (150 gm. of crystals in a litre + 4 or 5 c.c. of strong sulphuric acid). On passing a current,[1] the copper anode gets lighter and the kathode heavier. In other words, the copper kathode has been "electroplated" with copper. The battery need only be two accumulator cells.

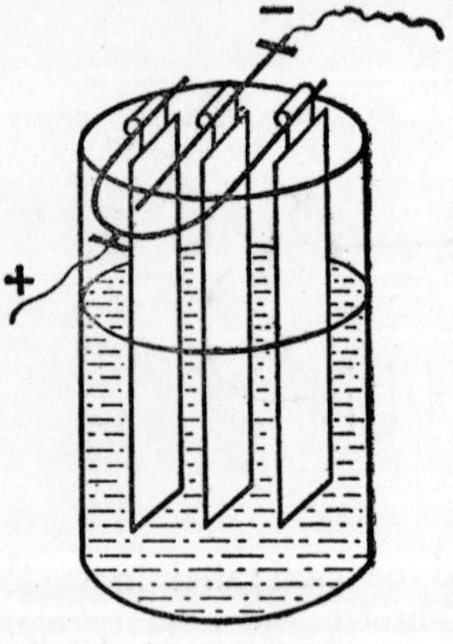

Fig. 269.

Generally there are two copper anodes joined to the same terminal (fig. 269). They are placed one on each side of the kathode to ensure that copper will be deposited on both sides of it. The kathode should be dipped for an instant in medium-strength nitric acid, rinsed in water and dried on a filter paper placed on a radiator. The clean surface should not be touched with fingers otherwise the copper will not adhere.

After weighing the kathode, the current should be passed for 10 min. The kathode is then dipped into water acidified with sulphuric acid, rinsed, dried, and weighed. The process should be repeated for 20 min. then 30 min. The increases in weight should be as 1 : 2 : 3, again agreeing with Faraday's first law.

When electrodes of silver are used with a solution of silver nitrate, similar results are obtained, the anodes being lighter and the kathode heavier in proportion to the quantity of electricity which passes.

So definite and regular are the results of these experiments, that it is from them that we now get our legal definition of the **ampère as that current which in 1 sec. will deposit 0·001118 gm. of silver from a solution of silver nitrate in water.**

[1] 1 amp. per 50 sq. cm. of kathode.

The *quantity* of electricity which passes in 1 sec. under these conditions is called a **coulomb, or an ampère-second.**

A coulomb will liberate—

0·00001035 gm. of Hydrogen
0·00008281 gm. of Oxygen
0·0003292 gm. of Copper
0·001118 gm. of Silver.

It may be asked whether there is any simple relation between these numbers. The answer is that they are in the same proportion to one another as their chemical equivalents, namely, 1 : 8 : 31·8 : 108. This is in accordance with Faraday's second Law of Electrolysis which says: "**If the same quantity of electricity passes through various electrolytes, then the weights of the elements liberated will be in the same proportion as their chemical equivalents.**"

Some Interesting Electrolytic Experiments.

(*a*) Using the hydrogen voltameter, interchange the tubes after a few minutes. Allow the current to run again for the same time. Each tube now contains **electrolytic gas.** Hold either tube to the Bunsen flame. There is a sharp explosion like a pistol shot.

(*b*) Add a salt-spoonful of potassium iodide to a beaker of water, then a few drops of phenolphthalein. Electrolyse by means of carbon electrodes taken from an old dry cell. These may be pushed through a piece of cardboard laid on the top of the beaker.

A brown colour due to liberated iodine appears at the anode. Potassium, like hydrogen and all metals, will be liberated at the kathode. Here it acts on the water forming caustic potash which turns the indicator pink.

This experiment has a medical application. It is sometimes desired to administer iodine through the skin into a joint, say the knee. Metal electrodes are wrapped in cotton-wool pads soaked in a weak solution of potassium iodide, the kathode pad being placed on the knee while the anode pad is placed some distance away on the same limb. When the current passes, iodine is driven into the knee under the kathode pad.

(*c*) Similar experiments with the same carbon electrodes may be carried out with solutions of zinc sulphate and lead acetate.

In the former we get a spongy mass of zinc on the kathode. In the latter case a lead tree forms.

Electrolysis with a Wimshurst Machine.

We may carry out a few of these electrolytic experiments with a Wimshurst machine and so illustrate the fact that current electricity and static electricity are really identical.

Support a gas jar cover glass so that it is nearer to the Wimshurst knobs than these are to one another (fig. 270). Dip a piece of filter paper into a solution of potassium iodide containing a little phenolphthalein. Lay it on the glass under the knobs and work the machine. Two brown iodine spots appear because the current travels first one way then the other. It is an oscillating current. We do not see pink spots due to caustic potash because they are masked by the brown.

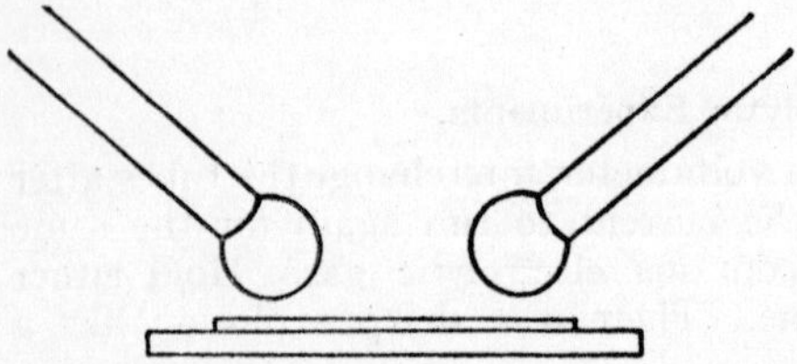

FIG. 270.

Repeat the experiment using sodium chloride instead of potassium iodide. Pink spots now appear due to caustic soda, but they quickly fade away.

Currents obtained from a Wimshurst have a much higher voltage and much lower amperage than ordinary electric currents. For this reason it is generally difficult to carry out the same experiments with the apparatus designed for current electricity and that intended for electrostatics.

While we are using the Wimshurst, it is worth noting another effect which is not exactly electrolytic but is nevertheless important—the production of **ozone.** Dip a piece of filter paper in starch solution containing a little potassium iodide and proceed as above. Blue spots will now be produced on the paper. This and the characteristic smell are sufficient indication that ozone is being produced.

Electrolysis in Industry.

(*a*) *Silver Plating.* In plating with silver, it is found best to use, instead of a solution of silver nitrate, a solution containing silver cyanide and potassium cyanide. The anode is a piece of silver, the kathode the article to be plated. The articles most frequently plated in this way are made of so-called "nickel silver" or "German silver," an alloy of copper, zinc, and nickel. After plating, the article is marked E.P.N.S.

(*b*) *Gold Plating*. The method is similar, the electrolyte being a solution of gold cyanide and potassium cyanide.

(*c*) *Chromium Plating*. This is much used for motor-car radiators and bathroom fittings. Steel is first plated with copper, then nickel, then chromium. In the final stage the bath usually contains chromic acid (CrO_3) and a lead anode. Since, in this case, the anode does not keep up the strength of the electrolyte, more chromic acid is added from time to time. Chromium-plated goods have the advantages that they do not readily tarnish nor are they easily scratched.

(*d*) *Copper Refining*. Copper is largely used for conducting wires and cables and its good conductivity depends on its purity. Copper refining is carried out entirely by electrolysis. The crude copper blocks are used as anodes in a bath of acidified copper sulphate, the copper being then deposited on thin sheets of pure copper acting as kathodes.

(*e*) *Manufacture of Sodium and Chlorine*. When a strong solution of brine is electrolysed, chlorine is liberated and collected at the anode while sodium goes to the kathode. The sodium acts on the water giving sodium hydroxide solution. This is evaporated to dryness and then electrolysed to obtain metallic sodium. The process of electrolysis finds many similar uses in industrial chemistry.

(*f*) *The Accumulator, Secondary Cell or Storage Cell*. The reader may be surprised to hear that the accumulator is an application of electrolysis. A few experiments, however, will soon show that this is really the case.

When dealing with the simple cell, we referred to the "back E.M.F. of polarization" caused by the formation of a "new pole." We have another example of this back E.M.F. in the hydrogen voltameter.

Experiment. Fit up the circuit shown in fig. 271. The battery is a 4-volt accumulator. K_1 and K_2 are tapping keys. The ammeter A is not absolutely essential but is useful to measure the current which is passing. V is a voltmeter to indicate the electrical pressure. HV is a hydrogen voltameter.

Close K_1 for a minute or so, then open K_1 and close K_2. The voltmeter will give a kick to about 1·5 volts and the reading will then quickly decrease. Since K_1 was open, this electrical pressure cannot be due to the accumulator but must be the back E.M.F. of the hydrogen voltameter caused by "new poles." The hydrogen voltameter will not give a reading on the ammeter unless the platinum plates are very large and very close together.

Whenever we electrolyse water, this back E.M.F. comes into action and has to be overcome by the battery. This is why we could not hope to electrolyse water with a single Daniell cell.

Experiment. Use the same circuit but replace the hydrogen voltameter by a pot containing two lead plates separated by a piece of wood about ¼-in. thick. Half-fill the pot with sulphuric acid which has been diluted by adding 1 volume of acid to about 4 of water. The lead plates are conveniently cut from a piece of lead roofing. A brass terminal should be fitted to each.

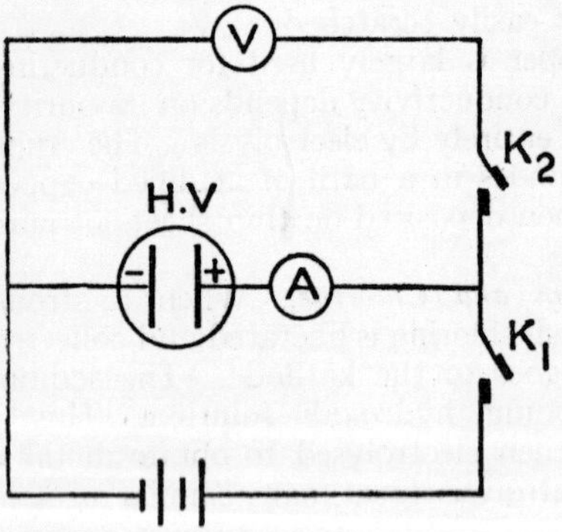

Fig. 271.

Proceeding as in the last experiment, we find a back E.M.F. of more than 2 volts! We may also replace the voltmeter by a lamp, a bell, or a buzzer. We have in fact made a toy accumulator which may be charged up and then discharged through lamp, bell, or buzzer. This time we shall be able to read the discharge current on the ammeter. During the charging, notice the bubbles coming off, especially from the negative electrode. Our little accumulator is gassing!

See if there is any difference of colour between the two electrodes. The positive will be slightly chocolate-coloured due to the formation of lead dioxide (PbO_2). This is the "new pole" causing a back E.M.F. of polarization.

The high back E.M.F. in the present case was discovered by Gaston Planté in 1860, and it is to his extensive work on polarization that we owe the idea of the common accumulator cell.

Simple Theory of the Accumulator. We do not of course in

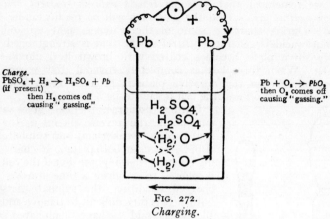

Charge.
$PbSO_4 + H_2 \rightarrow H_2SO_4 + Pb$
(if present)
then H_2 comes off causing "gassing."

$Pb + O_2 \rightarrow PbO_2$
then O_2 comes off causing "gassing."

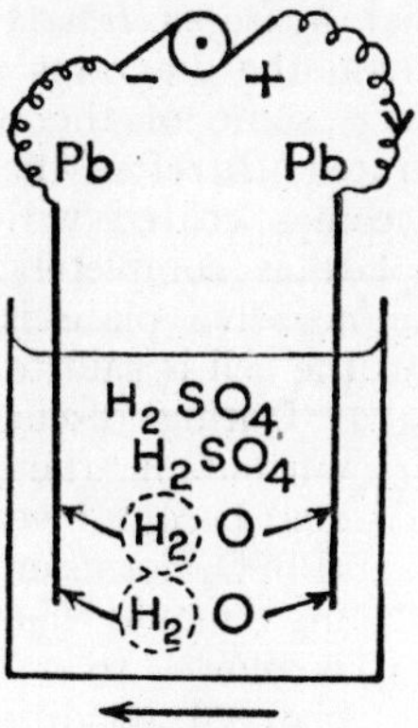

FIG. 272.
Charging.
Acid gets stronger and denser.

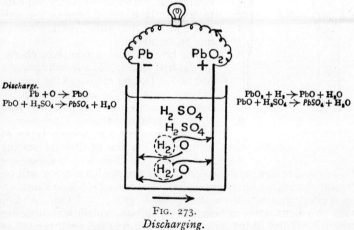

Discharge.
$Pb + O \rightarrow PbO$
$PbO + H_2SO_4 \rightarrow PbSO_4 + H_2O$

$PbO_2 + H_2 \rightarrow PbO + H_2O$
$PbO + H_2SO_4 \rightarrow PbSO_4 + H_2O$

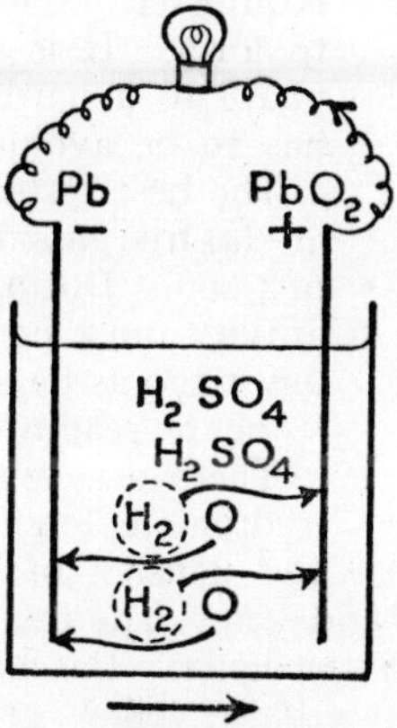

FIG. 273.
Discharging.
Acid gets weaker and less dense.

practice charge one accumulator from a larger one; a dynamo is generally used. Let us consider what happens during charge (fig. 272) and discharge (fig. 273).

If we remember that *hydrogen travels with the current and oxygen against the current,* the diagrams will be readily understood. During charging, some of the water is split up and sulphuric acid is generated, therefore the acid is strengthened. The positive plate becomes coated with brown lead dioxide (PbO_2). When this plate is completely covered, the oxygen comes off. When the negative plate is perfectly clean lead, hydrogen comes off and the cell is said to be "gassing."

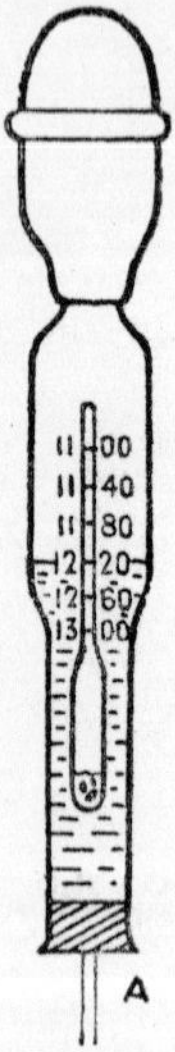

FIG. 274

FIG. 275.

During discharge, the cell gives a current in the reverse direction, the acid becomes weaker and lead sulphate ($PbSO_4$) forms on both plates. Recharging removes this sulphate, but if the cell is allowed to stand for a time in a discharged condition, the sulphate gets hard. It is then difficult to remove and the cell is said to have "sulphated." This is an unfortunate term, because it is quite natural for the ordinary sulphate to form. It is the change of this sulphate to a hard white coating which has to be avoided.

The best tests of a complete charge are (*a*) free gassing, (*b*) a specific gravity of 1·200. During discharge the specific gravity must not be allowed to fall below 1·170 as beyond this point the lead sulphate readily hardens.

There are two well-known types of hydrometer on the market for testing the density of the acid. These are illustrated in figs. 274 and 275. The method of using A will be readily understood from the figure. B is like an old-time fountain-pen filler containing three balls, yellow, green, and red. At C C are two bent strips of celluloid. Can you explain why they are there ? When all the balls are at the top of the acid, the cell is fully charged. When the red one sinks, it is a mild danger signal. If two sink the cell must be recharged.

We saw that our toy accumulator was quickly charged up to gassing point and was just as quickly discharged. To increase the capacity of the cell, the manufacturer uses lead grids, the positive being filled with a paste of lead dioxide and the negative with spongy lead. There is then a much larger quantity of active material on which the charging current can act.

Notice that an accumulator stores *chemical energy* which can be converted into electrical energy. It is for this reason that it is called a *storage* cell. It does not accumulate or store electricity.

You will probably meet the terms *primary cell* and *secondary cell.* The simple voltaic cell is a primary cell; its energy is generated within itself. The accumulator depends on some outside source of energy. Its energy is "second-hand." It is a *secondary cell.*

In recent years another kind of accumulator has appeared on the market. It was invented by the American electrician Edison. It is called the Nickel-Iron accumulator and bears the trade mark *NIFE*. Ask your chemistry master what he thinks of this trade mark. It will be useful to compare the two kinds of accumulator.

	Ordinary Accumulator.	*Edison Accumulator.*
+ Pole	Lead dioxide PbO_2	Nickel dioxide NiO_2
− Pole	Lead	Iron
Electrolyte . . .	Dilute sulphuric acid	Caustic potash KOH
Voltage	2·0 per cell	1·2 volts per cell
Internal resistance .	Low	Higher
Weight	Heavy	Lighter
Cost	High	Higher
Care of	(*a*) Must not be short circuited (*b*) Must not be shaken (*c*) Must be charged slowly (*d*) Must not be left run down	(*a*) Short circuiting does no harm (*b*) Stands vibration well. (*c*) May be charged at a high rate. (*d*) Can be left for a long time.

QUESTIONS

1. What contributions were made to our knowledge of electricity by the following men—

Galvani, Volta, Schweigger, Leclanché, Planté ?

2. Describe Oersted's experiment. State Ampère's Rule and the Right-hand Rule.

3. Describe the Tangent Galvanometer. Explain why it received its name and how it depends on the principle of moments.

4. Explain "Local Action" and "Polarization.' How are they avoided in a Daniell cell?

5. What is meant by short circuiting? When may it be done? When must it not be done?

6. Illustrate by diagrams how you would arrange 20 accumulator cells to give voltages of (*a*) 40 volts, (*b*) 20 volts, (*c*) 10 volts, (*d*) 4 volts, (*e*) 2 volts.

7. How would you show that an electric current has a heating effect, a magnetic effect, and a chemical effect?

8. What are (*a*) an ampère, (*b*) a coulomb? State Faraday's Laws of Electrolysis.

9. Draw (1) a circuit to illustrate the back E.M.F. of a hydrogen voltameter, (2) a circuit for charging and discharging a toy accumulator.

10. Explain sulphating, rheostat, depolarizer, secondary cell, gassing, amalgamation.

11. By means of diagrams and equations explain what happens in the ordinary accumulator cell during "charge" and "discharge."

12. Describe two forms of hydrometer and explain how to use them.

13. A certain current deposited 3·936 gm. of copper on a copper kathode in 40 min. What was the strength of the current? How many coulombs were used? How much oxygen would be liberated by the same quantity of electricity?

14. A current of 4 ampères was allowed to pass for 20 min. 15 sec. through various voltameters arranged in series. Calculate the weights of oxygen, hydrogen, copper, and silver which would be liberated.

15. A current of 1·5 amps. passes for 80 min. through a solution of copper sulphate. If the kathode has an area of 75 sq. cm., what is the thickness of the copper deposit? Density of copper is 9 gm. per c.c.

16. How long would a current of 2 ampères take to turn out from the appropriate electrolytes (*a*) a gram of copper, (*b*) a gram of silver?

17. Give a brief account of what happens when an electric current passes between two copper plates immersed in a solution of copper sulphate.

How could this arrangement be used to test the accuracy of an ammeter? In a particular case 0·802 gm. of copper was deposited in 30 min. when the ammeter reading was 1·3 amps.

What was the error in the reading of the instrument if the electrochemical equivalent of copper is 0·00033 gm. per coulomb? (B.)

CHAPTER XXVII

CURRENT ELECTRICITY: MORE ABOUT THE MAGNETIC EFFECT

In the last chapter we learnt that a wire carrying an electric current has a magnetic field and that lines of force form circles round the wire. It is difficult to show these lines of force going round a *single* wire unless we have a very powerful current. We can, however, send the same current through *several* wires and show the lines of force quite well.

Experiment. The coil shown in fig. 276 is made from 16 yd. of 20 d.c.c. wire bent into a square coil of 15 turns. The square

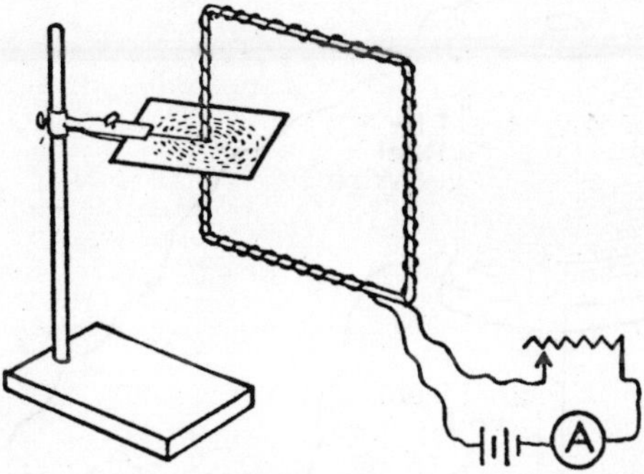

FIG. 276.

is 9 in. each way and the last turn is twisted spirally round the others to keep the coil together. The coil is connected to a 4-volt accumulator, a rheostat and an ammeter. The cardboard has a hole at the centre and a slit running to one side so that it may be slipped easily on to the coil.

Plotting compasses may be placed on the cardboard, or iron filings sprinkled on it. If a current of 2 to 4 amps. is sent through and the cardboard tapped gently, well-marked circles will be seen.

Such a coil may really be regarded as a short thick magnet, its two faces are the north and south poles. Just like a magnet it will attract a piece of iron. This effect is best shown when the coil is wound in the form of a spiral. It is then called a solenoid (fig. 277). Notice that Ampère's rule gives its polarity.

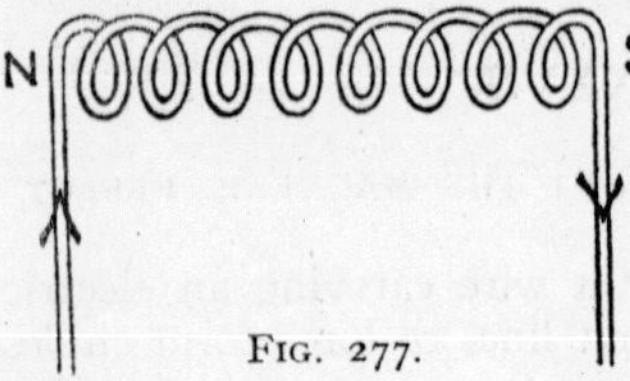

FIG. 277.

To show the attractive force of a solenoid, we do not need to make one; in every laboratory there is a very effective substitute—we may use a reel of copper wire!

Experiment. Fig. 278 represents a circuit in which a pound reel of 20 or 22 d.c.c. copper wire is joined in series with an 8-volt accumulator, an ammeter and a tapping key. The reel is held in the hand about 4 in. above the table, while a 6-in. rod of $\frac{1}{4}$-in. soft iron weighing about 40 gm. rests with one end on the table and the other in the hole of the reel.

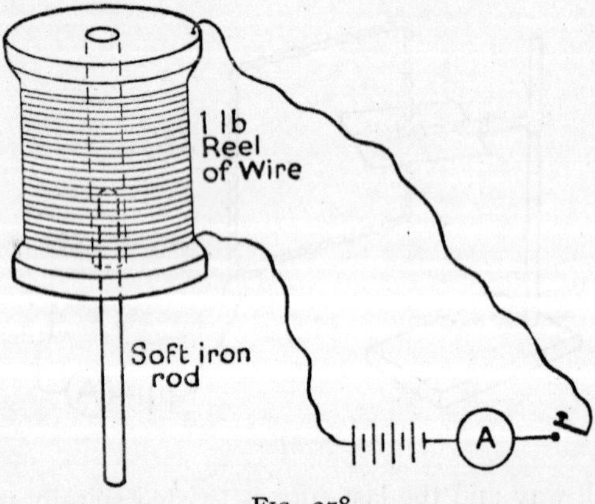

FIG. 278.

When the circuit is made through the tapping key, the rod is sucked into the reel and oscillates up and down. The increase in weight supported by the coil, and therefore the hand, is very striking. With a more powerful source of current, a heavier bar can be used.

In Chapter XXIV we learnt that magnets can be made by

"single touch" and "double touch." By means of a solenoid and a battery we are able to make much more powerful magnets. If a piece of steel is placed in the solenoid and a current is passed, it becomes converted into a permanent magnet. Under the same conditions a piece of soft iron becomes a temporary magnet; as soon as the current is stopped it ceases to be a magnet. The advantage here is that the magnetism is absolutely under control. These facts were discovered independently in 1820 by Sir Humphry Davy and the French scientist Arago.

In 1825 an English electrician, William Sturgeon, applied the discovery to the making of the first electromagnet. The wire may be coiled round a straight piece of soft iron or the iron may be bent into a horseshoe (fig. 279). Sturgeon's first electromagnet was

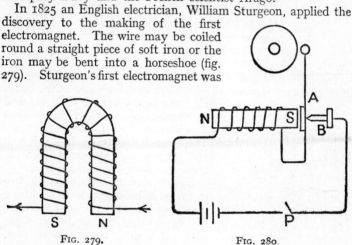

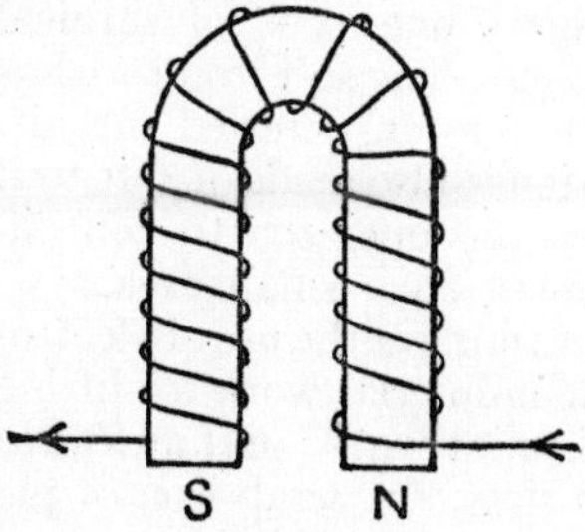

FIG. 279.

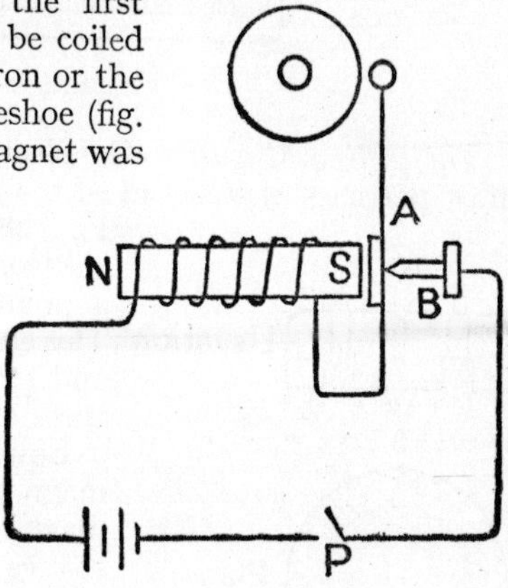

FIG. 280.

of the latter form. He used it as a lifting magnet. It was later improved upon by Faraday and Joule in England and Joseph Henry in America.

Simple Bell Circuit. Probably the commonest application of the electromagnet occurs in the working of electric bells and buzzers (fig. 280).

On pressing the push P, the circuit is completed. The soft iron core attracts the armature A to which the hammer is attached. The circuit is then broken at the contact screw B and the core no longer attracts the armature. The latter springs back, makes contact and is again attracted. Every time the armature is attracted, the hammer strikes the gong. The result is a rapid series of blows on the gong.

You will probably have seen an indicator, showing moving flags to indicate the room in which the bell push was used. These also work on the same principle. Later on you will meet the same idea in the induction coil, sparking coil or Ruhmkorff Coil.

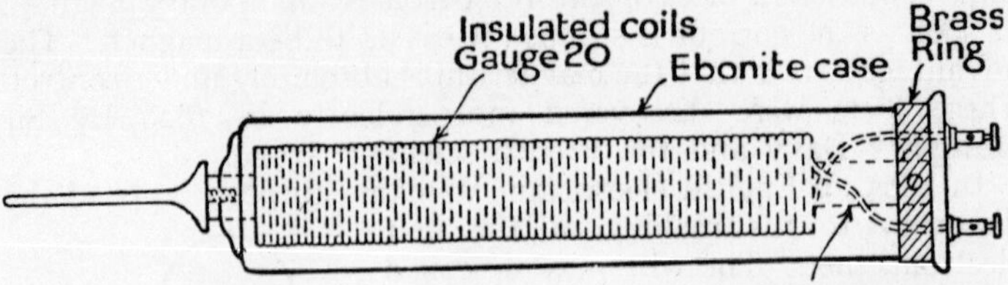

FIG. 281.

The Lifting Magnet. The electromagnet is frequently used to draw particles of steel out of the eye or other parts of the body. Fig. 281 shows one type of surgical electromagnet. The soft iron core has a pointed extension screwed into it. This extension is also made of soft iron and enables the operator to concentrate the force on a small area.

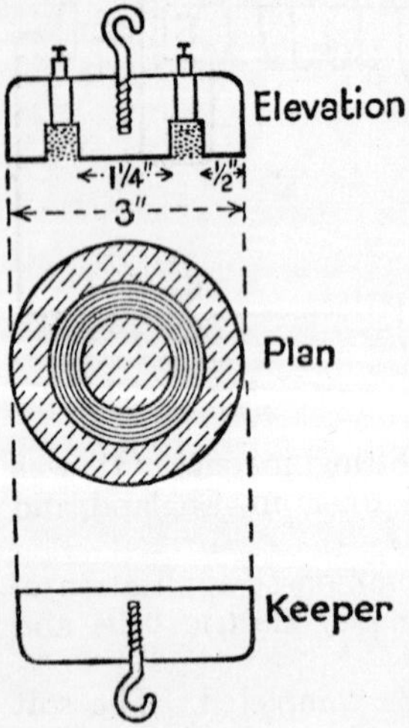

FIG. 282.

Equally striking is the use of electromagnets in industrial work for lifting masses of iron of varied and awkward shapes and sizes, *e.g.* scrap iron or pig iron. If a lathe is available a good working model, capable of lifting 40 or 50 lb., can easily be made (fig. 282).

A channel is cut out in a piece of soft iron. Two holes are bored and plugged with ebonite. The ebonite is drilled and tapped to carry the terminals. Two tiny holes must also be bored in the ebonite plugs to take the coil leads. Centre holes are drilled and tapped in the magnet and keeper to carry the screw hooks.

The channel is filled with 28-gauge insulated copper wire by first winding on a wooden former of the same cross-section as the central portion of the magnet, and then slipping it off into the channel, having first passed the ends through the plugs. Molten paraffin wax should now be run in.

To use the lifting magnet it is joined in series with a 4-volt accumulator and a rheostat. The hook of the keeper is attached to the weight, the rheostat moved to the "all out" position, and quickly restored to the "all in" position as soon as the weight is safely replaced on the table or floor.

Where are the poles of such a magnet? One is at the centre, the other is the ring of metal surrounding the coil.

Still another, perhaps the most important, use of electro-magnets will be met when you study dynamos and motors.

Experiment. Another method of showing that a flat coil carrying a current has magnetic properties (fig. 283).

Place a horseshoe magnet on the clamp of a burette stand. Wind thirty or forty turns of gauge 30 or 36 insulated copper wire round two fingers. Shape the wire into a circular coil and wrap the loose ends round the coil so as to hold the strands in position.

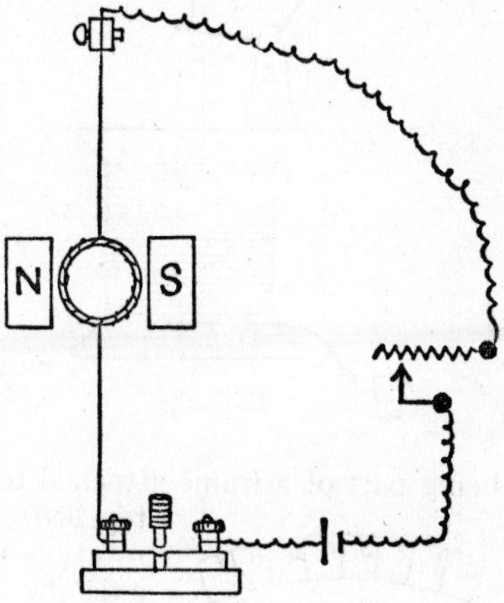

FIG. 283.

Suspend the coil vertically between the poles of the magnet, joining one end to a plug key and the other to another clamp on the same burette stand. Connect a 2-volt accumulator and a rheostat in series with the coil.

On passing a current, the coil faces acquire polarity and the coil will twist, its poles being attracted by the opposite poles of the magnet until there is equilibrium between the magnetic twist and the twist of the suspension wire. If, however, the coil is set in one particular way, there will be no twist. Explain.

Ammeters and Voltmeters. We are now in a position to understand something about the inner working of ammeters and voltmeters. They may be roughly divided into three classes:

(*a*) Moving Coil instruments. (*b*) Moving Iron.

(*c*) Hot Wire.

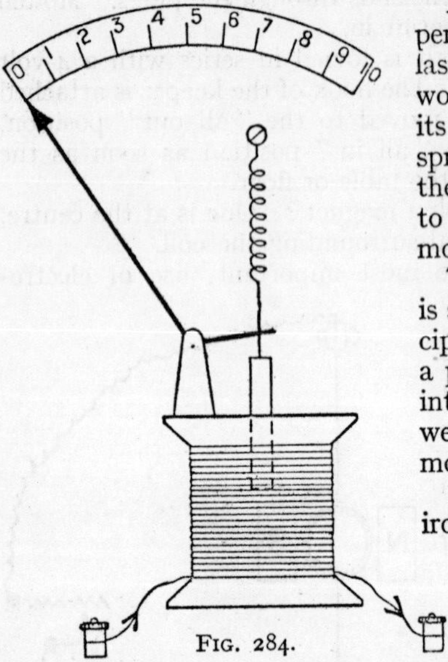

FIG. 284.

The moving coil type depends on the principle of the last experiment, but the coil is wound on a soft iron core and its movement is controlled by a spring instead of by the twist of the suspension wire. Attached to the coil is a pointer which moves over the arc of a circle.

The moving iron instrument is sometimes based on the principle of the experiment in which a piece of soft iron was sucked into a coil (p. 320). In fig. 284 we have a spring-controlled model working in that way.

In another type of moving iron instrument, the current running through a cylindrical coil magnetizes in the same sense two pieces of soft iron. One of these is fixed while the other, being part of a frame attached to the axle, is free to move when repelled. This movement causes the rotation of a pointer also attached to the axle (fig. 285).

In the "hot wire" instrument (fig. 286)

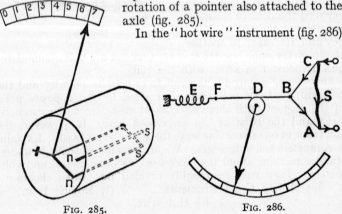

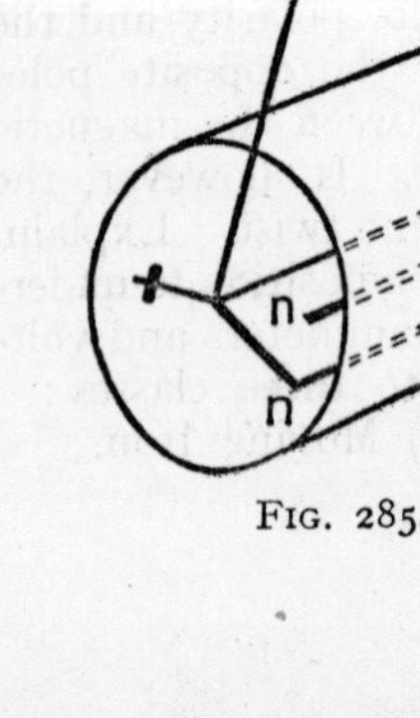

FIG. 285.

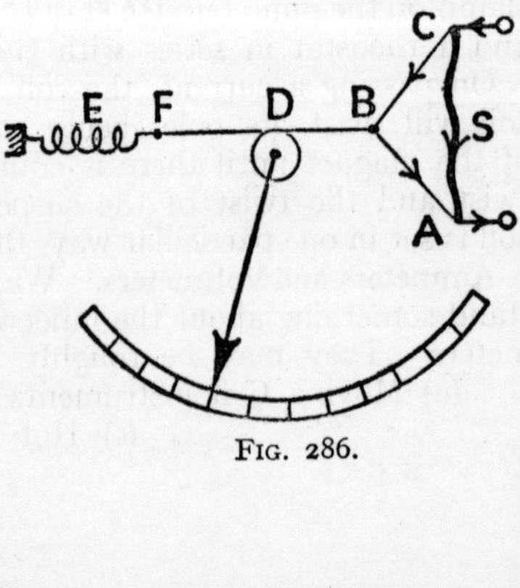

FIG. 286.

most of the current goes through a thick wire S, the *shunt*, but a certain definite fraction goes through the thin wire ABC. A silk fibre goes from B round a pulley D carrying the pointer and then to the spring E. When the wire ABC is heated by the current, it expands and the spring is then able to pull the pointer round.

The exact difference between an ammeter and a voltmeter will be better understood later. It will be sufficient here to mention that an ammeter is a *low*-resistance instrument placed *in* the circuit so that the current passes through it, while a voltmeter has a *high* resistance and acts as a sort of by-pass to the current.

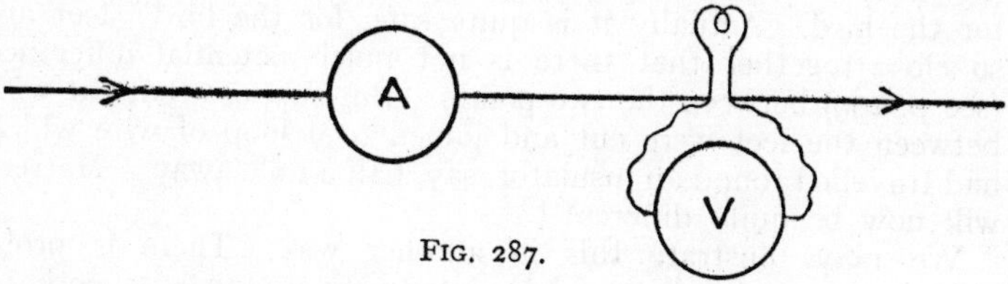

FIG. 287.

Thus if we wish to know the current passing through a lamp and the electric pressure acting across it, the instruments are connected up as shown in fig. 287, where A is the ammeter and V the voltmeter.

Moving Iron and Hot Wire instruments can also be used for A.C. (see p. 349).

Ammeters are calibrated by means of a silver voltameter (see p. 310).

QUESTIONS

1. Describe any two experiments illustrating the fact that a wire carrying an electric current has a magnetic field associated with it.

2. Draw an ammeter depending on the magnetic effect and one which does not.

3. What is a moving coil ammeter? How may the principle of such an instrument be demonstrated?

4. Make a list of the different uses to which electromagnets may be put and illustrate one of them.

5. Draw a simple bell circuit.

What would be the effect of substituting steel for soft iron in such a circuit?

CHAPTER XXVIII

POTENTIAL DIFFERENCE. OHM'S LAW. RESISTANCE

WHAT happens if a bird alights on an overhead power cable (fig. 288)? At first sight you may think it will be very bad for the bird. Actually it is quite safe, for the bird's feet are so close together that there is not much **potential difference** (see p. 299) between the two points. But suppose that the wire between the feet were cut and joined to a loop of wire which had travelled round an insulator, say, half a mile away. Matters will now be quite different!

We may illustrate this in another way. There is probably in your laboratory a board carrying a long wire perhaps

FIG. 288.

100 or 200 cm. long. Join a 4-volt accumulator to it by the usual thick copper leads (fig. 289). Fasten a piece of copper wire round a pocket flash bulb as shown on page 302. Connect the lamp to two points on the long wire: (*a*) close together, (*b*) far apart. What do you observe?

You may be helped to a clear idea about *potential difference* or *fall of potential* between two points by considering two other cases (fig. 290 A and B).

The amount of damage done by a falling brick will depend on the *height difference* through which it has fallen.

Water will spurt farther from a leak in a pipe when the *difference of water pressure* is greater.

In our electrical experiment there was a *potential difference* of 4 volts driving current round the circuit. Most of this electrical pressure was used in driving the current through the thin

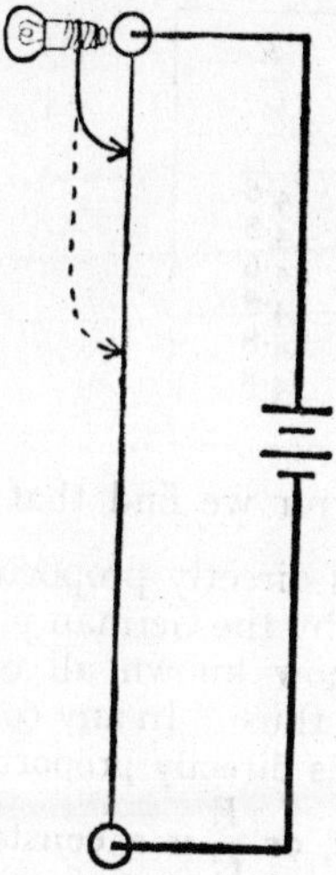

Fig. 289.

Fig. 290 A and B

wire. Between two points close together there will be very little potential difference so the lamp did not light, but when the lamp was joined to two points far apart, there was sufficient potential difference to drive a large current through the lamp.

Ohm's Law. Our previous work shows that the current travelling through a conductor depends on the electrical pressure driving it. Let us investigate this in more detail.

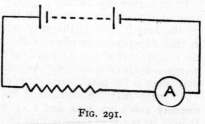

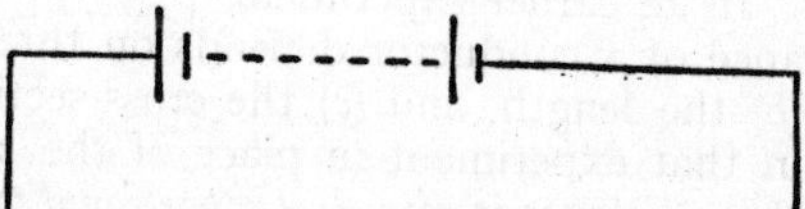

Fig. 291.

Experiment. Take as many freshly-charged accumulator cells as are available and join them up in series with an ammeter and a conductor, say 47 yd. of 26-gauge German silver wire (fig. 291).

Take readings on the ammeter using 1 cell, 2 cells, 3 cells and so on. Draw up a table of E.M.F.'s and currents, taking the E.M.F. of each cell to be 2 volts.

E (volts).	*C (ampères).*	$\frac{E}{C}$
2 volts	0·44 amp.	4·6
4	0·85	4·8
6	1·30	4·6
8	1·65	4·8
10	2·05	4·8
12	2·50	4·8

Within the limits of experimental error we find that $\frac{E}{C}$ is a constant, in other words, the current is directly proportional to the E.M.F. This is the fact discovered by the German physicist, Georg Simon Ohm (1787–1854) and now known all over the world as Ohm's Law. It may be stated thus, "In any conductor **at a constant temperature the current is directly proportional to the potential difference between its ends, or $\frac{E}{C}$ is a constant.**"

The constant $\frac{E}{C}$ is what is known as the *resistance* of the conductor, and we may say

$$\frac{E \text{ (volts)}}{C \text{ (ampères)}} = R \text{ (ohms) or } \frac{E}{R} = C \text{ or } \mathbf{E = RC}$$

In an earlier experiment (p. 307) it was shown that the resistance of a conductor depends on three things: (*a*) the material, (*b*) the length, and (*c*) the cross-section. By using an ammeter in that experiment in place of the lamp, it may be proved that the *resistance is directly proportional to the length and inversely proportional to the cross-section.* As regards material it may be shown that silver is the best conductor while copper takes second place.

An ohm may be defined as the resistance of a column of mercury 106·3 cm. long and 1 sq. mm. in cross-section at 0° C. It may be noted in passing that the temperature must be stated because the resistance of a metal increases as the temperature rises. On this fact depends the use of platinum resistance thermometers for the measurement of high and very low temperatures.

We have already learnt that the **ampère** is legally defined as the current which in 1 sec. will deposit 0·001118 gm. of silver from a solution of silver nitrate in water.

The **volt** is the potential difference which will drive a current of 1 ampère through a resistance of 1 ohm.

Resistances in Series. When two or more resistances are joined end to end, they are said to be joined "in series" (fig.

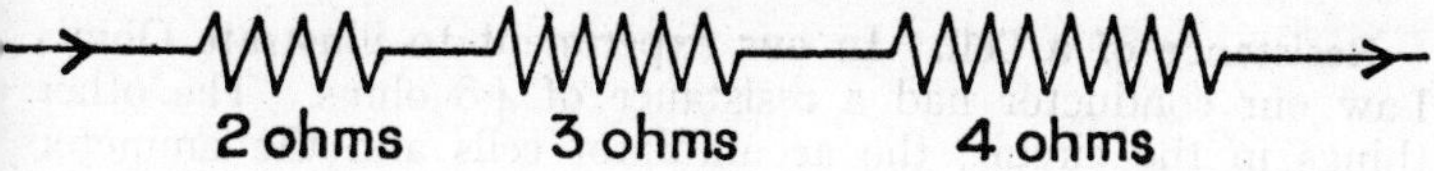

FIG. 292.

292). The combined resistance is then found by adding the separate resistances together. Thus in the example shown the total resistance is 9 ohms.

Resistances in Parallel. When the current has more than one path the conductors are said to be joined "in parallel" (fig. 293). The effect is the same as if we used a thicker conductor. Therefore the combined resistance will be less than that of any one of the separate conductors. In the example shown we proceed in this way.

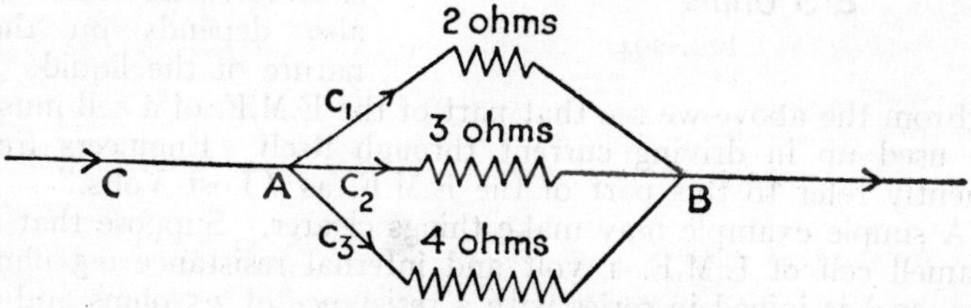

FIG. 293.

The current C divides at the point A into c_1, c_2, and c_3. The electromotive force acting between A and B will be the same along all the paths,

$$\therefore\ C = c_1 + c_2 + c_3$$

$$= \frac{E}{2 \text{ ohms}} + \frac{E}{3 \text{ ohms}} + \frac{E}{4 \text{ ohms}},$$

but $C = \frac{E}{R}$ where R is the combined resistance,

$$\therefore \frac{E}{R} = \frac{E}{2} + \frac{E}{3} + \frac{E}{4}$$

$$\therefore \frac{1}{R} = \frac{1}{2} + \frac{1}{3} + \frac{1}{4} = \frac{13}{12}$$

$$\therefore R = \frac{12}{13} \text{ ohm.}$$

Resistance of a Cell. In our experiment to illustrate Ohm's Law our conductor had a resistance of 4·8 ohms. The other things in the circuit, the accumulator cells and the ammeter had a negligible resistance. In some cells, however, the cell itself has a considerable resistance. It is in fact a liquid conductor and its resistance depends on the same factors as the resistance of a metallic conductor. Thus the closer the plates, the shorter the liquid conductor and the less the resistance. The bigger the cell, the greater the cross-section. This again diminishes the resistance. The resistance also depends on the nature of the liquid.

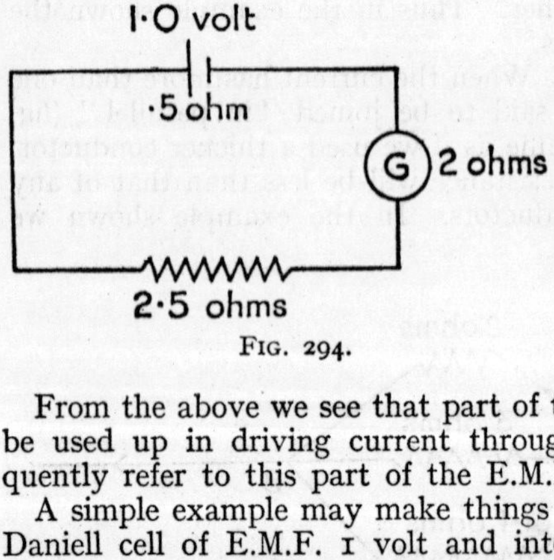

FIG. 294.

From the above we see that part of the E.M.F. of a cell must be used up in driving current through itself. Engineers frequently refer to this part of the E.M.F. as "Lost Volts."

A simple example may make things clearer. Suppose that a Daniell cell of E.M.F. 1 volt and internal resistance 0·5 ohm (fig. 294) is joined in series with a resistance of 2·5 ohms and a galvanometer of resistance 2 ohms. Applying Ohm's Law to the whole circuit, we have

$$\frac{E}{R} = \frac{1 \cdot 0}{2 \cdot 5 + 2 + 0 \cdot 5} = 0 \cdot 2 \text{ amp.} = C.$$

Applying Ohm's Law to the cell itself, we have

$$e = rC = 0 \cdot 5 \text{ ohm} \times 0 \cdot 2 \text{ amp.} = 0 \cdot 1 \text{ volt}$$

$\therefore$ Lost Volts = 0·1 volt.

Since Lost Volts = Resistance of cell × current, then the greater the current the greater will be the Lost Volts. Thus if we cut out the 2·5 ohms the current becomes 0·4 amp. and the lost volts will then be 0·2 volt.

This fact can be illustrated experimentally by the circuit shown in fig. 295. A Daniell cell is connected in series with a key, a variable resistance and an ammeter. A voltmeter is also connected across the cell.

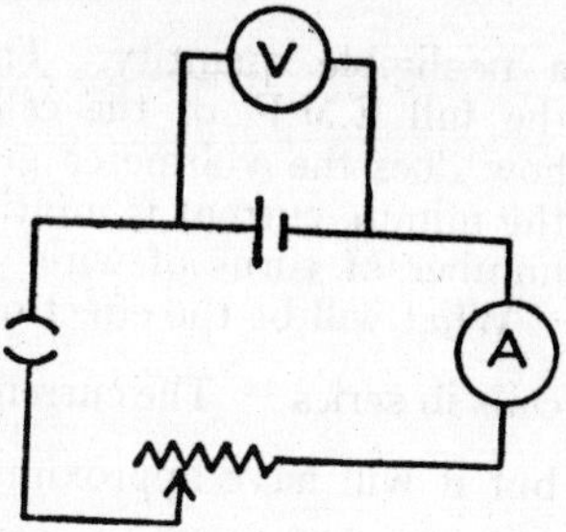

FIG. 295.

When the key is open, the voltmeter registers the E.M.F. of the cell. This is also called the "P.D. on open circuit." We will return to this point later. As soon as the key is closed, the voltmeter reading drops because of the lost volts used in driving a current through the cell. If the variable resistance is diminished, the current will increase, the product *rC* or lost volts will increase and the voltmeter reading will drop still more.

Resistance of an Accumulator Cell. An accumulator cell has a very small internal resistance so that the lost volts are generally negligible. This is one of the advantages of such a cell, but on the other hand the low resistance makes short-circuiting very dangerous to the cell. Thus suppose the internal resistance is 0·01 ohm and the terminals are accidentally "shorted" by a piece of wire of negligible resistance, then

$$\frac{2 \text{ volts}}{0{\cdot}01 \text{ ohm}} = 200 \text{ amps.},$$

a current much higher than the cell is meant to give. The plates get hot, the paste expands and breaks away from the grids. To avoid such a possibility it is a good plan when wiring up circuits to **fix leads to the accumulator last and remove first.**

Open Circuit. It was mentioned above that when a voltmeter is joined to the terminals of a cell, the latter is still said to be "on open circuit." If we look into this question, we shall see that the expression is quite reasonable.

A voltmeter always has a large number of turns of very thin wire. The resistance may be in the neighbourhood of 1000 ohms. Let it be connected to a Daniell cell of E.M.F. 1 volt and internal resistance 0·5 ohm. What current is flowing? $\frac{1}{1000{\cdot}5}$ amp. This is so small as to be negligible and the cell is to all intents and purposes "on open circuit."

What are the lost volts in this case? $\frac{1}{1000{\cdot}5} \times 0{\cdot}5$—again a negligible quantity. The voltmeter is therefore registering the full E.M.F. of the cell. But if the current is so minute how does the voltmeter give a reading? Because the effect of the minute current is multiplied over and over again by the vast number of turns of wire.

What will be the effect of joining the voltmeter to two Daniell cells in series? The current will now be $\frac{2}{1001}$ amp.—still minute but it will have approximately double the effect on the instrument. With 3 cells the current will be $\frac{3}{1001{\cdot}5}$ amp. and the effect will be approximately trebled. The important point to notice here is that the tiny currents are for all practical purposes proportional to the voltages. Therefore the instrument can be calibrated in volts.

A voltmeter must not provide an easy alternative path for the current. It must "taste the current and so judge the pressure." An ammeter must take all the current through itself and "resist" as little as possible—it is a low-resistance instrument.

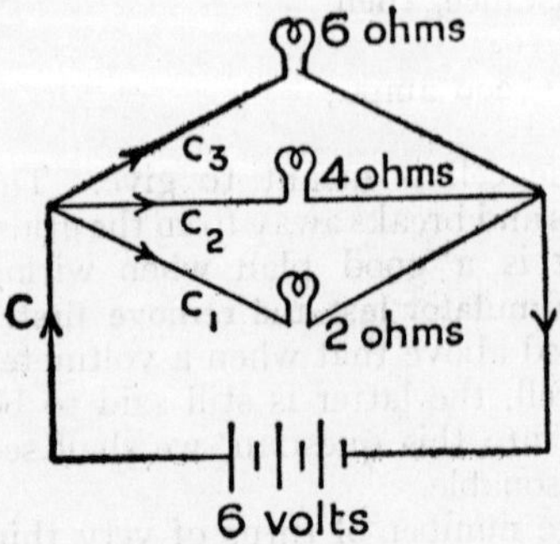

FIG. 296.

An Instructive Problem on Resistances.

A 6-volt accumulator of negligible resistance is joined to three lamps in parallel having resistances 2 ohms, 4 ohms and 6 ohms (fig. 296). Calculate the currents passing when (*a*) all the lamps are in their sockets, (*b*) first lamp removed, (*c*) first and second lamps are removed.

(*a*) ***All in.***

$$\text{Total Resistance } R = \frac{1}{\frac{1}{2}+\frac{1}{4}+\frac{1}{6}} = \tfrac{12}{11} \text{ ohms}$$

$$\therefore \text{ by Ohm's Law } C = \frac{6 \text{ volts}}{\frac{12}{11} \text{ ohms}} = 5\tfrac{1}{2} \text{ amps.}$$

Next apply Ohm's Law to each branch, noting that the fall of potential (the "*RC* drop" of the engineer) along any path is the same, viz. 6 volts,

then $r_1c_1 = 6$ or $2 \times c_1 = 6$, $\therefore c_1 = 3$ amps.
also $r_2c_2 = 6$ or $4 \times c_2 = 6$, $\therefore c_2 = 1\frac{1}{2}$ amps.
also $r_3c_3 = 6$ or $6 \times c_3 = 6$, $\therefore c_3 = 1$ amp.

(*b*) First lamp removed.

$$\text{Total Resistance } R = \frac{1}{\frac{1}{4}+\frac{1}{6}} = \tfrac{12}{5} \text{ ohms}$$

$$\therefore C = \frac{6}{\frac{12}{5}} = 2\tfrac{1}{2} \text{ amps.}$$

Also $r_2c_2 = 6$ or $4c_2 = 6$, $\therefore c_2 = 1\frac{1}{2}$ amps. as before.
Again $r_3c_3 = 6$ or $6c_3 = 6$, $\therefore c_3 = 1$ amp. as before.

(*c*) First and second lamps removed.

In this case again $c_3 = 1$ amp. as before.

What would happen if the lamps were in series? You will easily see that the same current, viz. $\frac{1}{2}$ amp., will flow through all the lamps, and when one is removed all will go out.

The important point that arises out of our problem is that when a building is to be wired up for lighting, the lamps must be in parallel. Each lamp then takes its own current under all circumstances and does not go out or flare up when others are switched off.

The Wheatstone Bridge. This is a method of comparing two resistances invented by Sir Charles Wheatstone (1802–75), one of the pioneers of telegraphy.

The principle will be readily understood from the theoretical circuit shown in fig. 297. *P* and *X* are fixed resistances. A wander key D divides a resistance wire into two sections of resistance *Q* and *R*. G is a sensitive galvanometer. A simple cell sends a current in at A. Suppose the current divides into c_1 and c_2. It will always be possible to find some point on the wire so that there is *no current through the galvanometer.*

In that case the same current c_1 will flow through *P* and *X* while c_2 flows through the wire.

Also Potential at B = Potential at D,

therefore Fall of potential from A to B = Fall of potential from A to D.

Also Fall of potential from B to E = Fall of potential from D to E.

But by Ohm's Law

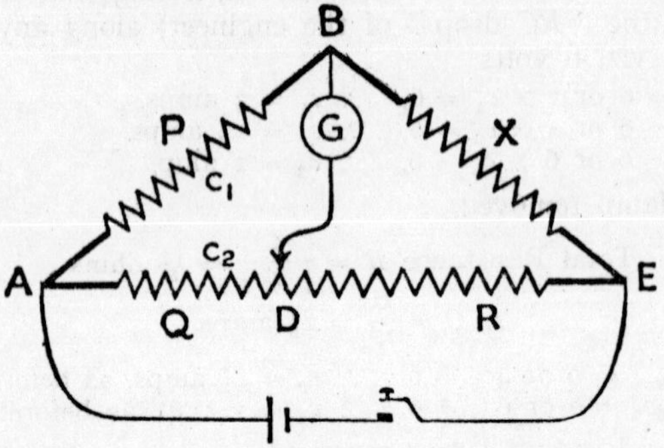

FIG. 297.

Fall of Potential in a Conductor = Resistance × Current

$$\therefore Pc_1 = Qc_2$$

and

$$Xc_1 = Rc_2$$

$$\therefore \frac{Pc_1}{Xc_1} = \frac{Qc_2}{Rc_2}$$

$$\therefore X = P.\frac{R}{Q} = P.\frac{l_2}{l_1}$$

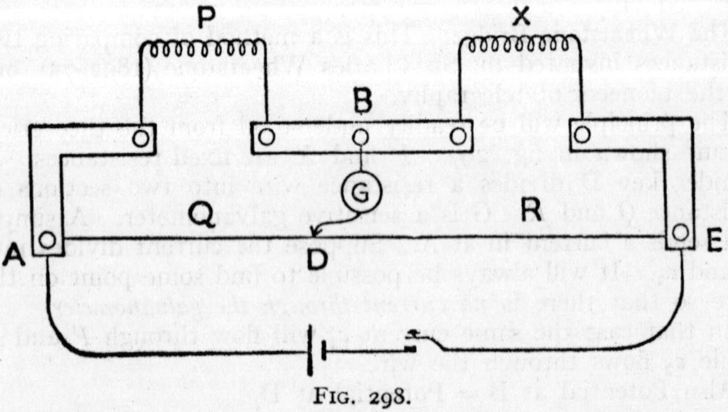

FIG. 298.

where l_1 and l_2 are the lengths of the two sections. Thus if we know P we can measure X.

The actual apparatus generally consists of copper strips of negligible resistance, terminals and a straight wire mounted on a board (fig. 298). It is then called a *metre bridge* or a *half-metre bridge* according to the length of the wire.

QUESTIONS

1. A certain piece of wire has a resistance of 5 ohms. What will be the resistance of another wire of the same material four times the length and half the diameter?

2. An electric current was passed through a solution of silver nitrate for half an hour. 10·062 gm. of silver were deposited. Find the strength of the current.

3. 8 ohms and 4 ohms are joined (*a*) in series, (*b*) in parallel. What is the resistance in each case?

4. A lamp joined to a 2-volt accumulator takes 0·2 amp. If connected to a 6-volt accumulator, what resistance would be needed to keep the current the same?

5. Four cells each of E.M.F. 1·1 volt and internal resistance 2 ohms are joined in parallel to an external resistance of $4\frac{1}{2}$ ohms. What is the current?

6. Three Daniell cells, each of E.M.F. 1·1 volts and internal resistance 4 ohms, are joined in series to a coil of resistance 4 ohms and a galvanometer of resistance 2 ohms. What is the current?

7. Calculate the "*RC* drop" in each part of the circuit in Question 6 and the total drop round the circuit.

8. What resistance would have to be placed in parallel with 8 ohms to make the total resistance 2 ohms?

9. The terminals of a galvanometer of resistance 40 ohms are joined by a *shunt* (parallel resistance) of 10 ohms. Find the resistance of this combination and the current which goes through the galvanometer when a potential difference of 16 volts is applied to its terminals.

10. A 6-volt accumulator is joined up to three lamps in parallel, each having resistance 5 ohms. Calculate the current flowing through one of the lamps when (*a*) all the lamps are in, (*b*) only one is in.

11. An unknown resistance is measured against a 5-ohm coil on a half-metre bridge. If balance occurs at 20 cm., what is the value of the unknown resistance?

12. Two feet of wire is put in the left gap of a metre bridge and a 1-ohm coil in the right. When the galvanometer shows no deflection, the left-hand reading on the wire is 56 cm. What would be the resistance of 1 mile of this wire?

13. What length of the wire in Question 12 would be needed to make 1 ohm?

14. Two coils joined in series have a total resistance of 10 ohms. When joined in parallel the resistance is $2\frac{2}{5}$ ohms. What are their resistances?

15. The potential difference at the terminals of a generator is 400 volts. If the current in the mains is 200 amps., what percentage of the volts will be lost in half a mile of main given that the resistance is 0·2 ohm per mile?

16. Three wires each having a resistance of 9 ohms are joined in parallel. If a current of 2 amps. flows through each, what E.M.F. is being used?

17. A 12-volt battery sends a current of 1·5 amps. through an external resistance of 6 ohms. What is the resistance of the battery?

18. Three cells each having an E.M.F. of 1·45 volts and an internal resistance of 4 ohms are connected in series; calculate the current which they will pass through a flash lamp, the resistance of which is 10 ohms. (C. part question.)

19. A 2-volt accumulator is joined up to three lamps A, B, and C in parallel, of resistances 2, 3, and 6 ohms respectively. Find the current through each lamp when (*a*) all are in, (*b*) B and C are in, (*c*) only C is left in.

20. Explain the meaning of Ohm's Law.

Power is supplied to a factory by two cables two miles long, and at the power-station the potential difference between the ends of the cable is maintained at 220 volts. The potential difference between the two ends at the factory must not fall below 200 volts and a maximum current of 40 amps. is needed. What is the greatest permissible resistance per mile of the cable? (O. and C.)

21. The lighting system of a country house takes 10 amps. at 100 volts. This is supplied by a dynamo that maintains 220 volts at its terminals. What is the resistance of the mains from the generating plant to the house? (O. and C.)

22. A cell of 1·5 volts E.M.F. and 5 ohms internal resistance is connected to two resistances of 100 ohms and 10 ohms respectively in parallel. How much current will pass through the cell and through each resistance? (O. and C.)

23. On what factors does the resistance of a wire depend? Given a voltmeter and a suitable battery how would you compare the resistances of two coils of wire? (J.M.B.)

CHAPTER XXIX

ELECTRICAL ENERGY

We learnt in Mechanics that *energy is the capacity for doing work.* A falling body possesses an amount of energy which depends on (a) the fall, (b) the mass which is falling. We also know that this energy can be converted into heat. Experiments by Joule and others have shown that **1 ft.-lb. will generate 0·32 cal.**

Everyday experience also teaches us that an electric current has energy. We have seen it used to drive an electric motor. It is only necessary to feel an electric-light bulb to prove that the energy of an electric current can be converted into heat. The energy of an electric current depends on (a) the fall in potential, (b) the quantity of electricity which is moving. The unit of electrical energy is called the *joule*; **one joule is equal to 0·24 cal. or 4·2 joules = 1 calorie.**

We may sum up the comparison between a falling body and an electric current by means of the following statements:

1 lb. falling 1 ft. has energy 1 ft.-lb. = 0·32 cal.
1 Coulomb falling 1 volt has energy 1 joule = 0·24 cal.

Notice that a ft.-lb. and a joule are both units of work, the joule being about $\frac{3}{4}$ of a ft.-lb.

In Mechanics we learnt that

550 ft.-lb. per second is a rate of working called 1 H.P.
so 1 joule ,, ,, ,, ,, ,, ,, 1 watt.

Horse-power and watt are units of *power*. How many watts in 1 H.P.?

Now a current flow of 1 coulomb per second is called an ampère, so we may also say that

1 amp.	driven by 1 volt	does 1 joule per second	
or 1 amp.	,, ,, 1 volt	has power	1 watt
or 2 amps.	,, ,, 200 volts	,, ,,	400 watts
or *C* amps	,, ,, *E* volts	,, ,,	*EC* watts.

Watts = Volts × Amps.

Now if you use a (theoretical) horse for an hour, how many ft.-lb. will he do? If you use a watt for an hour, how many joules will it do? This number of joules is called a **watt-hour.** If you use a watt for 1000 hours, the power station will charge for one Board of Trade (B.O.T.) unit. They call it a **kilowatt-hour.** How many joules will that be?

It should be noticed that there are many ways of using our unit. We may have

	1 watt	working	for	1000 hours
or	1000 watts	,,	,,	1 hour
or	500 watts	,,	,,	2 hours
or	10 watts	,,	,,	100 hours
or	2000 watts	,,	,,	½ hour, and so on.

The joules supplied and the bill will be the same.

Again, the watts may be produced in various ways. Thus we may have 1000 watts obtained from

	1000 amps.	driven	by	1 volt
or	1 amp.	,,	,,	1000 volts
or	2 amps.	,,	,,	500 volts, and so on.

It is interesting to observe that when we pay for a B.O.T. unit, we are really buying ft.-lb. of energy. Let us see how many ft.-lb. we get:

1000 watts = 1000 joules per second
1000 watts acting for an hour = 1000 × 60 × 60 joules
= 3,600,000 joules or 2,700,000 ft.-lb.—roughly enough energy to lift a ton through 1200 ft. against gravity.

We may also look upon it as a case of buying calories, thus—

1 joule = 0·24 calorie
∴ 1 watt = 0·24 cal. per second
∴ 1000 watts working for 1 hour will give 864,000 cals.

Electric Lamps. The best-known example of the use of electrical energy is undoubtedly the electric lamp. The two chief kinds are the vacuum lamp and the gas-filled lamp.

The current enters and leaves by short lengths of a reddish wire consisting of an alloy of 45% nickel and 55% iron coated with copper. This alloy was first made by M. Guillaume. Like platinum, it has the same coefficient of expansion as glass and can therefore be sealed into glass. Formerly platinum was used, but the amount of platinum in the world is so strictly limited that Guillaume's **nickel-iron alloy** has taken its place.

In both vacuum and gas-filled lamps the path of the current is from **alloy**, to stout **nickel** wire, through **tungsten** filament, to stout **nickel**, and out through **alloy**. The filament is supported by radiating "spokes" of either nickel (thick spokes) or, a springy metal called **molybdenum** (thin spokes).

Tungsten and molybdenum have very high melting-points, 3400° C. and 2500° C. respectively. They may, therefore, be heated to very high temperatures without risk of fusion. Note: the current does *not* pass through the molybdenum.

Both kinds of lamp have to be exhausted of air. This process formerly left a point on the bulb where the outlet had been sealed. Nowadays it is done in neater fashion. Careful examination of a modern lamp will reveal in the base a glass tube open on the inside and sealed on the outside. After exhaustion and before sealing, the gas-filled lamp is filled with a mixture of argon and nitrogen.

Have you ever noticed an electric lamp which has gone nearly black? This is due to "filament evaporation" caused by the high temperature. This not only makes the filament thinner and more liable to break, but the particles of filament are deposited on the glass and the light is obscured.

When there is an inert gas in the bulb the escaping tungsten molecules meet gas molecules and to a great extent bounce back on to the filament. The addition of the inert gas makes it possible therefore to use a higher temperature without increased blackening or shorter life. Now in all lamps only a very small percentage of the energy consumed is radiated as light, most of the energy being converted into useless heat. But the higher the temperature, that is the whiter the filament, the greater the percentage of energy converted into light.

Here, however, we meet a difficulty. In a vacuum lamp there is no cooling by conduction and convection (compare vacuum flask). These effects in a gas-filled lamp might easily cool the filament to such an extent that the high temperature advantage would be completely lost. To avoid this the filament is wound in a spiral so that it is in contact with as little gas as possible. The "coiled coil" lamp is a further development of the same idea.

But the convection currents have one advantage: in a hanging lamp any blackening particles are carried upwards to the neck where they can do no harm.

Simple Problems.

(i) A resistance wire is immersed in 1000 gm. of water. A current of 5 amps. at 20 volts pressure is sent through for 10 min. Calculate rise of temperature.

$$\begin{aligned}\text{Watts} &= \text{Volts} \times \text{Amps.}\\ &= 20 \times 5\\ &= 100\\ 100 \text{ watts} &= 100 \text{ joules per second}\\ &= 100 \times 0{\cdot}24 \text{ cal. per second.}\end{aligned}$$

In 10 min. 100 watts will generate 100 × 24 × 600 cals.

$$= 14{,}400 \text{ cals.}$$

$$\therefore \text{Rise of Temp.} = 14{\cdot}4^\circ \text{ C.}$$

Note also that

$$\text{Cals.} = 0{\cdot}24 \times \text{Amps.} \times \text{Volts} \times \text{Secs.} = 0{\cdot}24\ ECt$$

but $\text{Volts} = \text{Ohms} \times \text{Amps.}$

$$\therefore \text{Cals.} = 0{\cdot}24 \times \text{Ohms} \times \text{Amps.}^2 \times \text{Secs.} = 0{\cdot}24\ RC^2t$$

(ii) How many calories will be developed in 2 min. by a current of 40 ampères flowing through a resistance of 200 ohms?

$$\begin{aligned}\text{Cals.} &= 0{\cdot}24 \times \text{Ohms} \times \text{Amps.}^2 \times \text{Secs.}\\ &= 0{\cdot}24 \times 200 \times 40^2 \times 120\\ &= 9{,}216{,}000.\end{aligned}$$

(iii) A potential difference of 80 volts is applied to the ends of a coil whose hot resistance is 10 ohms. Find the heat generated in 20 sec.

$$\begin{aligned}\text{Cals.} &= 0{\cdot}24\ ECt\\ &= 0{\cdot}24\ E \times \frac{E}{R} \times t\\ &= 3072.\end{aligned}$$

(iv) An electric lamp bears the mark *200V 60W*. Explain the sign and say what further information can be derived from it.

The lamp is meant for a 200-volt supply. The mains in lighting this lamp would do work at the rate of 60 watts or the power used by the lamp is 60 watts. The current taken will be 60 ÷ 200 = 0·3 amp. The hot resistance of the lamp is 200 ÷ 0·3 = 667 ohms. It will use 1 B.O.T. unit in $16\frac{2}{3}$ hours. If used on a lower voltage the power consumed will be less than 60 watts, but the light will be less. When used on higher voltages the light increases, but the life of the lamp is shortened.

QUESTIONS

1. How many ft.-lb. of energy are there in a *joule*, a *watt-second*, *watt-hour*, and a *kilowatt-hour*?

2. A man does a kilowatt-hour in four 6-hour days; at what H.P. is he working?

3. If a man lifts a 10-lb. mass through 7 ft. 6 in. against gravity, how many joules does he do?

4. If 746 watts = 1 H.P., express the joule in terms of the foot-pound.

5. A man lifts a load of 55 lb. out of a well at the rate of 6 in. per second. At what H.P. is he working?

6. An electric lamp takes $\frac{1}{5}$ ampère on a 200-volt supply. At what rate is the lamp consuming energy?

7. An electric lamp working from 210-volt mains has a hot resistance of 735 ohms. What current does it take? In what time will it consume one B.O.T. unit?

8. A power of 50,000 kilowatts is sent out from a generating station at 132,000 volts. What is the strength of the current in the wires?

9. A lamp takes 0·5 amp. at 200 volts. If it has a candle-power of 180, find its *efficiency* in candle-power per watt and watts per candle-power.

10. Ten lamps similar to that in Question 9 are burning simultaneously. How long will a unit last? Calculate the heat generated in 1 hour.

11. In Question 10 what horse-power is being used?

12. Explain the expression "a power of 34 watts." Can it be expressed in terms of "horse-power"?

13. Which of the following are units of *energy* and which represent *rates of working*—ft.-lb., watt, joule, kilowatt, calorie, watt-hour, kilowatt-hour, B.O.T. unit, horse-power?

14. A wire is accidentally joined across an accumulator. Quote the equation which shows how the heat generated depends on the E.M.F. of the battery and the resistance of the wire.

15. A lamp takes 0·75 amp. at 220 volts. If its efficiency is 1·5 watts per candle-power, what is its candle-power?

16. A 50-candle-power lamp takes 0·5 amp. at 110 volts. What is its efficiency in watts per candle-power and candle-power per watt?

17. A generator drives a current of 2 amps. through a resistance of 373 ohms. What horse-power is being used?

18. A Hotpoint Electric Iron is marked WATTS [400] VOLTS [200/210]. What is its hot resistance? What current does it take? How long could it be used for a shilling at 3*d*. per unit?

19. An electric iron has a resistance of 100 ohms when used on a

220-volt supply. What will it cost to run it for 20 hours at $1\frac{1}{2}d.$ a unit?

20. The dim lamps and the rear lamp of a "baby" car are each marked 6V 6W. The head lights are stamped 6V 24W and the horn takes 2 amps. What current will be used when the driver sounds his horn at night (*a*) in the country, (*b*) in a well-lighted street?

21. Calculate the number of calories generated in 1 hour by the iron mentioned in Question 19.

22. An electric lamp takes a current of 0·55 amp. on a 220-volt circuit. Find (*a*) the power used by the lamp, (*b*) its hot resistance, (*c*) the cost of the energy used in 500 hours at 4*d.* a unit.

23. A current of 2 amps. is passed through a coil of wire immersed in 100 gm. of water. In 2 min. the temperature rises 7·2° C. What was the potential difference between the ends of the wire?

24. An electric lamp on a 200-volt supply has a hot resistance of 400 ohms. Calculate (*a*) the current, (*b*) the heat generated in 10 min.

25. If you run a 2000-watt electric fire for 2 hours, how many calories are you buying?

26. A certain electric power plant is said to have a *capacity of 236,000 KWH per annum.* What does this mean?

27. An electric heating coil of 80 ohms resistance is used on a supply of 230 volts. What will be the effect on the heat production of using two such coils (*a*) in series, (*b*) in parallel, instead of a single coil? (C.W.B.)

CHAPTER XXX

INDUCED CURRENTS

So far we have only studied one method of producing an electric current, namely, by using chemical energy. If there were no other method than this, electrical engineering would not have made much progress. We shall, however, soon learn that there is a much better method.

We have already seen how in 1819 Oersted showed that an electric current has magnetic properties, in other words, it is possible to produce **magnetism from electricity.**

It was natural then for scientists to wonder whether the opposite trick would be possible—can we produce **electricity from magnetism**?

In 1831 this question was definitely answered in the affirmative by Michael Faraday in England and Joseph Henry in America. The results of their work can easily be illustrated in any physical laboratory.

Experiment. Support a horseshoe magnet in a suitable stand (fig. 299). Connect an old tuning coil to a sensitive galvanometer. Move the coil rapidly down over one of the poles so as to cut lines of force. The galvanometer needle is deflected. If the coil is now allowed to remain at rest, the needle comes back to zero, but on moving the coil rapidly upwards, the needle is deflected the other way. If the movements are now carried out more slowly the kicks of the needle are feebler. On using the other pole of the magnet the effects are reversed.

Experiment. Instead of the horseshoe use a bar magnet. Holding the coil stationary, thrust the N. end of the magnet into it. Rapidly withdraw it. Repeat the movements slowly. Use the other pole. Record your observations.

Our experiments show that an electric current is generated whenever there is relative motion between lines of force and a coil of wire. Such a current is called an **induced current.** The corresponding electromotive force is referred to as an **induced e.m.f.** and the method of producing these currents is called **electromagnetic induction.**

So far we have always had to use chemical energy or do work in order to produce electrical energy. Further investigation proves that the present case is no exception. We are still subject to the Law of Conservation of Energy. We are really doing work to produce this electrical energy.

We know that when a current flows in a coil its faces acquire polarity. Imagine the coil in the last experiment being

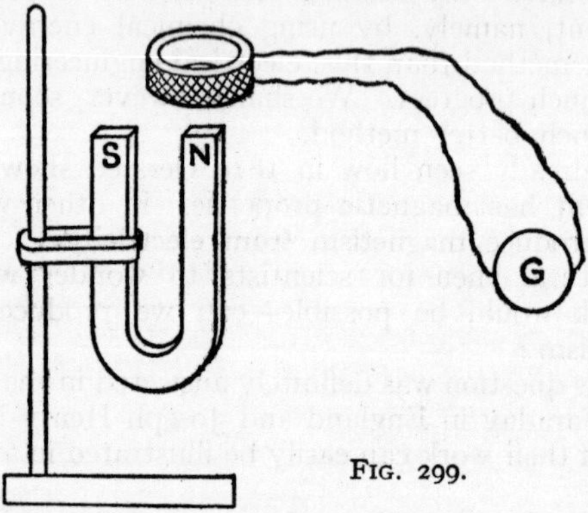

FIG. 299.

approached by the N. end of the bar magnet. A more detailed experiment would show that the induced current gives the near face N. polarity. There is therefore a repulsive force between the coil and the magnet and it is by doing work against this repulsive force that the electrical energy is generated. The matter is neatly stated in a Law due to a Russian scientist, H. F. E. Lenz (1804–1865).

Lenz's Law: The direction of the induced current is always such that its electromagnetic action tends to oppose the motion which produces it.

Two other illustrations of electromagnetic induction are worth noticing.

Experiment. Two old tuning coils are placed one on top of the other. One is joined to a galvanometer, the other to a battery and tapping key (fig. 300).

Close the battery circuit by means of the key. Open the circuit. Close the circuit and draw one coil rapidly away. Restore it quickly to its first position. Record your observations.

Experiment. Faraday's Ring. Faraday used a soft iron ring of external diameter 6 in. (fig. 301). Its cross-section was circular and $\frac{7}{8}$ in. in diameter. The primary circuit consisted of 72 ft.

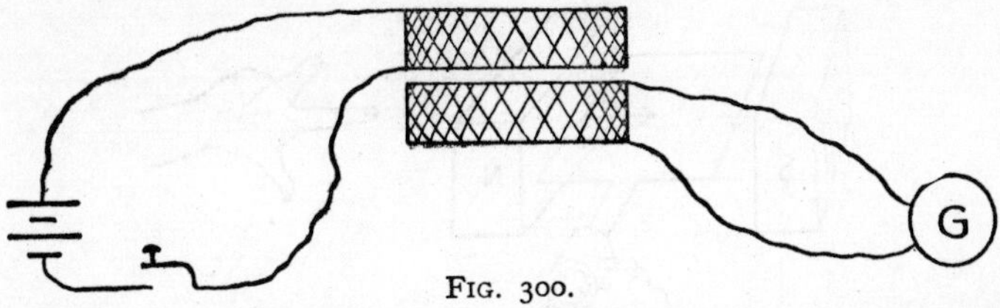

FIG. 300.

of insulated copper wire wound on one side of the ring and connected to a battery of voltaic cells. The secondary circuit consisted of 60 ft. of similar copper wire wound on the other side of the ring. The ends of the secondary were connected and made to pass over a magnetic needle.

On making the circuit, the needle is deflected and then comes to rest. At break the needle is deflected the other way.

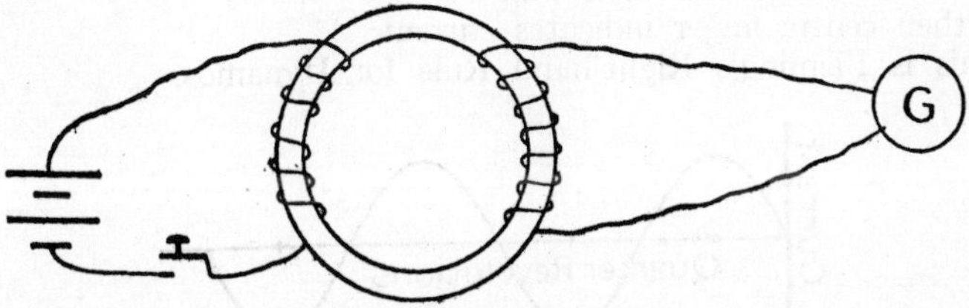

FIG. 301.

Using a sensitive galvanometer instead of the needle, well-marked deflections are given with a couple of cells in the primary circuit. A ring from a retort stand carrying two lots of 10 yd. of 22 d.c.c. wire will be found satisfactory.

The foregoing experiment is the basis of an important piece of electrical apparatus called the *transformer*.

Dynamos. Consider a loop of wire rotating clockwise between the poles of a magnet (fig. 302). It is cutting the lines of force or the "magnetic flux." Suppose that the loop is connected to two slip rings rubbed by brushes of carbon or copper gauze. Let the brushes be connected to a galvanometer having a central zero.

The direction of the induced current will be related to the directions of flux and motion in the manner shown by the three

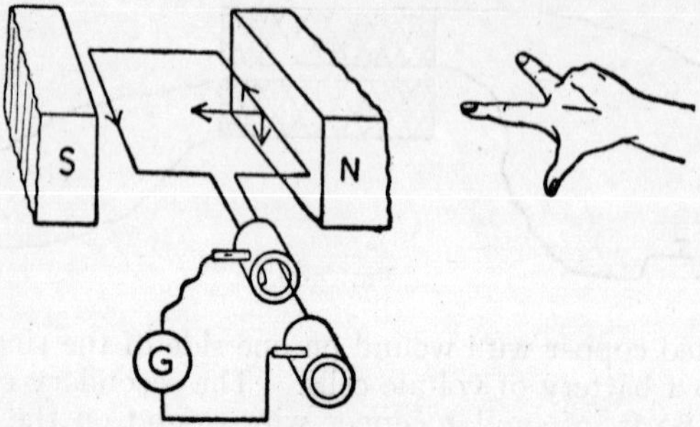

FIG. 302.

arrows or by a right hand having the thumb, forefinger and centre finger extended so that they are at right angles to each other.

If thumb indicates motion
and forefinger indicates flux
then centre finger indicates current.

This is Fleming's Right-hand Rule for Dynamos.

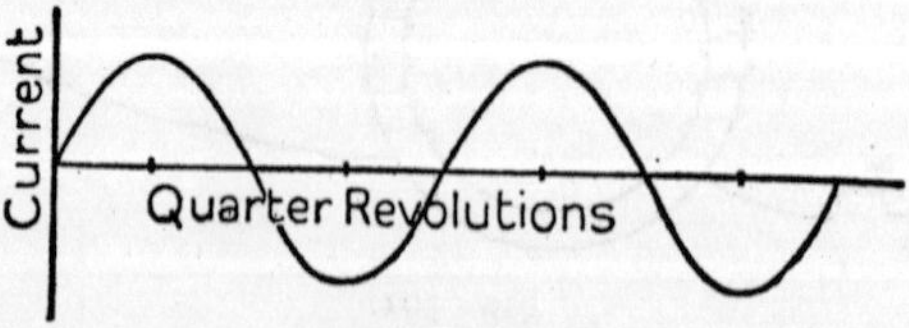

FIG. 303.

Careful thought will show that:

(*a*) The induced current is a maximum when the coil is passing through the horizontal position.

(*b*) The induced current is zero when the coil is passing through the vertical position.

(*c*) In one revolution there are two maxima and two zeros.

(*d*) The two maximum currents are in opposite directions in the external circuit.

These facts are conveniently shown on a diagram in which current is graphed against quarter revolutions (fig. 303). Such a current is said to be *alternating* (A.C.) and the dynamo producing it is called an *alternator*. Each complete series of changes is called a *cycle*. Alternators are generally made to have a *frequency* of 50 cycles per second.

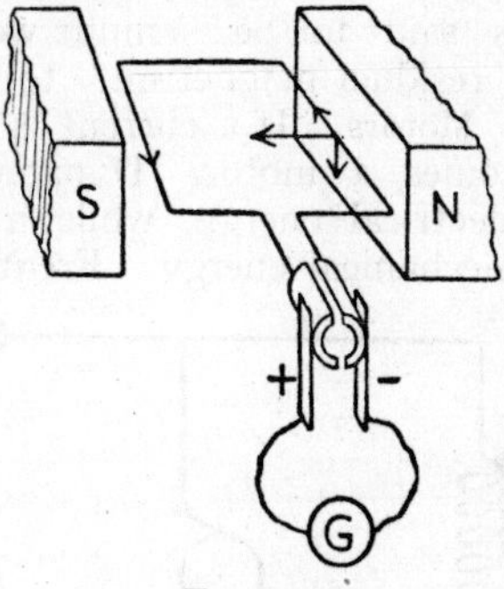

FIG. 304.

Actual machines have many loops of wire and these are wound on a soft iron core to increase the magnetic flux. The core and windings form the *armature* and the slip rings revolve with it. If direct current (D.C.) is desired, the slip rings are replaced by a split ring called a *commutator* (fig. 304). The sections of the commutator are separated from each other by mica or other insulating material. In this case one brush will be always positive and the other always negative. Whenever the current changes its direction in the loop, at that same instant each commutator section

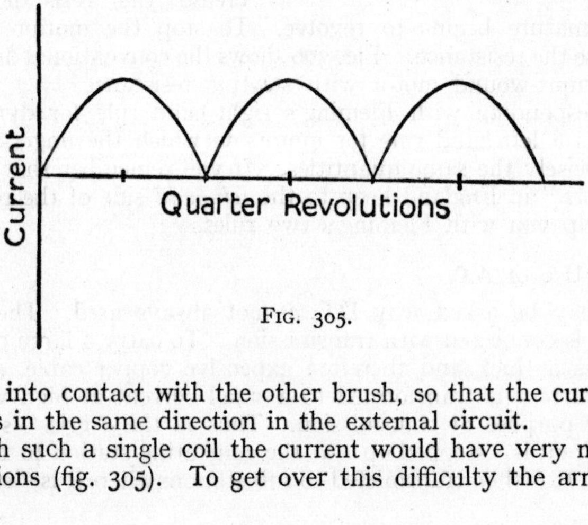

FIG. 305.

moves into contact with the other brush, so that the current is always in the same direction in the external circuit.

With such a single coil the current would have very marked pulsations (fig. 305). To get over this difficulty the armature is made of several coils wound in different planes and joined to a commutator of several sections.

The magnetic field is produced by an electromagnet of the horseshoe type. It is generally excited by "shunting" part of the current generated through the field coils. Such a dynamo is said to be "shunt wound." There is always sufficient "residual magnetism" to produce a starting current.

Motors. If a current is sent *into* a dynamo, the dynamo becomes a motor. Dynamos convert mechanical energy into electrical energy, while motors convert electrical energy into mechanical energy. Frequently they are identical in construction and the same machine can be used for either purpose.

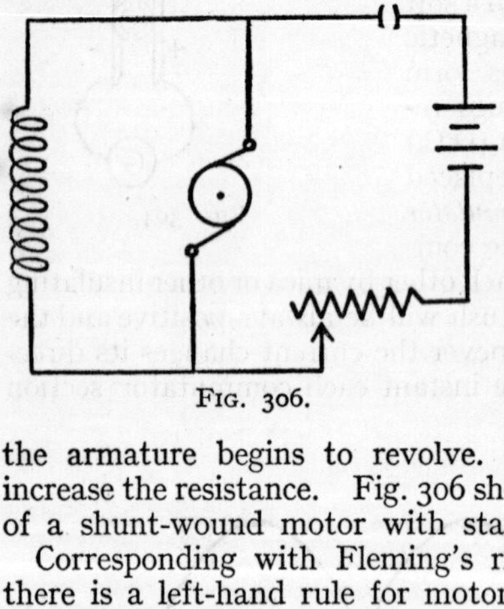

FIG. 306.

If a small D.C. dynamo is available, it is interesting to send current into its brushes from a couple of accumulator cells. The brushes should be joined in series with the cells and a rheostat set at maximum resistance. Gradually decrease the resistance till the armature begins to revolve. To stop the motion, again increase the resistance. Fig. 306 shows the conventional diagram of a shunt-wound motor with starting resistance.

Corresponding with Fleming's right-hand rule for dynamos, there is a left-hand rule for motors in which the fingers stand for precisely the same quantities. If you remember that petrol "motors" in England keep to the *left-hand* side of the road, it will help you with Fleming's two rules.

The Use of A.C.

It may be asked why D.C. is not always used. The main reason is connected with transmission. To carry a large current requires a thick and therefore expensive copper cable, so this large current is transformed to a small current at high voltage for the purpose of transmission. Thus in the "grid" system, the current is "stepped up" at the generating station to 132,000 volts. It is then transmitted to sub-stations where it is "stepped down" to 11,000 volts. Before being supplied to the public, it is again stepped down to voltages of about 200.

This stepping up and down is carried out by means of transformers based on Faraday's iron ring. These transformers generally consist of a thin coil and a thick coil wound on an iron core. If the thin coil has 1500 turns and the thick coil 300 turns, then any alternating current sent through the thin coil will have its voltage stepped down in the ratio 5 to 1.

This procedure is not possible with D.C. Further, there are several methods available for converting A.C. to D.C. in those cases, *e.g.* battery charging, and electroplating, where A.C. would be unsuitable. For these reasons current is generally supplied as A.C.

In doing experiments with the A.C. supply, great care is necessary because the voltage is much higher than in the ordinary D.C. experiments. Also, a nominal voltage of 230 means that twice in the cycle there is a " peak " voltage of 325 (*i.e.* 230 × 1.414). Such experiments should therefore only be done at school and under supervision. A safe rule is, **never touch any metallic part of the apparatus while the switch is on.** Bearing this precaution in mind, it is worth while trying the following:

(*a*) Using a transformer which steps the ordinary A.C. supply down to 25 volts or less, connect the low voltage side to the hydrogen voltameter.

(*b*) Hold the twin flex leading to a lamp over a compass needle. Switch on the current. Separate the flex and try each branch in the same way. Why is there no effect ?

(*c*) Using the transformer of (*a*), connect the low voltage side to a voltmeter (of suitable range) of the moving iron type, or the hot wire type (page 324). Why do you get readings now ?

(*d*) Rotate the poles of a horseshoe magnet slowly round a lighted carbon filament lamp.[1]

The Induction Coil. In garages you will sometimes hear people talking about " coil ignition " and " magneto ignition." They are discussing the two methods of igniting the mixture of air and petrol vapour, the explosion of which gives the force which drives the car.

[1] See also Articles by Mr. E. G. Savage, C.B. (*S.S.R.*, No. 65) and Mr. H. E. Dance (*S.S.R.*, No. 66).

In order to understand these two methods of ignition, we must study an instrument sometimes called the Induction Coil and sometimes the Ruhmkorff Coil (fig. 307). It consists of two

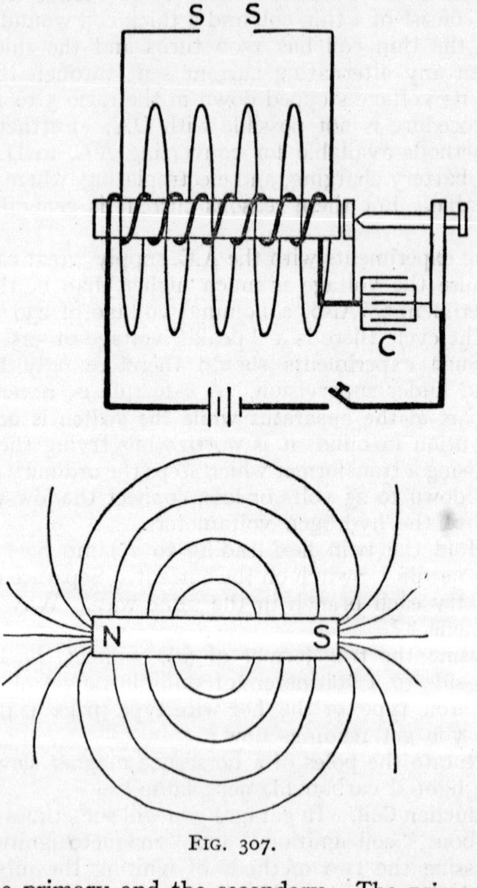

FIG. 307.

circuits, the primary and the secondary. The primary is very similar to the simple bell circuit (p. 321). A layer or two of thick insulated copper wire is wound round a bundle of soft iron rods. The current from a couple of cells passes through this coil then into a soft iron hammer in contact with an adjusting screw and so back to the battery through a key. The screw and hammer both have platinum contacts.

The core of soft iron rods becomes a temporary magnet, the hammer is attracted and the circuit broken. Since the hammer is mounted on a piece of springy metal, it flies back into contact with the screw and the circuit is complete again. The hammer and screw are together called the "interrupter" or "make-and-break."

Round the primary coil and insulated from it is wound a very large number of turns of thin wire. This, the secondary, may be several miles in length.

At "make," lines of force spread out from the temporary magnet cutting across the coils of the secondary. But we have seen that when lines of force pass across a coil there is an induced E.M.F. set up between the ends of the coil.

At "break," the lines of force collapse into the soft iron core again cutting across the secondary. There is thus an induced E.M.F. at make and at break, but in opposite directions. The E.M.F. at break is found to be greater than that at make because the break is a more sudden action.

Across the interrupter there is joined a condenser C generally consisting of sheets of tinfoil separated by waxed paper. The effect of this condenser is to reduce sparking between the platinum points and to make the break still more sudden, thus still further increasing the E.M.F. at break.

If the secondary terminals S S are close enough together, the induced E.M.F. will be great enough to overcome the resistance of the air and a spark will pass. The longer the secondary coil, the longer will be the spark. A coil was once made to give a spark of 42 in. Its secondary was 280 miles long!

The experiments usually carried out with a Wimshurst machine can be done with an induction coil, but care must be taken not to touch the secondary terminals unless the coil is a very small one.

Ignition Systems.

We are now in a better position to understand ignition, a question of great importance in the working of petrol motors of all descriptions. In the early days of motor-cars and cycles, the ignition of the explosive mixture was brought about by means of a battery and an induction coil similar to the one we have considered. This type of coil is sometimes called a *trembler coil*.

The coil ignition method was rather inconvenient for motorcycles, because of the cumbersome battery which had to be carried. To get over this difficulty, the magneto was invented.

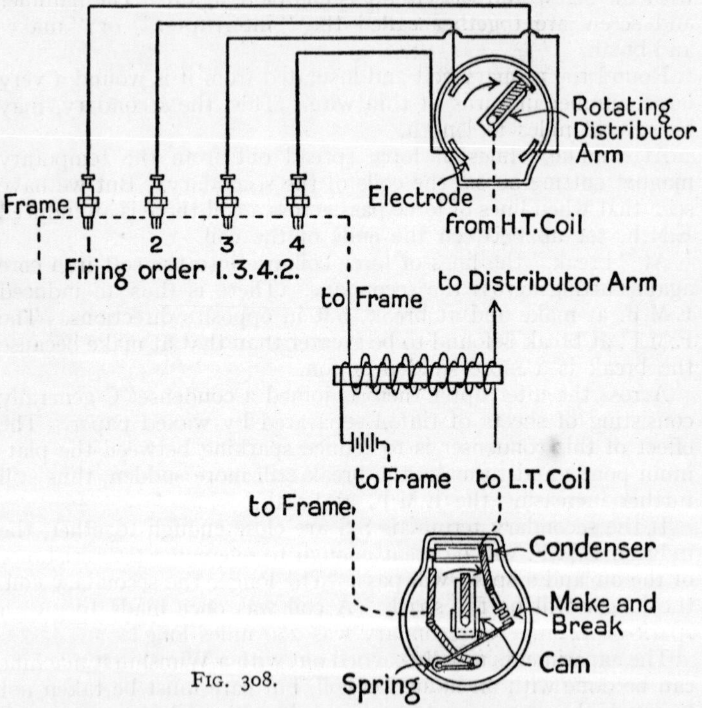

FIG. 308.

This instrument is to all intents and purposes a small dynamo and induction coil combined. The armature is wound with two coils, the primary consisting of a few turns of thick wire, while the secondary is a coil of many turns of thin wire. The dynamo is of course driven by the engine itself.

The primary has a " make and break " or " contact breaker " in it and across this is the usual condenser. One end of the secondary is connected to earth which in this case is the metal-work or " frame " of the car. The other end goes to the central electrode of the sparking plug. The spark jumps across the air gap to the outer part of the plug which is in contact with the frame and the secondary circuit is thus complete.

Not only did the magneto become popular on motor-cycles but cars also adopted magneto ignition.

To-day, fashion has changed once more and coil ignition is again fitted on the majority of cars although the motor-cycle still retains its compact magneto.

But the coil ignition of to-day is rather different. The coil is generally a **plain** coil, that is, it has no moving parts. Its make and break is located elsewhere, generally in the *base* of the distributor where the condenser may also be found (fig. 308).

It will be seen from the diagrams that both in the low-tension and the high-tension circuits, the circuit is completed through the " frame." The cam on the rotating distributor arm causes a break four times per revolution. At each instant, the metal piece on the top of the arm engages with one of the four electrodes in the distributor *cover*, causing a spark in one of the cylinders. The firing order 1·3·4·2 is found to be best for smooth working.

Having regard to the fact that the plug points are generally fairly close together, it might be thought that only a comparatively low voltage would be necessary to produce a spark. It is found, however, that the greater the pressure of the gas, the higher the voltage necessary. Since at the moment of firing, the gas is under compression, a voltage in the neighbourhood of 10,000 volts is necessary.

In conclusion it is worth noting that any ignition system may be compared with an induction coil in that it must have a spark gap in the secondary, a contact breaker somewhere in the primary, and a condenser across this contact breaker.

Experiments with the Induction Coil.

1. Copper wire is wound round the handle of a clean metal spoon (fig. 309), one end of the wire being attached to one of the secondary terminals of the coil. Another wire is joined to the other terminal and its free end brought near to a few drops of ether in the spoon. On passing sparks, the ether will burst into flame. While the spoon is still warm, methylated spirit is

poured in and the experiment repeated. Petrol or benzole may also be used.

2. A piece of paper is held between the ends of two wires

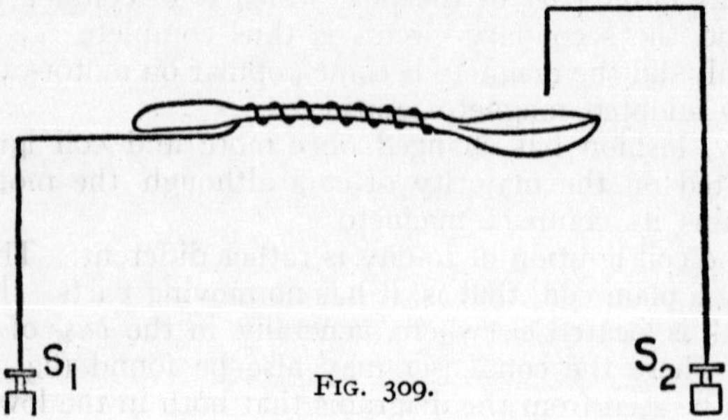

FIG. 309.

joined to the secondary terminals. After passing sparks a number of tiny perforations will be seen on holding the paper up to the light.

3. *Spectrum Tubes.* We have seen that to make a spark pass across the small gap in a sparking plug a voltage of about 10,000 volts is necessary. But here the gas is under pressure and the greater the pressure the higher the voltage needed. It is found, however, that the discharge of electricity will take place across a very long gap if the gas is rarefied, or across a short gap with only a small voltage acting. The former fact is used in spectrum tubes and X-ray tubes; the latter fact is used in working discharge tubes and lamps, which give characteristic colours on the ordinary town voltage.

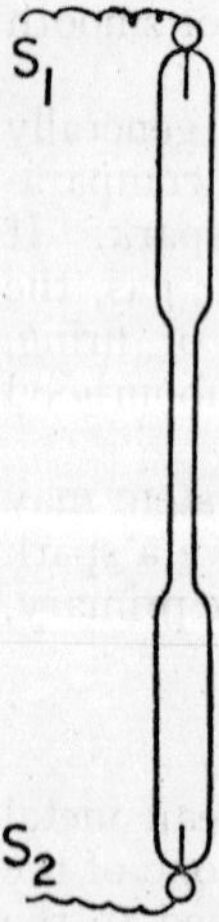

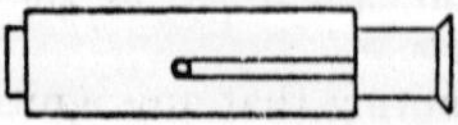

FIG. 310.

A spectrum tube containing rarefied hydrogen gives a striking appearance when joined to the terminals of the induction coil (fig. 310). The discharge may be examined with a direct vision spectroscope when the characteristic hydrogen lines will be plainly seen in the orange and blue.

Discharge Tube Lighting. The discharge lamps now so often seen in town lighting or for advertisement signs contain a rarefied gas or vapour. Neon, nitrogen and carbon dioxide gases give respectively red, buff, and artificial daylight. Sodium and mercury vapours give yellow and blue respectively. The various shades of green may be produced by cadmium, thallium, and magnesium. Some coloured lights, however, are merely filament lamps with tinted glass.

House Lighting. Useful knowledge may be gained by a careful examination of the electric lighting system of your house. Where the supply leads come in you will find a "fuse box," a meter and a double-pole main switch. Such a switch makes a gap in both leads. If the fuse box has a glass front you will see two strips or wires of a white metal mounted on porcelain and let into the leads. The metal may be tin, lead, or tinned copper. A current of 10 amps. will melt a tin wire of S.W.G. 21, a lead wire of S.W.G. 20 and a copper wire of S.W.G. 33. These are called 10-amp. fuses. The meter and the main fuses are chosen to suit the maximum current likely to be used in the house.

Following these and the main switch you will find a number of smaller fuse wires also mounted on porcelain. These are let into the leads travelling to different parts of the house. If in any part of the house a very easy path were made for the current by the touching of two leads, an excessive current would flow and sufficient heat would be generated to burn the insulation on the wiring or even set fire to the building. This is prevented by the "blowing of the fuse" and the breaking of the circuit. At the instant of melting, a spark jumps across and hot drops of molten metal are produced. Hence the use of a porcelain mounting.

Each lamp in the building is connected to two fuse wires thus —fuse, wall switch, lamp, fuse. It will readily be understood that all the lamps must be in parallel with each other. On referring to p. 333 it will also be evident why each lamp always takes the same current and does not flare up when others are switched off.

QUESTIONS

1. Draw a diagram to illustrate the essentials of a D.C. motor. Show one armature coil and mark the directions of (*a*) lines of force, (*b*) current, (*c*) motion. See fig. 302.

2. With the help of fig. 306 draw the conventional diagram for a shunt-wound dynamo with a lamp in the external circuit.

3. What are the main differences between A.C. and D.C.? State the advantages which each has over the other.

4. Draw the primary circuit of an induction coil. Show how it resembles and differs from a simple bell circuit.

5. Describe the principle and mode of action of the "make and break," such as is found in many electrical instruments.

Give **two** examples of its use in everyday life. (J.M.B.)

6. Why is an induction coil sometimes called a "transformer"?

7. In what way does an induction coil illustrate electromagnetic induction? Under what conditions will the instrument give (*a*) only an induced E.M.F., (*b*) an induced current?

8. Describe the ignition system of any motor-car with which you are acquainted.

9. What is meant by a "short circuit" in the electric supply to a house and why is it likely to cause damage unless the circuit is protected by a "fuse"? Explain the action of a fuse.

An electric cable whose resistance per yard is 0·005 ohm carries a current of 30 ampères. How much heat is produced per minute in each mile of the cable? The mechanical equivalent of heat is 4·2 joules per calorie. (D.)

ANSWERS TO NUMERICAL EXAMPLES

INDEX

INDEX